THE STRUCTURE
OF LIE GROUPS

HOLDEN-DAY SERIES MATHEMATICS

Earl A. Coddington and Andrew M. Gleason, Editors

G. Hochschild, *The Structure of Lie Groups*
Sze-Tsen Hu, *Elements of General Topology*
Sze–Tsen Hu, *Elements of Modern Algebra*
McCoart, Oliphant, and Scheerer, *Elementary Analysis*

THE STRUCTURE
OF LIE GROUPS

G. HOCHSCHILD

Department of Mathematics
University of California, Berkeley

HOLDEN-DAY, INC.

San Francisco, London, Amsterdam

1965

Library of Congress Catalog Card Number: 65–25766

Printed in the United States of America

PREFACE

Taken in its broad sense, Lie group theory involves all of the major branches of mathematics: algebra, analysis, topology, differential geometry, and algebraic geometry. This book takes up the subject in the narrow sense, omitting differential geometry and algebraic geometry from the above list, and minimizing the analysis. It is addressed primarily to the student who wants to learn the basic techniques and results of Lie group theory quickly, without having to weave his way in and out of many books and papers. The reader is assumed to have at least a superficial acquaintance with multilinear algebra, group theory, general topology, and real variable theory. This means that he should know the initial definitions and their immediate consequences, and be familiar with the grammar of mathematics in a general way. For a student at this stage, the book is technically self-contained. Its plan is to reach the most important results as directly as possible, developing the mathematical tools only to the extent to which they are used here. The development of the main theme is limited by my decision to resist the temptation to introduce and use the theory of algebraic linear groups, which would make it difficult to reach an end before the author and/or the reader is too tired to care.

Almost all of the content of this book represents standard mathematical equipment from the tool chest of the specialist. Although much of this is of comparatively recent and hence easily traceable origin, I have shied away completely from the task of revealing the original sources and giving due credit. The fact that this task is rather awkward is illustrated by the situation of Theorem 3.1 of Chapter XV. The names to be attached to this result are: É. Cartan, C. Chevalley, K. Iwasawa, A. Malcev, G. D. Mostow. Moreover, in the proof of its hardest part, I have made use of an unpublished simplification due to Chevalley (the proof of Theorem 1.2 of Chapter XV) of Mostow's simplification of Cartan's original proof. The only sources listed are a few of the most important books that can serve to amplify and support what is presented here and to enlarge the reader's view of the theory. One of these, Chevalley's *Theory of Lie Groups*, is, of course, the very foundation on which everything given here rests, although an acquaintance with it is not presupposed.

The organization of this book is as follows. Chapter I contains the generalities concerning locally compact topological groups, and in particular the existence and uniqueness of the Haar integral. It also contains a few basic facts from general topology, such as the Stone-Weierstrass Theorem. Chapter II contains the general theory of compact groups and their representations. The most important results here are the Peter-Weyl Theorem and the Tannaka Duality Theorem. Chapter III deals with a number of basic results on the structure of locally compact groups, chiefly abelian groups, that can be proved by elementary methods. Chapter IV develops the topological theory of covering spaces and covering groups, which plays a dominant role in Lie group theory. All the classical analysis that is used later on is given in Chapter V. Chapter VI introduces analytic manifolds. No more than the basic definitions and the main facts concerning analytic maps is given here, and no more than this is used later on.

Lie group theory proper begins with Chapter VII. The Lie algebra of an analytic group is defined, and the main properties of the exponential map of the Lie algebra into the group are established. Chapter VIII deals with the closed subgroups of analytic groups, homogeneous spaces, and factor groups. The main results are that a closed subgroup of a Lie group is a Lie group and that the factor group of an analytic group by a closed normal subgroup is an analytic group. Chapter IX establishes the technique of semidirect product constructions, which is used extensively later on. The bulk of Chapter X is the purely algebraic development of the Campbell-Hausdorff formula which is basic for the subsequent deeper analysis of the exponential map in the theory of analytic groups. From this, the theory of analytic subgroups is then readily obtained at the end of the chapter. At this stage, the road is cleared for the applications of Lie algebra theory to the theory of analytic groups.

Chapter XI is the first instalment of pure Lie algebra theory, sufficient for the first serious application, which is made in Chapter XII. The main result here is that every finite-dimensional real Lie algebra is the Lie algebra of an analytic group. The proof is based on semi-direct product constructions, and yields topological results concerning normal analytic subgroups of simply connected analytic groups, which play an important role in the structure and representation theory. Chapter XIII deals with the general structure theory of compact analytic groups. Chapter XIV brings Lie algebra theory to the stage required for the rest of this book.

The main result concerns the existence of real forms of compact type for the semisimple complex Lie algebras. This is applied in Chapter XV in order to obtain the basic results concerning the maximal compact subgroups of Lie groups with finite component groups. The principal concern of Chapter XVI is Malcev's criterion for an analytic subgroup of an analytic group to be closed. This requires results on the centers of analytic groups and on closures of analytic subgroups that are of independent interest. Chapter XVII introduces complex analytic groups and the universal complexifications of real analytic groups; in particular, it characterizes the universal complexifications of the compact analytic groups in representation-theoretical terms. Finally, Chapter XVIII gives the main results concerning the existence of faithful representations of analytic groups and the structure of linear analytic groups.

There are a few exercises at the end of each chapter. These are not to be taken in the sense of gymnastics; they are meant to clarify and supplement the material of the chapter, and indications of proofs are frequently included. A few times, the result of an exercise is made use of later on.

Consciously and subconsciously, I have incorporated many suggestions and used much advice of my friends and colleagues, but I am especially indebted to G. D. Mostow whose share of involuntary contributions to this exposition is large, having accumulated in years of collaboration. My special thanks are due to Siegfried Grosser whose notes on a course I gave at Berkeley in 1963–64 form the nucleus around which the present exposition has been built.

G. H.

Berkeley, June 1965

TABLE OF CONTENTS

I. TOPOLOGICAL GROUPS [6, 7, 8, 10]

1

We shall take the elementary notions and results of general topology for granted. The word "space" will be used to mean "topological Hausdorff space". By the topology of a space we mean the collection of its open sets.

Since the notion of compactness will play an important role, we recall the usual frequently used facts concerning it. A compact subset of a space is closed, and a closed subset of a compact space is compact. A continuous map $f: S \to T$ of a space S into a space T sends every compact subset of S onto a compact subset of T. If S is compact and f is bijective then f is necessarily a homeomorphism. A Cartesian product of a family of compact spaces is always compact. Finally, every compact space is *normal*, in the sense that, for every pair (A, B) of disjoint closed sets, there are disjoint open sets U and V such that $A \subset U$ and $B \subset V$.

The importance of normality resides in the following result, known as *Urysohn's Lemma*.

Let A and B be disjoint closed subsets of a normal space S. Then there is a continuous map f of S into the closed interval [0, 1] *such that f takes the value 0 at every point of A and the value 1 at every point of B.*

We sketch the proof. Using the normality, and induction on n, one constructs, for each proper dyadic fraction $k/2^n$, an open set $U(k/2^n)$ such that the following conditions are satisfied: $U(1) = S - B$; if $r < r'$ then the closure of $U(r)$ is contained in $U(r')$; every $U(r)$ contains A. Now one defines $f(x)$ to be equal to 1 if x does not lie in $U(1)$ and to be equal to $\inf[r \mid x \in U(r)]$ if x lies in $U(1)$. Next, one notes the following two facts:

if $0 < t \leq 1$, then $[x \mid f(x) < t] = \bigcup_{r<t} U(r)$;

if $0 \leq t < 1$, then $[x \mid f(x) > t] = \bigcup_{r>t} (S - U(r)^*)$,

where the star denotes topological closure. The fact that these sets are open implies that f is continuous, while the other requirements on f are evidently satisfied.

Let S be a compact space, and let $\mathscr{C}(S)$ denote the algebra (over the field of the real numbers) of all continuous real-valued functions on S. One has a norm on $\mathscr{C}(S)$, defined by $\|f\| = \max_{x \in S} |f(x)|$, and we view $\mathscr{C}(S)$ as a topological space, with the metric topology derived from this norm. It is clear that addition, multiplication and scalar multiplication in $\mathscr{C}(S)$ are all continuous with respect to this topology. The fundamental result concerning $\mathscr{C}(S)$ is the *Stone-Weierstrass Theorem*, and reads as follows.

Let A be a subalgebra of the algebra $\mathscr{C}(S)$ of the continuous real-valued functions on the compact space S, and suppose that A separates the points of S. Then the closure A^* of A in $\mathscr{C}(S)$ either coincides with $\mathscr{C}(S)$ or is the algebra of all continuous functions that vanish at some fixed point a of S.

In order to prove this result, one shows first that if $f \in A^*$ then $|f| \in A^*$. In doing this, one may evidently suppose that $\|f\| \leq 1$. Since $|f| = (f^2)^{1/2}$, it then suffices to show that, on $[0, 1]$, the function $(x)^{1/2}$ is the uniform limit of a sequence of polynomials $p_n(x)$ with constant terms 0. Such a sequence is given by

$$p_0(x) = 0, \qquad p_{n+1}(x) = p_n(x) + \tfrac{1}{2}(x - p_n(x)^2).$$

Next, one notes that

$$\sup(f_1, f_2) = \tfrac{1}{2}(f_1 + f_2 + |f_1 - f_2|)$$

and
$$\inf(f_1, f_2) = \tfrac{1}{2}(f_1 + f_2 - |f_1 - f_2|).$$

Hence one may conclude that if f_1 and f_2 belong to A^* then $\sup(f_1, f_2)$ and $\inf(f_1, f_2)$ belong to A^*.

Now let us suppose that there is no point in S at which all the elements of A take the value 0. Let x and y be distinct points of S. By the assumption of the theorem, there is an element u in A such that $u(x) \neq u(y)$. We may suppose (interchanging x and y if necessary) that $u(x) \neq 0$. By our additional assumption, there is an element v in A such that $v(y) \neq 0$. Now we can evidently choose a real number ρ such that, if $f = u + \rho v$, we have $f(x) f(y) (f(x) - f(y)) \neq 0$. Then, given arbitrary real numbers α and β, there are real numbers γ and δ such that $\gamma f(x) + \delta f(x)^2 = \alpha$ and $\gamma f(y) + \delta f(y)^2 = \beta$. Thus, given distinct points x and y in S and real numbers α and β, there is always an element g in A such that $g(x) = \alpha$ and $g(y) = \beta$.

Keeping our assumption in force, let h be any element of $\mathscr{C}(S)$, and let e be any positive real number. If x and y are distinct points of S then, by what we have just proved, there is an element $g_{x,y}$ in A such that $g_{x,y}(x) < h(x) + e$ and $g_{x,y}(y) > h(y) - e$. Let S_y be the set of all points z in S such that $g_{x,y}(z) > h(z) - e$. Then S_y is an open neighborhood of y in S. Since S is compact, there is a finite set of points $y_1, \cdots, y_n$ in S such that S is the union of the family of sets S_{y_i}. Put $k_x = \sup(g_{x,y_1}, \cdots, g_{x,y_n})$. Then we have $k_x(x) < h(x) + e$ and $k_x(z) > h(z) - e$ for every z in S. From what we have proved in the beginning, we know that k_x belongs to A^*. Now let S'_x be the set of all points z in S such that $k_x(z) < h(z) + e$. One sees as before that there is a finite set of points $x_1, \cdots, x_m$ in S such that S is the union of the family of sets S_{x_i}. Put $k = \inf(k_{x_1}, \cdots, k_{x_m})$. Then $k \in A^*$ and $h(z) + e > k(z) > h(z) - e$ for all z in S. Hence it is clear that $h \in A^*$, so that $A^* = \mathscr{C}(S)$.

Now consider the remaining case where there is a point a in S at which every element of A takes the value 0. Let A_1 be the subalgebra $R + A$ of $\mathscr{C}(S)$, where R stands for the algebra of the constant functions. Then the above applies to A_1, whence $A_1^* = \mathscr{C}(S)$. Now let f be an element of $\mathscr{C}(S)$ such that $f(a) = 0$. Let (f_n) be a sequence of elements of A_1 that converges to f. Then, clearly, $f_n - f_n(a) \in A$, and the limit of the sequence $(f_n - f_n(a))$ is $f - f(a) = f$. Thus $f \in A^*$, q.e.d.

2

A *topological group* is a group G that is endowed with a Hausdorff topology such that the map $G \times G \to G$ that sends (x, y) onto xy^{-1} is continuous. It follows at once from this definition that the inversion map on G is continuous, because this map can be factored according to the scheme $x \to (1, x) \to 1x^{-1} = x^{-1}$, where 1 stands for the neutral element of G. Hence the multiplication is also a continuous map $G \times G \to G$, because it can be factored according to the scheme $(x, y) \to (x, y^{-1}) \to x(y^{-1})^{-1} = xy$. In particular, this implies that if x is any element of G then the left and right translations effected by x on G, sending an element y of G onto xy or yx, respectively, are homeomorphisms of G onto G.

The topology of a topological group G is easily seen to be determined by any *fundamental system of neighborhoods* of 1, i.e., a family of neighborhoods of 1 such that every neighborhood of 1 contains a member of the family. In fact, if S is a fundamental system of neighborhoods of 1, then a subset A of G is open if and only if, for every point x of A, there is a member V of S such that $Vx \subset A$ (or such that $xV \subset A$).

It is frequently convenient to define a topology on a group G by giving a fundamental system of neighborhoods of 1. A family S of subsets of a group G is a fundamental system of neighborhoods of 1 for a topology with which G is a topological group if and only if the following conditions are satisfied:

N_1. The intersection of S is the set consisting of 1 alone.

N_2. The intersection of every pair of members of S contains a member of S.

N_3. For every member V of S, there is a member W of S such that $WW^{-1} \subset V$.

N_4. If x is a point of G and V is a member of S then xVx^{-1} contains a member of S.

We leave the verification that these conditions indeed characterize fundamental systems of neighborhoods of 1 to the reader.

If G is a topological group and H is a subgroup of G then the topology induced on H from that of G evidently makes H into a topological group. It is equally important to define an appropriate topology on the set G/H of the cosets xH of H in G. Let π denote the canonical map $G \to G/H$ that is defined by $\pi(x) = xH$ for every x in G. If we view this situation in the category of (not necessarily Hausdorff) topological spaces and continuous maps we can give a precise meaning to "appropriate": π should be continuous and, for every continuous map α of G into a topological space S that is constant on each coset of H in G, the corresponding map $\alpha^H: G/H \to S$, where $\alpha^H \circ \pi = \alpha$, should be continuous. It is clear that there can be at most one such topology on G/H. Actually, it exists, and its open sets are precisely all those subsets T of G/H for which $\pi^{-1}(T)$ is an open subset of G. Moreover, it clearly has the additional property that the canonical map $\mu: G \times (G/H) \to G/H$, where $\mu(x, yH) = xyH$, is continuous.

There is one unavoidable drawback: in general, G/H is not a Hausdorff space. In fact, it is easily seen that G/H is a Hausdorff space if and only if H

is closed in G. For this reason, one usually refrains from considering the topology of G/H if H is not closed in G.

We shall derive a sufficient condition for a subgroup H of a topological group G to be closed in G, which is sometimes useful. Generally, let us say that a subset T of a space S is *locally closed* if every point t of T has a neighborhood V_t in S such that $V_t \cap T$ is closed. Let V_t° denote the interior of V_t. If $x \in V_t^\circ \cap T^*$ then every neighborhood of x meets $V_t \cap T$, whence $x \in V_t \cap T$. Thus we have $V_t^\circ \cap T^* = V_t^\circ \cap T$. Hence $T = V \cap T^*$, where $V = \bigcup_{t \in T} V_t^\circ$, i.e., T is the intersection of an open subset of S with T^*.

PROPOSITION 2.1. *Let H be a subgroup of the topological group G. If H is locally closed, in particular if H is locally compact with its induced topology, then H is closed in G.*

Proof. If H is locally closed then, by the above, we have $H = V \cap H^*$, where V is open in G. Let $x \in H^*, y \in H$. Let W be a neighborhood of 1 in G such that $yW \subset V$. Since x lies in H^*, there is an element z in H such that zx lies in W, whence $yzx \in V$. On the other hand, since yz lies in H, it is clear that $yzx \in H^*$. Thus $yzx \in V \cap H^*$, and so $yzx \in H$, whence $x \in H$. We have shown that $H^* = H$, i.e., that H is closed. It remains only to observe that a locally compact subspace T of a space S is locally closed in S. Indeed, if t is a point of T and U_t is a compact neighborhood of t in T, then U_t is closed in S and $U_t = V_t \cap T$, where V_t is a neighborhood of t in S.

It is clear from the definition of the topology on the coset space G/H that if H is a closed normal subgroup of G then G/H is a topological group. Now let γ be a continuous surjective group homomorphism of G onto a topological group K, and let H denote the kernel of γ. Evidently, H is a closed normal subgroup of G, and the induced map $\gamma^H \colon G/H \to K$ is a bijective continuous homomorphism. However, in general, it is not a homeomorphism. The map γ^H is a homeomorphism if and only if γ is an open map. The next two theorems cover cases in which γ can be proved to be open. For the first of these theorems, we require the following simple fact.

LEMMA 2.2. *Let G be a topological group, K a compact subset of G, and T a closed subset of G. Then TK is closed in G.*

Proof. Let x be any element of $G - TK$. Then $T^{-1}x$ does not meet K. Since T is closed, so is $T^{-1}x$. Hence, for every point t of K, there is a neighborhood V_t of 1 in G such that tV_tV_t does not meet $T^{-1}x$. The compact set K is covered by a finite subfamily of the family of tV_t's. If V is the intersection of the corresponding finite family of V_t's then V is still a neighborhood of 1 in G, and KV does not meet $T^{-1}x$. Hence xV^{-1} does not meet TK, and we have shown that $G - TK$ is open, q.e.d.

THEOREM 2.3. *Let G be a topological group, L a closed subgroup of G, and H a compact subgroup of G. Let π denote the canonical map $G \rightarrow G/H$, let $\pi_L\colon L \rightarrow \pi(L)$ and $(\pi_L)^{L \cap H}\colon L/(L \cap H) \rightarrow \pi(L)$ denote the continuous maps canonically induced by π. Then π_L is both an open map and a closed map, and $(\pi_L)^{L \cap H}$ is a homeomorphism.*

Proof. Let T be a closed subset of L. Then T is also closed in G, and it follows from Lemma 2.2 that TH is closed in G. Since π is an open map, $\pi(G - TH)$ is open in G/H. Clearly, $\pi(T) = G/H - \pi(G - TH)$. Thus $\pi(T)$ is closed in G/H and hence also in $\pi(L)$. This proves that π_L is a closed map.

Now let μ denote the canonical map $L \rightarrow L/(L \cap H)$. If X is a closed subset of $L/(L \cap H)$ then $\mu^{-1}(X)$ is closed in L. Hence, by what we have just proved, $\pi_L(\mu^{-1}(X))$ is closed in $\pi(L)$, i.e., $(\pi_L)^{L \cap H}(X)$ is closed in $\pi(L)$. Thus $(\pi_L)^{L \cap H}$ is a closed map. Since it is bijective, it is therefore also an open map, and hence a homeomorphism. Finally, $\pi_L = (\pi_L)^{L \cap H} \circ \mu$, which shows that π_L is also an open map.

In particular, consider the case where H is normal in G. Then LH is a subgroup of G, and is closed, by Lemma 2.2. Quite generally, if S and T are arbitrary subgroups of G such that $T \subset S$ then the continuous bijective map $(\pi_S)^T\colon S/T \rightarrow \pi(S)$ induced by the canonical map $\pi\colon G \rightarrow G/T$ is a homeomorphism, by means of which we may identify S/T with $\pi(S)$. Indeed, the open sets of S/T are the sets of cosets vT with v ranging over an open subset V of S such that $VT = V$. Hence $V = W \cap S$, where W is an open set of G such that $WT = W$. From this, one sees immediately that $\pi(W \cap S) = \pi(W) \cap \pi(S)$, which shows that this is an open set of $\pi(S)$. Since this set is the image under $(\pi_S)^T$ of the open set of S/T we started with, this shows that $(\pi_S)^T$ is an open map and thus a homeomorphism. Hence Theorem 2.3 gives the result that *the canonical map $L/(L \cap H) \rightarrow (LH)/H$ is a homeomorphism whenever H is a compact normal subgroup of G and L a closed subgroup of G.*

For the next theorem, we need the following well-known topological result.

LEMMA 2.4. *Let S be a locally compact space, and suppose that S is the union of* *a countable family of closed sets A_n, $n = 1, 2, \cdots$. Then one of the A_n's contains a non-empty open set of S.*

Proof. Suppose this is not true. Since S is locally compact, there is a non-empty open set V in S such that V^* is compact. Now there is a point v_1 in V that does not lie in A_1. Using that $(V^* - V) \cup (V^* \cap A_1)$ is compact, we see easily that there is an open neighborhood V_1 of v_1 such that $V_1^* \subset V$ and $V_1^* \cap A_1 = \varnothing$. Next, there is a point v_2 in V_1 that does not lie in A_2. Continuing in this fashion, we obtain a sequence of non-empty closed subsets V_n^* of V^* such that $V_{n+1}^* \subset V_n^*$ and V_n^* does not meet any A_k with $k \leq n$. Since V^* is compact, the intersection of this nested family of V_n^*'s is non-empty, and it does not meet any one of the A_n's, so that we have a contradiction.

Let V be a space, G a topological group. Suppose that we are given a map $\mu: G \times V \to V$ such that, abbreviating $\mu(g, v)$ by $g \cdot v$, all the partial maps $g \to g \cdot v$ and $v \to g \cdot v$ are continuous and $g_1 \cdot (g_2 \cdot v) = (g_1 g_2) \cdot v$ for all elements g_1, g_2 of G and all points v of V. Suppose also that G acts transitively on V, i.e., that $G \cdot v = V$ for some (and hence every) point v of V. Then we shall say that V is a *homogeneous G-space*.

THEOREM 2.5. *Let G be a locally compact topological group that is a union of a countable family of compact subsets. Let V be a locally compact homogeneous G-space, and let v be a point of V. Then the continuous surjective map $\gamma: G \to V$ such that $\gamma(g) = g \cdot v$ is an open map, and the given map $\mu: G \times V \to V$ is continuous.*

Proof. Both assertions follow once it is shown that if U is any neighborhood of 1 in G then $U \cdot v$ is a neighborhood of v in V. Choose an open neighborhood X of 1 in G such that $X^{-1}X \subset U$. Since G is locally compact, X contains a compact neighborhood Y of 1. From the fact that G is the union of a countable family of compact sets, we see easily that there is a countable set of points g_n ($n = 1, 2, \cdots$) in G such that G is the union of the family of compact sets $g_n Y$. Since γ is continuous and surjective, the sets $\gamma(g_n Y)$ are closed and cover V. By Lemma 2.4, there is an index n such that $\gamma(g_n Y)$ contains a non-empty open set P of V. Let y be a point in Y such that $\gamma(g_n y) \in P$. Then we have

$$(g_n y)^{-1} \cdot P = y^{-1} \cdot (g_n^{-1} \cdot P) \subset y^{-1} \cdot (Y \cdot v) \subset U \cdot v.$$

Since $(g_n y)^{-1} \cdot P$ is evidently a neighborhood of v in V, this completes the proof.

7

The most important case covered by Theorem 2.5 is the case where V is a topological group and γ is a surjective continuous homomorphism $G \to V$.

We shall devote the rest of this section to the standard facts concerning compactness and local compactness of topological groups and their coset spaces. One sees almost immediately that if G is locally compact and H is a closed subgroup of G then both H and G/H are locally compact. It is completely obvious that if G is compact then so are H and G/H. The converse of each statement is also true, but much harder to prove.

THEOREM 2.6. *Let G be a topological group, and suppose that G has a closed subgroup H such that H and G/H are locally compact. Then G is locally compact. If H and G/H are compact then G is compact.*

Proof. Let π denote the canonical map $G \to G/H$. Since H is locally compact, there is a closed neighborhood U of 1 in G such that $H \cap (U^{-1}U)^*$ is compact. Choose a closed neighborhood U_1 of 1 in G such that $U_1^{-1}U_1 \subset U$. Since G/H is locally compact, there is a compact neighborhood C of $\pi(1)$ in G/H such that $C \subset \pi(U_1)$. Put $V = U_1 \cap \pi^{-1}(C)$. Then V is a closed neighborhood of 1 in G, and we shall prove that V is compact.

Let $\mathscr{B}$ be any family of subsets of V that is maximal with respect to the finite intersection property. In order to conclude that V is compact, it suffices to show that the intersection of the family consisting of the closures in V of the members of $\mathscr{B}$ is non-empty. Since V is closed, closures in V are closures in G. Thus we must show that $\bigcap_{B \in \mathscr{B}} B^* \neq \varnothing$.

Now $\pi(\mathscr{B})$ is a family of subsets of the compact set $\pi(V) = C$ with the finite intersection property. Hence $\bigcap_{B \in \mathscr{B}} \pi(B)^* \neq \varnothing$, so that there is a point v in V such that $\pi(v)$ lies in each $\pi(B)^*$. Now $H \cap (v^{-1}U)$ is a closed subset of the compact set $H \cap (U^{-1}U)^*$ and hence is compact, whence $(vH) \cap U$ is compact.

Now suppose that $\bigcap_{B \in \mathscr{B}} B^*$ is empty. Then, for each point x of $(vH) \cap U$, we can find a neighborhood V_x of 1 in G and a member B_x of $\mathscr{B}$ such that $V_x V_x x$ does not meet B_x. Since $(vH) \cap U$ is compact, it is covered by a finite family $(V_{x_i} x_i)$, $i = 1, 2, \cdots, n$. Put $B = B_{x_1} \cap \cdots \cap B_{x_n} \in \mathscr{B}$, and $W = U_1 \cap V_{x_1} \cap \cdots \cap V_{x_n}$. Then $W((vH) \cap U)$ does not meet B. On the other hand, $\pi(Wv)$ is a neighborhood of $\pi(v)$ in G/H and hence must meet $\pi(B)$. But this means that there is a point w in W, a point b in B and a point h in H such that $wvh = b$. Then $vh = w^{-1}b \in U_1^{-1}U_1 \subset U$, so that $b \in W((vH) \cap U)$, which contradicts the above. Thus the first part of Theorem 2.6 is proved.

If H and G/H are compact we may take $C = G/H$ and $U_1 = G$ in the above. Then we have $V = G$, so that G is compact. This completes the proof.

3

Let f be a function defined on a space S. We define the *support* of f as the closure of the set of non-zeros of f in S, and we denote it by S_f. Let G be a locally compact topological group, and let $\mathscr{C}$ denote the algebra of all continuous real-valued functions on G with compact support. Let $\mathscr{C}^+$ denote the set of the non-negative functions belonging to $\mathscr{C}$. If f is a function on G and x is an element of G we define the function $x \cdot f$ on G by putting $(x \cdot f)(y) = f(yx)$ for every element y of G. A real linear map I of $\mathscr{C}$ into the field of the real numbers is called a *Haar integral* for G if it is not the zero map, takes only non-negative values on $\mathscr{C}^+$, and is such that $I(x \cdot f) = I(f)$ for every element f of $\mathscr{C}$ and every element x of G. In order that such an I should exist, it is necessary and sufficient that there exist a real-valued function I^+ on $\mathscr{C}^+$ satisfying the following conditions:

(1) I^+ is not identically 0 and takes only non-negative values;
(2) $I^+(rf) = rI^+(f)$ for every f in $\mathscr{C}^+$ and every non-negative real number r;
(3) $I^+(f + g) = I^+(f) + I^+(g)$ for all elements f and g of $\mathscr{C}^+$;
(4) $I^+(x \cdot f) = I^+(f)$ for every x in G and every f in $\mathscr{C}^+$.

Indeed, if a Haar integral I exists then we may take for I^+ the restriction of I to $\mathscr{C}^+$. Conversely, every I^+ satisfying the above conditions has a unique extension to a Haar integral I as follows. For every f in $\mathscr{C}$ define the elements f_+ and f_- of $\mathscr{C}^+$ by $f_+(x) = \max(f(x), 0), f_-(x) = \max(-f(x), 0)$. Then we have $f = f_+ - f_-$, and we define

$$I(f) = I^+(f_+) - I^+(f_-).$$

We proceed to the existence proof. Let f and g be elements of $\mathscr{C}^+$. Suppose that $g \neq 0$. Then there is a non-empty open set A in G such that $g(x) > \gamma$ for all x in A, where γ is some positive real number. Since the support G_f of f is compact, there is a finite set of points $x_1, \cdots, x_n$ in G such that the sets Ax_i cover G_f. Hence, if M denotes the maximum value of f, we have $f \leq \sum_{i=1}^n (M/\gamma) x_i^{-1} \cdot g$. In particular, we see that there are

9

elements $z_1, \cdots, z_n$ in G and positive real numbers $\gamma_1, \cdots, \gamma_n$ such that $f \leq \sum_{i=1}^{n} \gamma_i z_i \cdot g$. We define $(f:g)$ as the infimum of all sums $\sum_{i=1}^{n} \gamma_i$ that arise in this fashion. If m is the maximum value of g then we have evidently $f \leq m(f: g)$, so that $(f: g) > 0$ whenever $f \neq 0$.

It follows immediately from the definition that if h is another non-zero element of $\mathscr{C}^+$ then $(f: h) \leq (f: g)(g: h)$, and so $(f: h)/(g: h) \leq (f: g)$. Similarly, if $f \neq 0$, we have $(g: h) \leq (g:f)(f: h)$, and so $1/(g:f) \leq (f: h)/(g: h)$. Let K_f denote the closed interval $[1/(g:f), (f: g)]$ if $f \neq 0$, and let $K_f = [0]$ if $f = 0$. Let K stand for the Cartesian product space $\prod_{f \in \mathscr{C}^+} K_f$. By the above, we have $(f: h)/(g: h) \in K_f$ for every f in $\mathscr{C}^+$. Keeping g fixed, let $K(h)$ denote the point of K whose projection on K_f is $(f: h)/(g: h)$ for every f.

For any neighborhood V of 1 in G, denote by $\mathscr{C}_V^+$ the set of all elements of $\mathscr{C}^+$ whose supports lie in V and that do not take the value 0 at 1. Since G is locally compact, it follows from Urysohn's Lemma that $\mathscr{C}_V^+$ is non-empty. Let $K(V)$ denote the closure in K of the set of $K(h)$'s with h in $\mathscr{C}_V^+$. It is clear that the family of these $K(V)$'s has the finite intersection property. Since K is compact, there is a point I^+ in K that belongs to each $K(V)$. Clearly, I^+ may be viewed as a real-valued function on $\mathscr{C}^+$, $I^+(f)$ being the projection of I^+ on K_f. We claim that I^+ satisfies the four conditions listed above.

The fact that I^+ lies in $K(V)$ may be spelled out as follows: given $f_1, \cdots, f_n$ in $\mathscr{C}^+$ and a positive number ε, there is an element h in $\mathscr{C}_V^+$ such that $(f_i: h)/(g: h)$ differs from $I^+(f_i)$ by less than ε for each i. Hence conditions (1), (2) and (4) follow from the corresponding properties of $(f: h)$, which are either obvious or have been proved above.

The additivity property (3) is not obvious. However, it is clear from the definition that $((f_1 + f_2): h) \leq (f_1: h) + (f_2: h)$, whence $I^+(f_1 + f_2) \leq I^+(f_1) + I^+(f_2)$. In order to prove the reversed inequality, choose an element p in $\mathscr{C}^+$ that has a positive minimum on $G_{f_1 + f_2}$; this is possible by applying Urysohn's Lemma on a compact subset of G containing the compact set $G_{f_1 + f_2}$ in its interior. Now define functions q_1 and q_2 on G with support contained in $G_{f_1 + f_2}$ and q_j coinciding with $f_j/(f_1 + f_2 + \varepsilon p)$ on $G_{f_1 + f_2}$, where ε is a positive real number. Then we have, evidently, $q_j \in \mathscr{C}$, $q_j(f_1 + f_2 + \varepsilon p) = f_j$, and $q_1 + q_2 \leq 1$.

There is a neighborhood V of 1 in G such that, for $j = 1, 2$, $|q_j(y) - q_j(x)| < \varepsilon$ whenever y lies in Vx. Write q for $f_1 + f_2 + \varepsilon p$, let h be an element of $\mathscr{C}_V^+$, and suppose that $q \leq \sum_{i=1}^{n} \gamma_i(x_i \cdot h)$. Then we have $q(x) \leq \sum'_i \gamma_i h(xx_i)$, where $\sum'_i$ is the sum over those indices i for which xx_i lies in V. For these indices i, we have $|q_j(x) - q_j(x_i{}^{-1})| < \varepsilon$. Hence

$$q_j(x)q(x) \leq \sum'_i \gamma_i(q_j(x_i{}^{-1}) + \varepsilon)h(xx_i)$$

for every x, which shows that $((q_jq):h) \leq \sum^n_{i=1} \gamma_i(q_j(x_i{}^{-1}) + \varepsilon)$. Adding these inequalities for $j = 1, 2$, and using that $q_1 + q_2 \leq 1$, we obtain $((q_1q): h) + ((q_2q): h) \leq (1 + 2\varepsilon)\sum^n_{i=1} \gamma_i$. We may therefore conclude that the left-hand side is less than or equal to $(1 + 2\varepsilon)(q: h)$. Thus we have

$$(f_1: h) + (f_2: h) \leq (1 + 2\varepsilon)((f_1 + f_2 + \varepsilon p): h)$$
$$\leq (1 + 2\varepsilon)[((f_1 + f_2): h) + \varepsilon(p: h)].$$

It follows from this that we must have

$$I^+(f_1) + I^+(f_2) \leq (1 + 2\varepsilon)[I^+(f_1 + f_2) + \varepsilon I^+(p)],$$

and hence that $I^+(f_1) + I^+(f_2) \leq I^+(f_1 + f_2)$. This completes the proof of the existence of a Haar integral.

Now let J be any Haar integral for G. If f and g are elements of $\mathscr{C}^+$ and $g \neq 0$ we see immediately from the definition of $(f: g)$ that $J(f) \leq (f: g)J(g)$. Since there is an f such that $J(f) > 0$, this shows that $J(g) > 0$ for every non-zero element g of $\mathscr{C}^+$.

Let P be a compact subset of G, and let $\mathscr{C}_P$ denote the subalgebra of $\mathscr{C}$ consisting of the elements of $\mathscr{C}$ whose supports lie in P. There is an element p of $\mathscr{C}^+$ such that $p(x) = 1$ for every point x in P. Now if f belongs to $\mathscr{C}_P$ and if M is the maximum value taken on by its absolute value then we see easily that $|J(f)| \leq J(|f|) \leq MJ(p)$. *Hence the restriction to $\mathscr{C}_P$ of J is continuous with respect to the norm that is given by* $\|f\| = \max_{x \in G}|f(x)|$.

Now let I and J be any two Haar integrals for G. We wish to prove that there is a positive real number γ such that $I(f) = \gamma J(f)$ for every f in $\mathscr{C}$. For this purpose, we consider the continuous functions with compact support on $G \times G$. If f is such a function, and if we define $_xf(y) = f(x,y)$, then $_xf$ evidently belongs to $\mathscr{C}$, and we may define a function $_If$ by setting $_If(x) = I(_xf)$. It is clear from the continuity property of a Haar integral that $_If$ belongs to $\mathscr{C}$, so that we may form $J(_If)$. Similarly, define $f_y(x) = f(x,y)$ and $f_J(y) = J(f_y)$. We shall show that $J(_If) = I(f_J)$ for every f.

Observe first that if $f(x,y) = u(x)v(y)$, where u and v belong to $\mathscr{C}$, we have $J(_If) = J(u)I(v) = I(f_J)$. In the general case, we deduce the equality by approximating f with sums of such product functions. Given f, there is a compact subset A of G such that the support of f is contained in

$A \times A$. Let T denote the algebra consisting of the functions of the type $g(x, y) = \sum_{i=1}^{n} u_i(x)v_i(y)$, where the u_i's and the v_i's belong to $\mathscr{C}_A$. Clearly, it will suffice to show that T is dense in the algebra of the continuous functions on $G \times G$ whose supports lie in $A \times A$, which may be identified with the algebra of the continuous functions on $A \times A$ that vanish on the boundary of $A \times A$. Let B denote the space obtained from $A \times A$ by collapsing the boundary of $A \times A$ to a single point b_0. Then the algebra of the continuous functions on $A \times A$ that vanish on the boundary of $A \times A$ may be identified with the algebra of the continuous functions on B that take the value 0 at b_0. Clearly, the subalgebra corresponding to T separates the points of B. Hence it follows from the Stone-Weierstrass Theorem that this is a dense subalgebra, so that T is indeed dense in the algebra of the continuous functions on $G \times G$ whose supports lie in $A \times A$.

Now we are in a position to prove that I and J are proportional. Let f be an element of $\mathscr{C}^+$, and choose an open subset U of G such that $G_f \subset U$ and U^* is compact. Also choose an element p of $\mathscr{C}^+$ that takes the value 1 at every point of U. Given a positive number ε, choose a symmetric neighborhood $V = V^{-1}$ of 1 in G such that $|f(xy) - f(yx)| < \varepsilon$ for all x whenever y lies in V, and such that $(G_f V) \cup (V G_f) \subset U$. This last condition ensures that $f(xy) = f(xy)p(x)$ and $f(yx) = f(yx)p(x)$ whenever y lies in V, so that, by the first condition, $|f(xy) - f(yx)| < \varepsilon p(x)$ for all x.

Define $u(x, y) = h(y)f(xy)$, where h is an element of $\mathscr{C}^+$ such that $h(y) = h(y^{-1})$ for every y and the support of h lies in V. Evidently, u is continuous and has compact support. We compute $I(u_J)$. Since $u_y = h(y)y \cdot f$, we have $u_J(y) = h(y)J(y \cdot f) = h(y)J(f)$, whence $I(u_J) = I(h)J(f)$. On the other hand, define $v(x, y) = h(y)f(yx)$, and let us compute $I(v_J)$. We know that $I(v_J) = J(_I v)$. Now $_x v = h(x \cdot f)$, whence $_I v(x) = I(h(x \cdot f)) = I((x^{-1} \cdot h)f) = _I w(x)$, where $w(x, y) = h(yx^{-1})f(y) = h(xy^{-1})f(y)$. Thus $J(_I v) = J(_I w) = I(w_J)$. Now $w_y = (y^{-1} \cdot h)f(y)$, so that $w_J(y) = f(y)J(y^{-1} \cdot h) = f(y)J(h)$, which gives $I(w_J) = J(h)I(f)$. Thus $I(u_J) = I(h)J(f)$ and $I(v_J) = J(h)I(f)$.

Now we have $|u(x, y) - v(x, y)| < \varepsilon p(x)h(y)$, so that we obtain

$$|I(h)J(f) - J(h)I(f)| < \varepsilon I(h)J(p).$$

If g is another element of $\mathscr{C}^+$ we proceed with g as we did above with f, using a suitable element q of $\mathscr{C}^+$ to take the place of p and restricting h so that it will serve for g as well as for f. Then we have, in addition to the last inequality,

$$|I(h)J(g) - J(h)I(g)| < \varepsilon I(h)J(q).$$

Take f and g different from 0 and divide the above inequalities by $I(f)I(h)$ or $I(g)I(h)$, respectively. Then we obtain

$$|J(f)/I(f) - J(h)/I(h)| < \varepsilon J(p)/I(f)$$

and
$$|J(g)/I(g) - J(h)/I(h)| < \varepsilon J(q)/I(g).$$

Hence

$$|J(f)/I(f) - J(g)/I(g)| < \varepsilon[J(p)/I(f) + J(q)/I(g)].$$

Since p and q may be fixed independently of ε when f and g are given, it follows that $J(f)/I(f) = J(g)/I(g)$, so that we have proved that, *up to a positive constant factor, there is only one Haar integral for G.*

EXERCISES

1. Noting that every open subgroup of a topological group is also closed, show that a connected topological group is generated by every neighborhood of the neutral element. Hence show that every discrete normal subgroup of a connected topological group is central, and that a continuous surjective homomorphism of a locally compact connected group onto a locally compact group is open.

2. Let G be a connected topological group, and let C be a discrete normal subgroup of G. Show that if G/C is compact then C is finitely generated. [First show that there is a compact neighborhood U of 1 such that $G = UC$, and hence that there is a finite subset C_1 of C such that $UUU^{-1} \subset UC_1$. By considering the canonical image of U in G/D, where D is the subgroup of C generated by C_1, deduce that $G = UD$, from which point the proof is easily completed.]

3. Let G be a locally compact group that has a semidirect product decomposition $G = N \cdot K$, where N and K are closed subgroups, N is normal in G, and the multiplication induces a homeomorphism of $N \times K$ onto G. Let I and J be Haar integrals for N and K, respectively. If f is a continuous function with compact support on G, define the function $_I f$ on K by setting $_I f(x) = I((x \cdot f)_N)$, where the subscript N means restriction of the function to N. Show that $_I f$ is continuous and has compact support, and that the map sending each f onto $J(_I f)$ is a Haar integral for G. Use this to find an explicit Haar integral for the multiplicative group of the matrices $\begin{pmatrix} a & b \\ 0 & 1 \end{pmatrix}$, where a ranges over the set of all positive real numbers and b ranges over the set of all real numbers.

II. COMPACT GROUPS [1, 2, 10]

1

We shall require a certain amount of operator theory for the space $\mathscr{C}$ of the continuous real-valued functions with compact support on the locally compact group G. For this purpose, we introduce the positive definite inner product given by $[f, g] = I(fg)$, where I is a Haar integral for G. This satisfies the *Schwarz inequality* $[f, g]^2 \leq [f,f][g,g]$, which follows immediately from the fact that, for all real numbers α and β, we have $0 \leq [\alpha f + \beta g, \alpha f + \beta g] = \alpha^2[f,f] + 2\alpha\beta[f, g] + \beta^2[g, g]$. We write $[f]$ for $[f,f]^{1/2}$. Then the Schwarz inequality may be written $|[f, g]| \leq [f][g]$. From this, one easily deduces the triangle inequality $[f + g] \leq [f] + [g]$. In fact, we have

$$[f + g]^2 = [f]^2 + 2[f, g] + [g]^2 \leq [f]^2 + 2[f][g] + [g]^2$$
$$= ([f] + [g])^2.$$

A subset $(e_\alpha)_{\alpha \in A}$ of $\mathscr{C}$ is called an *orthonormal set* if $[e_\alpha] = 1$ for each α and $[e_\alpha, e_\beta] = 0$ whenever $\alpha \neq \beta$. We recall the *Bessel inequality*, which says that, for every finite subset B of A and every element f of $\mathscr{C}$, $\sum_{\beta \in B}[f, e_\beta]^2 \leq [f]^2$. For the proof, one merely has to observe that

$$[f]^2 - \sum_{\beta \in B}[f, e_\beta]^2 = [f - \sum_{\beta \in B}[f, e_\beta]e_\beta]^2.$$

Let T be a linear endomorphism of $\mathscr{C}$ that is continuous with respect to the metric defined by our norm [ ]. Then the set of real numbers $[T(f)]$, where f ranges over the elements of $\mathscr{C}$ such that $[f] = 1$, is bounded. For otherwise there would be a sequence of elements f_n of $\mathscr{C}$ such that $[f_n] = 1$ while $[T(f_n)] \geq n$. Hence the sequence $[(1/n)f_n]$ converges to 0 and $[T((1/n)f_n)] \geq 1$, which contradicts the continuity of T.

The *norm* of the operator T is defined by $[T] = \sup_{[f]=1}([T(f)])$. We say that T is *symmetric* if $[T(f), g] = [f, T(g)]$ for all f and g.

14

LEMMA 1.1. *If T is symmetric then $[T] = \sup_{[f]=1}(|[T(f),f]|)$.*

Proof. If $[f] = 1$ the Schwarz inequality gives $|[T(f),f]| \leq [T(f)]$. Hence the supremum written in the statement of the lemma exists as a non-negative real number $\mu \leq [T]$. Hence it suffices to show that if $[f] = 1$ then $[T(f)] \leq \mu$. Assuming, as we may, that $T(f) \neq 0$, put $g = [T(f)]^{-1}T(f)$. Then $[g] = 1$, and $[T(f),g] = [T(f)] = [g, T(f)] = [T(g),f]$. Hence we find that

$$[T(f+g),f+g] = [T(f),f] + 2[T(f)] + [T(g),g]$$
and $$[T(f-g),f-g] = [T(f),f] - 2[T(f)] + [T(g),g],$$

whence

$$4[T(f)] = [T(f+g),f+g] - [T(f-g),f-g]$$
$$\leq \mu[f+g,f+g] + \mu[f-g,f-g] = 4\mu, \quad \text{q.e.d.}$$

From now on, we shall suppose that G is compact, so that $\mathscr{C}$ is the space of all continuous real-valued functions on G. In particular, the constant function 1 belongs to $\mathscr{C}$, and we normalize the Haar integral I so that $I(1) = 1$. Then we have, for every element f of $\mathscr{C}$, $[f] \leq \|f\|$.

By a *special operator* on $\mathscr{C}$ we shall mean a symmetric continuous linear endomorphism with the additional property that it maps the unit sphere $(f \mid [f] = 1)$ of $\mathscr{C}$ onto a uniformly bounded and equicontinuous set of functions. We shall need the result that every infinite sequence in such a set has an infinite subsequence that converges uniformly to an element of $\mathscr{C}$. In order to prove this, one proceeds as follows: given such a sequence (f_n) and a positive ε, choose a neighborhood V of 1 in G such that $\|x \cdot f_n - f_n\| < \varepsilon$ for all n whenever x lies in V. Next, choose a finite set of points $x_1, \cdots, x_p$ in G such that the sets $x_i V$ cover G. Since (f_n) is uniformly bounded, there is a finite set of indices $(n_1, \cdots, n_q)$ such that for every m there is an m' belonging to $(n_1, \cdots, n_q)$ satisfying $|f_m(x_i) - f_{m'}(x_i)| < \varepsilon$ for each i. It follows that $\|f_m - f_{m'}\| < 3\varepsilon$. Hence there is an infinite subsequence $(f_n^{(1)})$ of the sequence (f_n) such that $\|f_m^{(1)} - f_n^{(1)}\| < 6\varepsilon$ for all m and n. In this fashion, taking ε to be $1/k$, $k = 1, 2, \cdots$, successively, we construct a sequence of subsequences $(f^{(k)})$, the sequence for $k + 1$ being a subsequence of the sequence for k, such that the diagonal sequence $(f_k^{(k)})$ converges uniformly to an element of $\mathscr{C}$.

LEMMA 1.2. *If T is a special operator then one of $[T]$ or $-[T]$ is a characteristic value for T. If $\alpha > 0$ then every orthonormal set of characteristic functions belonging to characteristic values β with $|\beta| \geq \alpha$ is finite.*

Proof. By Lemma 1.1, we can find a sequence of elements f_n of $\mathscr{C}$ such that $[f_n] = 1$ and $[T(f_n), f_n]$ converges to γ, where $\gamma^2 = [T]^2$. By the above, we can ensure furthermore that the sequence of functions $T(f_n)$ converges uniformly to an element f of $\mathscr{C}$. Now we have $[T(f_n) - \gamma f_n]^2 = [T(f_n)]^2 + \gamma^2 - 2\gamma[T(f_n), f_n]$. The expression on the right evidently converges to $[f]^2 - [T]^2$, whence we have $[f]^2 \geq [T]^2$. Now if $T \neq 0$ then $[T] > 0$, so that we have then $f \neq 0$. Hence, in order to conclude that γ is a characteristic value, it suffices to show that $T(f) = \gamma f$, because if $T = 0$ then $[T] = 0$ and so is trivially a characteristic value for T.

Since $[T(f_n)]^2 \leq [T]^2 = \gamma^2$, the above equality shows that $[T(f_n) - \gamma f_n]$ converges to 0, whence also $[T^2(f_n) - \gamma T(f_n)]$ converges to 0. On the other hand, $[T(f_n) - f]$ converges to 0, so that also $[T^2(f_n) - T(f)]$ converges to 0. We have

$$[T(f) - \gamma f] \leq [T^2(f_n) - T(f)] + [T^2(f_n) - \gamma T(f_n)] + |\gamma|[T(f_n) - f].$$

Hence we conclude that $[T(f) - \gamma f] = 0$, i.e., that $T(f) = \gamma f$.

Now let E be an orthonormal set as in the statement of the lemma. For every element e of E, write $T(e) = \beta_e e$, where $|\beta_e| \geq \alpha$. Then, if e and f are distinct elements of E, we have $[T(e - f)]^2 = \beta_e^2 + \beta_f^2 \geq 2\alpha^2$, whence $\|T(e - f)\|^2 \geq 2\alpha^2$. Now if E were infinite we could find an infinite sequence (e_n) in E such that the sequence $(T(e_n))$ is uniformly convergent, and this would evidently contradict what we have just proved. Thus E must be finite, and Lemma 1.2 is proved.

We see immediately from the last result that every maximal orthonormal set of characteristic functions for T belonging to non-zero characteristic values is countable. We arrange such a set in a sequence (e_n), and we call such a sequence a *basic orthonormal sequence* for T. Then every characteristic function f belonging to a characteristic value $\beta \neq 0$ is a finite linear combination of e_n's. In order to see this, let S_β denote the *finite* set of indices n such that e_n belongs to the characteristic value β, and put $g = f - \sum_{n \in S_\beta}[f, e_n]e_n$. Then we have $[g, e_i] = 0$ for every index i; indeed, this is clear for i in S_β, and it holds for the other indices because we have $[u, v] = 0$ whenever u and v are characteristic functions belonging to different characteristic values. Hence we would obtain a contradiction to the maximality of (e_n) if g were different from 0. Hence we have $f = \sum_{n \in S_\beta}[f, e_n]e_n$.

PROPOSITION 1.3. *Let T be a special operator on $\mathscr{C}$, and let (e_n) be a basic* *orthonormal sequence for* T. *For* f *in* $\mathscr{C}$, *put* $f_{(p)} = T(\sum_{n \leq p}[f, e_n]e_n)$. *Then the sequence* $(f_{(p)})$ *converges uniformly to* $T(f)$.

Proof. Since T is special, there is a real number $|T|$ such that $\|T(g)\| \leq |T|[g]$ for all elements g of $\mathscr{C}$. Hence, if $p < q$, we obtain

$$\|f_{(q)} - f_{(p)}\| \leq |T|(\sum_{p < n \leq q}[f, e_n]^2)^{1/2}.$$

It is clear from Bessel's inequality that the expression on the right approaches 0 as p and q both become large. Hence $(f_{(p)})$ is a uniform Cauchy sequence and therefore converges uniformly to an element g of $\mathscr{C}$. It remains to prove that $g = T(f)$.

Define the operator T_p by $T_p(u) = T(u) - \sum_{n \leq p}[u, e_n]T(e_n)$. One verifies immediately that T_p is a special operator. Evidently, $T_p(f) = T(f) - f_{(p)}$. Hence the proposition will follow immediately if we show that $[T_p]$ converges to 0 as p becomes large, for then $[T_p(f)]$ must converge to 0, and this means that the limit g of $(f_{(p)})$ must be equal to $T(f)$.

By Lemma 1.2, there is a characteristic function u_p for T_p that belongs to a characteristic value μ_p, with $\mu_p^2 = [T_p]^2$. Using the symmetry of T, one verifies directly that $[T_p(u), e_n] = 0$ for all u and all $n \leq p$. Hence, if $\mu_p \neq 0$, we get $[u_p, e_n] = 0$ for all $n \leq p$. But this means that $T_p(u_p) = T(u_p)$, so that u_p is also a characteristic function for T, whence $u_p = \sum_{n \in S_{\mu_p}}[u_p, e_n]e_n$. In particular, since $u_p \neq 0$, this shows that S_{μ_p} must contain an index larger than p. Now, given a positive number α, choose p larger than all those indices (finite in number) n for which e_n belongs to a characteristic value β_n with $|\beta_n| \geq \alpha$. Then our last result shows that we must have $|\mu_p| < \alpha$, i.e., $[T_p] < \alpha$. Thus $[T_p]$ converges to 0 as p becomes large, and Proposition 1.3 is proved.

Before we make an application of Proposition 1.3, we must discuss additional properties of the Haar integral for a *compact* group G. For f in $\mathscr{C}$, denote by $f \cdot x$ the element of $\mathscr{C}$ that is given by $(f \cdot x)(y) = f(xy)$. Then the map sending each f onto $I(f \cdot x)$ is evidently a Haar integral, whence $I(f \cdot x) = p(x)I(f)$ for every f, where p is some fixed function on G taking only positive real values. Taking for f the constant function with value 1, we find that $p(x) = 1$ for every x. Thus $I(f \cdot x) = I(f)$ for every f in $\mathscr{C}$ and every x in G. Now denote by f' the function given by $f'(x) = f(x^{-1})$. Then $(x \cdot f)' = f' \cdot x^{-1}$, so that $I((x \cdot f)') = I(f' \cdot x^{-1}) = I(f')$. Thus the map that sends each f onto $I(f')$ is also a Haar integral, and it follows as above that $I(f) = I(f')$ for every f in $\mathscr{C}$.

If f and g are elements of $\mathscr{C}$ then their *convolution* $f * g$ is the element of $\mathscr{C}$

17

that is defined by $(f * g)(x) = [x \cdot f, g']$. The Schwarz inequality and the invariance properties of I yield $|(f * g)(x)| \leq [x \cdot f][g'] = [f][g]$, whence $\|f * g\| \leq [f][g]$. Furthermore, we have $|(f * g)(xy) - (f * g)(x)| \leq [xy \cdot f - x \cdot f][g']$ which gives $\|y \cdot (f * g) - (f * g)\| \leq [y \cdot f - f][g]$. Thus we see that the map $g \to f * g$ is not only a continuous linear endomorphism of $\mathscr{C}$ with respect to the norm [ ] but also sends the unit sphere of $\mathscr{C}$ onto a uniformly bounded and equicontinuous set of functions. We shall show next that $[f * g, h] = [g, f' * h]$ for all elements f, g, h of $\mathscr{C}$. Once this has been done, we shall know that *if $f = f'$ then the convolution with f is a special operator on $\mathscr{C}$*.

Put $u(x, y) = f(yx)g(y^{-1})h(x)$. Then, in the notation used in connection with the Haar integral in Section 3 of Chapter I, we have $_x u = (x \cdot f)g'h(x)$, $_l u = (f * g)h$, and hence $[f * g, h] = I(_l u)$. On the other hand, we have $_l u(x) = I(_x u) = I((_x u)') = _l v(x)$, where $v(x, y) = f(y^{-1}x)g(y)h(x)$. Hence $[f * g, h] = I(_l v) = I(v_l)$. Now we have $v_y = (f \cdot y^{-1})g(y)h = (y \cdot f')'g(y)h$, whence $v_l(y) = g(y)I((y \cdot f')'h) = g(y)I((y \cdot f')h') = (g(f' * h))(y)$, so that $I(v_l) = [g, f' * h]$, as we wished to prove.

A continuous function f on a topological group G is called a *representative function* if the space spanned by the translates $x \cdot f \cdot y$, where x and y range over G, is finite-dimensional. One verifies immediately that it suffices for this that the one-sided translates $x \cdot f$ or $f \cdot x$ span a finite-dimensional space. Clearly, the representative functions constitute a subalgebra $\mathscr{R}$ of the algebra of all continuous functions. We are now ready to obtain the fundamental *Peter-Weyl Theorem*.

THEOREM 1.4. *The space $\mathscr{R}$ of the representative functions on the compact group G is uniformly dense in the space $\mathscr{C}$ of all continuous functions on G.*

Proof. Let us observe first that, for all elements f and g of $\mathscr{C}$ and all elements x of G, we have $(f * g) \cdot x = f * (g \cdot x)$. Indeed,

$$((f * g) \cdot x)(y) = [xy \cdot f, g'] = [y \cdot f, x^{-1} \cdot g'] = [y \cdot f, (g \cdot x)']$$
$$= (f * (g \cdot x))(y).$$

Now let t be an element of $\mathscr{C}$ such that $t = t'$, and let T be the *special* operator on $\mathscr{C}$ defined by $T(f) = t * f$. It is clear from what we have just proved that if e is a characteristic function for T belonging to a characteristic value γ then, for every x in G, $e \cdot x$ is again a characteristic function belonging to γ. If $\gamma \neq 0$ then we know that the space of the corresponding characteristic functions is finite-dimensional. In particular, e is then a representative function. Hence it is clear from Proposition 1.3 that *every function of the type t ∗ f is in the uniform closure of $\mathscr{R}$.*

Now let x be an element of G that is not equal to 1. Then we can find a compact neighborhood V of 1 in G such that x does not lie in VV. Next, we can find a non-zero element t in $\mathscr{C}$ such that $t = t'$ and the support of t lies in V. Then we have $(t \ast t)(x) = 0$, while $(t \ast t)(1) = [t, t] > 0$. Thus $t \ast t$ separates 1 and x. Hence $(t \ast t) \cdot y$ separates y and yx. Since $(t \ast t) \cdot y = t \ast (t \cdot y)$, this shows that the functions $t \ast f$, where f ranges over $\mathscr{C}$, separate the points of G. Now it evidently follows from the Stone-Weierstrass Theorem that the uniform closure of $\mathscr{R}$ must coincide with $\mathscr{C}$.

2

Let G be a topological group, and let V be a real or complex *topological vector space*, which is to mean that V is a vector space endowed with a topology making it into a topological group and such that the scalar multiplication $F \times V \to V$ is continuous, where F is the field of the real or the complex numbers. Suppose that we are given a homomorphism ρ of G into the group of all linear automorphisms of V such that the map $G \times V \to V$ that sends each (g, v) onto $\rho(g)(v)$ is continuous. Then we say that V is a *continuous G-module* and that ρ is a *continuous representation* of G on V. We shall refer to V as the *representation space* of ρ. Usually, we shall write $g \cdot v$ for $\rho(g)(v)$.

Let A be any topological vector space, and consider the vector space $F(G, A)$ of all continuous maps of G into A. We topologize $F(G, A)$ by the *compact-open topology*, in which a fundamental system of neighborhoods of 0 consists of the sets $N(K, U)$, where K is a compact subset of G and U is a neighborhood of 0 in A, and $f \in N(K, U)$ means that $f(K) \subset U$. Clearly, this makes $F(G, A)$ into a topological vector space. If x is in G and f in $F(G, A)$ we define, as before, the element $x \cdot f$ of $F(G, A)$ by $(x \cdot f)(y) = f(yx)$. Now one verifies easily that, *if G is locally compact*, then this makes $F(G, A)$ into a continuous G-module. In particular, if G is compact and A is the field of the real numbers then $F(G, A) = \mathscr{C}$, with the topology of the uniform norm $\| \; \|$.

In what follows, it will be convenient to have the extension of the Haar integral to complex-valued functions. Let G be a locally compact group. If f is any complex-valued continuous function with compact support on G then we have evidently a unique decomposition $f = u + iv$, where u and v

are functions belonging to $\mathscr{C}$. Now, if I is a Haar integral on $\mathscr{C}$, we define $I(f) = I(u) + iI(v)$. Clearly, all the basic properties of I are preserved. The inequality $|I(f)| \leqq I(|f|)$ remains true for complex-valued functions f, and it is proved as follows. We have $|v| = (|f| - |u|)^{1/2}(|f| + |u|)^{1/2}$. Hence $I(|v|)^2 = [(|f| - |u|)^{1/2}, (|f| + |u|)^{1/2}]^2$. By the Schwarz inequality, the last expression is no greater than $I(|f| - |u|)I(|f| + |u|)$. Hence we have

$$I(|f|)^2 \geqq I(|u|)^2 + I(|v|)^2 \geqq |I(u)|^2 + |I(v)|^2 = |I(f)|^2.$$

Now let G be a compact group, and let V be a finite-dimensional real or complex continuous G-module. Let v be an element of V, and let δ be an element of the dual space V° to V. Define the continuous function δ/v on G by $(\delta/v)(x) = \delta(x \cdot v)$. With I the normalized Haar integral for G, consider the linear functional on V° that sends each δ onto $I(\delta/v)$. By the duality of finite-dimensional vector spaces, there is one and only one element $I(v)$ in V such that $\delta(I(v)) = I(\delta/v)$ for every δ in V°. Clearly, the map $v \to I(v)$ is a linear endomorphism of V. Denote the G-fixed subspace of V by V^G. If v belongs to V^G then δ/v is evidently the constant function with value $\delta(v)$, whence $I(v) = v$. If v is any element of V and x is an element of G we have, if ρ denotes the representation of G on V,

$$\delta(x \cdot I(v)) = I((\delta \circ \rho(x))/v) = I((\delta/v) \cdot x) = I(\delta/v) = \delta(I(v)).$$

Hence we conclude that $I(v)$ lies in V^G. Thus *the endomorphism of V that is induced by I is a projection of V onto V^G.*

In a more rigorous notation, we should denote this endomorphism of V by I_V. The omission of the subscript V is justified by the following facts. If V is a submodule of the G-module of all continuous functions on G then $I_V(v) = I(v)$ for every element of V. In general, the association of I_V with V is *natural*, in the sense that if α is a G-module homomorphism $V \to W$ then $I_W \circ \alpha = \alpha \circ I_V$. The proof of each of these facts is immediate.

We recall a few notions of representation theory, in which the topologies are disregarded. A G-module is said to be *simple* if its only G-submodules are (0) and the whole module. A G-module is called *semisimple* if it is a sum of simple submodules. It is an elementary result of the theory of groups with operators that a G-module is semisimple if and only if every submodule is a direct G-module summand of the whole module.

Let us consider an arbitrary group G and G-modules over an arbitrary field F. If V and W are any two such modules we make the F-space $\mathrm{Hom}_F(W, V)$ of all F-linear maps of W into V into a G-module. If α

belongs to $\mathrm{Hom}_F(W, V)$ and x belongs to G then the transform $x \cdot \alpha$ is defined as an element of $\mathrm{Hom}_F(W, V)$ by putting $(x \cdot \alpha)(w) = x \cdot \alpha(x^{-1} \cdot w)$ for every w in W. Then $(\mathrm{Hom}_F(W, V))^G$ is evidently the space of all G-module homomorphisms of W into V. A *class* of G-modules over F is any family S of such modules having the following closure properties: if V belongs to S and if U is a submodule of V then U and V/U both belong to S; if V and W belong to S then $\mathrm{Hom}_F(W, V)$ belongs to S. If V is a G-module we denote by V_G the submodule consisting of all sums of elements of the form $x \cdot v - v$ with v in V and x in G.

LEMMA 2.1. *Let S be a class of G-modules over the field F such that every member V of S is the sum of its submodules V^G and V_G. Then every member of S is semisimple.*

Proof. Let V be a member of S, and let U be a submodule of V. Consider the G-module $\mathrm{Hom}_F(V/U, V)$. The elements μ of this module with the property that, for every x in G, $(x \cdot \mu - \mu)(V/U) \subset U$ evidently constitute a submodule M of $\mathrm{Hom}_F(V/U, V)$. By the assumption of our lemma, we have $M = M^G + M_G$. Let π denote the canonical map $V \to V/U$. We can evidently find an F-linear map α of V/U into V such that $\pi \circ \alpha$ is the identity map on V/U. Using that π is a G-module homomorphism, one verifies immediately that α belongs to M. Hence we may write $\alpha = \beta + \gamma$, where $\beta \in M^G$ and $\gamma \in M_G$. By the definition of M, we have $\gamma(V/U) \subset U$, which means that $\pi \circ \gamma = 0$, so that $\pi \circ \beta$ is still the identity map on V/U. Since $\beta \in M^G$, it is a G-module homomorphism, whence it is clear that $\beta(V/U)$ is a G-submodule of V, and that $V = U + \beta(V/U)$ and $U \cap \beta(V/U) = (0)$. Thus U is a direct G-module summand in V, and our lemma is proved.

Now let G be a compact group, and consider the (real or complex) finite-dimensional continuous G-modules. We observe that on a finite-dimensional real or complex vector space V there is only one topology making it into a (Hausdorff) topological vector space. This is the coarsest topology for which all the linear maps into the base fields are continuous. We do not need to prove the uniqueness result if we simply agree to topologize every finite-dimensional vector space in this fashion. Then, if ρ is a representation of G on V, it is easy to see that ρ is continuous if and only if $\mu \circ \rho$ is a continuous function on G for every linear functional μ on the space of all linear endomorphisms of V. In particular, it is clear that the finite-dimensional continuous G-modules constitute a class in the sense of Lemma 2.1.

Now let V be any finite-dimensional continuous G-module. Let π denote the canonical map $V \to V/V_G$. Clearly, $V/V_G = (V/V_G)^G = I(V/V_G) = (I \circ \pi)(V) = (\pi \circ I)(V)$, so that we have $V = I(V) + V_G = V^G + V_G$. Hence Lemma 2.1 applies to give the following basic result.

THEOREM 2.2. *Every finite-dimensional continuous module for a compact group is semisimple.*

Let ρ be a finite-dimensional representation of a group G, and let U be the representation space of ρ. Let $E(U)$ stand for $\mathrm{Hom}_F(U, U)$, where F is the base field. The composites $\eta \circ \rho$ with η in $E(U)^\circ$ are F-valued functions on G. We call them the *representative functions associated with ρ.* We shall also denote this space by $S(U)$, when it is inconvenient to name the representation.

LEMMA 2.3. *Let U and V be finite-dimensional modules for a group G over a field F. Then $S(\mathrm{Hom}_F(U, V)) = S(U)'S(V)$, i.e., the elements of $S(\mathrm{Hom}_F(U, V))$ are the sums of the products $f'g$, where f belongs to $S(U)$ and g belongs to $S(V)$.*

Proof. There is a linear map of the tensor product $E(U) \otimes E(V)$ into $E(\mathrm{Hom}_F(U, V))$, which is obtained in the evident fashion from the composition maps $E(V) \times \mathrm{Hom}_F(U, V) \to \mathrm{Hom}_F(U, V)$ and $\mathrm{Hom}_F(U, V) \times E(U) \to \mathrm{Hom}_F(U, V)$. This map is easily seen to be injective. Since the dimensions of $E(U) \otimes E(V)$ and $E(\mathrm{Hom}_F(U, V))$ are equal, our map is therefore a linear isomorphism. Let τ be its inverse: $E(\mathrm{Hom}_F(U, V)) \to E(U) \otimes E(V)$. The dual τ° of τ is a linear isomorphism $(E(U) \otimes E(V))^\circ \to E(\mathrm{Hom}_F(U, V))^\circ$. If we compose τ° with the canonical isomorphism $\eta : E(U)^\circ \otimes E(V)^\circ \to (E(U) \otimes E(V))^\circ$, we obtain a linear isomorphism $E(U)^\circ \otimes E(V)^\circ \to E(\mathrm{Hom}_F(U, V))^\circ$. Now let α, β, γ denote the representations of G on U, V, $\mathrm{Hom}_F(U, V)$, respectively. Then we have, directly from the definitions, $\tau(\gamma(x)) = \alpha(x^{-1}) \otimes \beta(x)$ for every element x of G.

Let f be an element of $S(\mathrm{Hom}_F(U, V))$. Then $f = f^\circ \circ \gamma$, where f° is an element of $E(\mathrm{Hom}_F(U, V))^\circ$. This gives

$$f(x) = f^\circ(\gamma(x)) = f^\circ(\tau^{-1}(\alpha(x^{-1}) \otimes \beta(x)))$$
$$= (\tau^{-1})^\circ(f^\circ)(\alpha(x^{-1}) \otimes \beta(x)).$$

Now write $(\tau^{-1})^\circ(f^\circ) = \eta(p)$ with p in $E(U)^\circ \otimes E(V)^\circ$. Noting that, if $r \in E(U)^\circ$ and $s \in E(V)^\circ$, we have

$$\eta(r \otimes s)(\alpha(x^{-1}) \otimes \beta(x)) = r(\alpha(x^{-1}))s(\beta(x))$$
$$= ((r \circ \alpha)'(s \circ \beta))(x),$$

we see that $f \in S(U)'S(V)$. Reversing the above computation, we see that $(r \circ \alpha)'(s \circ \beta)$ belongs to $S(\operatorname{Hom}_F(U, V))$, whence $S(U)'S(V) \subset S(\operatorname{Hom}_F(U, V))$. This completes the proof of Lemma 2.3.

We shall say that two semisimple G-modules U and V are *independent* if no simple G-submodule of U is isomorphic with a simple G-submodule of V. Clearly, this is the case if and only if $\operatorname{Hom}_F(U, V)^G = (0)$.

THEOREM 2.4. *Let G be a compact group, and let U and V be independent finite-dimensional continuous G-modules. Then the Haar integral I annihilates every element of $S(U)'S(V)$.*

Proof. Since $\operatorname{Hom}_F(U, V)^G = (0)$, we must have $I(\operatorname{Hom}_F(U, V)) = (0)$. In view of Lemma 2.3, it suffices therefore to show that if W is any finite-dimensional continuous G-module such that $I(W) = (0)$ then also $I(S(W)) = (0)$. By choosing a basis for W and the dual basis for W°, one finds easily that $S(W)$ coincides with the space spanned by the functions μ/w where $w \in W$ and $\mu \in W^\circ$. Since $I(\mu/w) = \mu(I(w))$, this gives the desired result.

Now let us consider a single finite-dimensional continuous G-module U over the field C of the complex numbers. We consider the algebra $E(U) = \operatorname{Hom}_C(U, U)$. Let T stand for the trace function on $E(U)$. For every element a of $E(U)$, define the element T_a of $E(U)^\circ$ by $T_a(b) = T(ab)$. It is easily verified that the map $a \to T_a$ is a linear isomorphism of $E(U)$ onto $E(U)^\circ$. Hence if ρ is our representation of G on U then every element of $S(U)$ may be written in the form $T_a \circ \rho$ with some element a of $E(U)$.

THEOREM 2.5. *Let ρ be a finite-dimensional continuous simple representation of the compact group G on the complex vector space U of dimension n. Let a and b be arbitrary elements of $E(U)$. Then*

$$I((T_a \circ \rho)(T_b \circ \rho)') = \frac{1}{n} T(ab).$$

Proof. By Schur's Lemma, $E(U)^G$ is one-dimensional, and so consists of the scalar multiples of the identity map e on U. (This is the only place in the proof where we use the assumption that the base field is the field of the complex numbers rather than that of the real numbers.) Hence, for every a in $E(U)$, we have $I(a) = \alpha e$, where α is a complex number. Hence $T(I(a)) = n\alpha$. On the other hand, $T(x \cdot a) = T(\rho(x)a\rho(x^{-1})) = T(a)$ for every element x of G, so that $T(E(U)_G) = (0)$. We know that $a - I(a)$ lies in $E(U)_G$. Hence we have $T(I(a)) = T(a)$. From the above, we

23

have therefore $\alpha = (1/n)\,T(a)$, so that $I(a) = (1/n)\,T(a)e$. Applying T_b and noting that $T_b(I(a)) = I(T_b/a)$, we find $I(T_b/a) = (1/n)\,T(a)\,T(b)$.

We may identify $E(U)$ with the tensor product $U \otimes U^\circ$; if $u \in U$ and $\mu \in U^\circ$ this identifies $u \otimes \mu$ with the element of $E(U)$ that maps each element v of U onto $\mu(v)u$. Evidently, $T(u \otimes \mu) = \mu(u)$. Let $a = s \otimes \sigma$ and $b = t \otimes \tau$. We have $(T_b/a)(x) = T(b\rho(x)a\rho(x^{-1}))$. Now

$$\rho(x)a\rho(x^{-1}) = (x \cdot s) \otimes (\sigma \circ \rho(x^{-1})),$$

so that $\qquad b\rho(x)a\rho(x^{-1}) = \tau(x \cdot s)t \otimes (\sigma \circ \rho(x^{-1})).$

Hence we find

$$(T_b/a)(x) = \tau(x \cdot s)\sigma(x^{-1} \cdot t),$$

whence $\qquad\qquad\qquad T_b/a = (\tau/s)(\sigma/t)'.$

Hence our above result gives $I((\tau/s)(\sigma/t)') = (1/n)\sigma(s)\tau(t)$. Now put $h = s \otimes \tau$ and $k = t \otimes \sigma$. Then our last result becomes

$$I((T_h \circ \rho)(T_k \circ \rho)') = \frac{1}{n}\,T(hk).$$

Since each side of the identity to be proved is the value at (a, b) of a bilinear map of $E(U) \times E(U)$ into C, the special case we have just established implies the general result.

Theorem 2.4 leads to an important result concerning the structure of the algebra of representative functions on a compact group. We may deal simultaneously with the real and the complex case if we agree that $[f, g] = I(f\bar{g})$, where $\bar{g}$ denotes the complex conjugate of g. This leaves things as they were in the real case. In the complex case, the map sending (f, g) onto $[f, g]$ is a positive definite Hermitian inner product on the space of the complex-valued representative functions.

Let U be a finite-dimensional G-module. We have already remarked that $S(U)$ consists of the sums of the functions μ/u, where μ ranges over U° and u ranges over U. Let us now apply this remark to the G-module $S(U)$. Clearly, $S(U)^\circ$ is spanned by the evaluations x° corresponding to the elements x of G, where $x^\circ(f) = f(x)$. One verifies immediately that if f is in $S(U)$ then $x^\circ/f = f \cdot x$. Since $S(U)$ is stable also under the action of G from the right, we conclude that $S(S(U)) = S(U)$.

Now let j stand for the complex conjugation on the algebra of representative functions. For g in $j(S(U))$, denote by $\sigma(g)$ the element of $S(U)^\circ$ given by $\sigma(g)(f) = [f, j(g)]$. Since our inner product $[\ ,\ ]$ is positive definite Hermitian, it is clear that σ is a linear isomorphism of $j(S(U))$ onto $S(U)^\circ$. From the invariance of the Haar integral, we have $[x \cdot h, x \cdot k] = [h, k]$ for every x in G. From this and the obvious fact that $x \cdot j(g) = j(x \cdot g)$, one verifies immediately that σ is actually a G-module isomorphism. Hence we have $S(j(S(U))) = S(S(U)^\circ)$. From Lemma 2.3, we know that $S(S(U)^\circ) = S(S(U))'$, which is $S(U)'$, by the above. Thus we have $S(j(S(U))) = S(U)'$. On the other hand, one sees easily that $S(j(S(U))) = j(S(S(U))) = j(S(U))$. Finally, this gives $j(S(U)) = S(U)'$.

Hence Theorem 2.4 is equivalent to the statement that *if U and V are independent finite-dimensional continuous modules for the compact group G then* $[S(U), S(V)] = (0)$. We shall refer to this as the *orthogonality theorem*.

It is contained in the following structure theorem.

THEOREM 2.6. *Let G be a compact group, and let A be either the G-module of all real-valued representative functions on G or that of the complex-valued representative functions. Let P be a complete system of representatives for the isomorphism classes of the non-zero finite-dimensional simple continuous (real or complex, respectively) G-modules. Let B be any G-submodule of A. Then B is the sum of the family of submodules $B \cap S(U)$ where U ranges over P, these submodules are mutually orthogonal with respect to the inner product $[\ ,\ ]$, and B is closed in A with respect to the inner product topology and, a fortiori, with respect to the topology of the uniform norm $\|\ \|$.*

Proof. Let f be any element of A, and let (f) denote the finite-dimensional G-submodule of A that is spanned by the transforms $x \cdot f$ with x in G. We may write (f) as a direct sum of simple G-submodules $V_1, \cdots, V_n$. Accordingly, $f = f_1 + \cdots + f_n$, with f_i in $V_i \subset S(V_i)$. Now P contains a U_i that is isomorphic with V_i, so that $S(U_i) = S(V_i)$. Thus we have shown that A is the sum of the family of submodules $(S(U))_{U \in P}$. By the orthogonality theorem, this sum is direct. Let π_U denote the projection $A \to S(U)$ that corresponds to this decomposition of A. We show first that $\pi_U(B) \subset B$ for every U in P. Since B is a sum of simple submodules, it suffices to prove this in the case where B is simple (and $\neq (0)$). In that case, the restriction of the G-module homomorphism π_U to B must be either 0 or must map B isomorphically onto a non-zero simple submodule of $S(U)$. It follows immediately from the orthogonality theorem, and the fact that $S(S(U)) = S(U)$, that every non-zero simple submodule of $S(U)$ is isomorphic with U. Hence $\pi_U(B) = (0)$, except for the single U in P that is isomorphic with B. Hence we must have $\pi_U(B) = B$, for this U, and our above assertion is proved. Hence it is clear that B is the sum of the family of submodules $(B \cap S(U))_{U \in P}$.

The second statement of our theorem is simply the orthogonality theorem. In order to prove the third statement, let f be an element of A that lies in the closure (for the inner product topology) of B. It is clear from the orthogonality that, for every h in A and every U in P, $[\pi_U(h), \pi_U(h)] \leq [h, h]$. Taking $h = f - b$, with b ranging over B, we see from this that $\pi_U(f)$ lies in the closure of $\pi_U(B)$ in $S(U)$. Since $S(U)$ is finite-dimensional, this gives $\pi_U(f) \in \pi_U(B)$. Hence f belongs to the sum of the $\pi_U(B)$'s, i.e., $f \in B$. Thus the third statement of our theorem is proved. Finally, since $[f] \leq \|f\|$, the closure of B for the topology of the uniform norm lies in the closure of B for the inner product topology, and so coincides with B.

3

We denote by R the field of the real numbers, and by $\mathscr{R}(G)$ the R-algebra of the real-valued continuous representative functions on the topological group G. If H is another topological group we have a canonical map of $\mathscr{R}(G) \otimes \mathscr{R}(H)$ into $\mathscr{R}(G \times H)$, which we denote by π and which is characterized by the formula $\pi(u \otimes v)(x, y) = u(x)v(y)$.

LEMMA 3.1. *The canonical map π defined above is an isomorphism of R-algebras.*

Proof. Evidently, π is a homomorphism of R-algebras. Thus it suffices to show that π is bijective. Regarding $\mathscr{R}(H)$ merely as an R-space of maps of the set H into R, we see from elementary linear algebra that if S is any finite dimensional R-subspace of $\mathscr{R}(H)$ we can find an R-basis $(s_1, \cdots, s_n)$ for S and elements $y_1, \cdots, y_n$ in H such that $s_i(y_j)$ is equal to 1 or 0 according to whether $i = j$ or $i \neq j$. Clearly, given any element p of $\mathscr{R}(G) \otimes \mathscr{R}(H)$, we can find such a system $(s_1, \cdots, s_n; y_1, \cdots, y_n)$ with which we have $p = \sum_i u_i \otimes s_i$, where each u_i lies in $\mathscr{R}(G)$. Then we have $\pi(p)(x, y_j) = u_j(x)$, whence it is clear that our map π is injective.

Now let f be an element of $\mathscr{R}(G \times H)$. Let S be the finite-dimensional subspace of $\mathscr{R}(H)$ that is spanned by the restrictions to H of the translates $x \cdot f$ with x in G. Let $(s_1, \cdots, s_n; y_1, \cdots, y_n)$ be a system as above. Then we have $(x \cdot f)_H = \sum_i u_i(x)s_i$, where the u_i's are certain real-valued functions on G. Hence $f(x, y) = \sum_i u_i(x)s_i(y)$. This gives $u_j(x) = f(x, y_j)$, whence it is clear that the u_i's actually belong to $\mathscr{R}(G)$, and hence that π is surjective.

In particular, consider the case where $H = G$. If f is any element of $\mathscr{R}(G)$ then the map sending each pair (x, y) of elements of G onto $f(xy)$ is evidently an element of $\mathscr{R}(G \times G)$. Let $\gamma(f)$ be the corresponding element of $\mathscr{R}(G) \otimes \mathscr{R}(G)$. Then γ is clearly an algebra homomorphism $\mathscr{R}(G) \to \mathscr{R}(G) \otimes \mathscr{R}(G)$, by which we mean to imply also that γ sends the identity element of $\mathscr{R}(G)$ (i.e., the constant function with value 1) onto the identity element of $\mathscr{R}(G) \otimes \mathscr{R}(G)$. The associativity of the multiplication in G implies that γ makes $\mathscr{R}(G)$ into an *associative coalgebra*, in the sense that, if i stands for the identity map on $\mathscr{R}(G)$, the two maps $(i \otimes \gamma) \circ \gamma$ and $(\gamma \otimes i) \circ \gamma$ of $\mathscr{R}(G)$ into $\mathscr{R}(G) \otimes \mathscr{R}(G) \otimes \mathscr{R}(G)$ coincide. Moreover, there is a *counit* for this coalgebra structure, i.e., an R-module homomorphism $c \colon \mathscr{R}(G) \to R$ such that $(c \otimes i) \circ \gamma$ and $(i \otimes c) \circ \gamma$ are both the identity map on $\mathscr{R}(G)$; we identify $R \otimes \mathscr{R}(G)$ and $\mathscr{R}(G) \otimes R$ with $\mathscr{R}(G)$, of course. In fact, we simply define $c(f) = f(1)$, where 1 stands for the neutral element of G. Clearly, c is then actually an algebra homomorphism. We denote the multiplication $\mathscr{R}(G) \otimes \mathscr{R}(G) \to \mathscr{R}(G)$ by μ, and the canonical map $R \to \mathscr{R}(G)$ by u. Then $c \circ u$ is evidently the identity map on R. The map u is called the *unit* of $\mathscr{R}(G)$; $\mu \circ (u \otimes i)$ is our identification $R \otimes \mathscr{R}(G) \to \mathscr{R}(G)$, and $\mu \circ (i \otimes u)$ is our identification $\mathscr{R}(G) \otimes R \to \mathscr{R}(G)$.

If we abstract the structure we have just described from the group G, retaining only the R-module $\mathscr{R}(G)$, the algebra structure μ on $\mathscr{R}(G)$ with the algebra homomorphism $u \colon R \to \mathscr{R}(G)$ as a unit and the coalgebra structure γ with the algebra homomorphism $c \colon \mathscr{R}(G) \to R$ as a counit, and if we assume that the above identities are satisfied by these maps and that γ is an algebra homomorphism, we have what is called a *Hopf algebra* $(\mathscr{R}(G), \mu, u, \gamma, c)$. In this general concept, the base ring need not be the field R but may be any commutative ring with identity.

In our special case, there is one further important structural item. Let η denote the algebra endomorphism of $\mathscr{R}(G)$ that is defined from the inversion in G, i.e., $\eta(f) = f'$, where $f'(x) = f(x^{-1})$. Then one sees immediately that $\mu \circ (\eta \otimes i) \circ \gamma = u \circ c$. Let us agree to call an algebra endomorphism η with this last property a *symmetry* of our Hopf algebra.

Note that to every element x of G there corresponds an algebra homomorphism $x^\circ \colon \mathscr{R}(G) \to R$, where $x^\circ(f) = f(x)$. If we identify $R \otimes R$ with R, we see immediately that $(xy)^\circ = (x^\circ \otimes y^\circ) \circ \gamma$. Abstracting from all the special non-formal features of this situation, we may invert our above considerations and obtain the following general result.

PROPOSITION 3.2. *Let (A, μ, u, γ, c) be a Hopf algebra over an arbitrary commutative ring K with identity. Let S denote the set of all K-algebra homomorphisms $A \to K$. Define a composition of elements of S by $s_1 s_2 = (s_1 \otimes s_2) \circ \gamma$. Then this is an associative map $S \times S \to S$, and $sc = s = cs$, for all s in S. If the given Hopf algebra has a symmetry, this makes S into a group.*

Proof. It is evident that $s_1 s_2 \in S$ whenever s_1 and s_2 belong to S. The associativity follows from the associativity of γ, as follows:

$$(s_1 s_2) s_3 = [((s_1 \otimes s_2) \circ \gamma) \otimes s_3] \circ \gamma = (s_1 \otimes s_2 \otimes s_3) \circ (\gamma \otimes i) \circ \gamma$$
$$= (s_1 \otimes s_2 \otimes s_3) \circ (i \otimes \gamma) \circ \gamma = (s_1 \otimes ((s_2 \otimes s_3) \circ \gamma)) \circ \gamma$$
$$= (s_1 \otimes (s_2 s_3)) \circ \gamma = s_1 (s_2 s_3).$$

Clearly, $c \otimes s = s \circ (c \otimes i)$, so that $cs = s \circ (c \otimes i) \circ \gamma = s$. Similarly, $sc = (s \otimes c) \circ \gamma = s \circ (i \otimes c) \circ \gamma = s$.

Now suppose that η is a symmetry. Then we have

$$(s \circ \eta) s = ((s \circ \eta) \otimes s) \circ \gamma = (s \otimes s) \circ (\eta \otimes i) \circ \gamma = s \circ u \circ c = c.$$

This shows that S is a group, with neutral element c, the inverse of s being $s \circ \eta$.

In the case where the base ring K is the field R of the real numbers, we give to S the finite-open topology, i.e., the topology in which a fundamental system of neighborhoods of c consists of the sets $N(f_1, \cdots, f_n, e)$, where the f_i's belong to A, e is a positive real number, and $s \in N(f_1, \cdots, f_n, e)$ means that $|s(f_i) - c(f_i)| < e$ for each i. One verifies easily that this makes S into a topological group. If $A = \mathcal{R}(G)$ then one sees immediately that the map $G \to S$ that sends each element x of G onto the element x° of S is a continuous group homomorphism.

Now suppose that G is compact. Then a Haar integral for G gives us an R-module homomorphism $J: \mathcal{R}(G) \to R$. The invariance property $J(y \cdot f) = J(f)$ for all y in G and all f in $\mathcal{R}(G)$ is easily seen to be equivalent to the relation $(J \otimes i) \circ \gamma = u \circ J$. Moreover, we have $J(f^2) > 0$ for every non-zero element f. If (A, μ, u, γ, c) is any Hopf algebra over R, let us call an R-module homomorphism $J: A \to R$ with these last two properties a *gauge* of the Hopf algebra. Then we have the following lemma.

LEMMA 3.3. *Let (A, μ, u, γ, c) be a Hopf algebra over R having a symmetry and a gauge. Then the group S of all algebra homomorphisms $A \to R$ is compact.*

Proof. We note first that, for every s in S, we have $J \circ (i \otimes s) \circ \gamma = J$. Indeed, the expression on the left is equal to $(J \otimes s) \circ \gamma = s \circ (J \otimes i) \circ \gamma = s \circ u \circ J = J$. Next, observe that, for every fixed element f of A, the set

$((i \otimes s)(\gamma(f)))_{s \in S}$ lies in a finite-dimensional R-subspace F of A. Let $(f_1, \cdots, f_p)$ be an orthonormal basis of F with respect to the positive definite inner product $[g, h] = J(gh)$. Let us write $(i \otimes s)(\gamma(f)) = \sum_{q=1}^p s_q f_q$, with real coefficients s_q depending on s. Then we have

$$J(f^2) = J((i \otimes s)(\gamma(f))^2) = \sum_{q=1}^p s_q{}^2.$$

On the other hand, $s = cs = (c \otimes s) \circ \gamma = c \circ (i \otimes s) \circ \gamma$, so that $s(f) = \sum_{q=1}^p s_q c(f_q)$. Hence it is clear that the set of real numbers $s(f)$, where s ranges over S, is bounded, and so lies in some closed finite interval T_f.

Let T denote the compact space $\prod_{f \in A} T_f$. Let α denote the map $S \to T$ such that $\alpha(s)$ is the point of T whose projection on T_f is $s(f)$. Clearly, α maps S homeomorphically onto the subspace $\alpha(S)$ of T. As a subset of T, $\alpha(S)$ is determined by the conditions $t_{u(1)} = 1$, $t_{fg} = t_f t_g$, $t_{f+g} = t_f + t_g$, $t_{rf} = r t_f$, for all elements f and g of A and all real numbers r. Hence it is clear that $\alpha(S)$ is closed in T and therefore compact. Hence S is compact, and Lemma 3.3 is proved.

Let (A, μ, u, γ, c) be any Hopf algebra with symmetry over R, and let S be the topological group of the algebra homomorphisms $A \to R$. For every element f of A, denote by f° the function on S defined by $f^\circ(s) = s(f)$. Then $s \circ f^\circ = ((i \otimes s)(\gamma(f)))^\circ$, so that it is clear from what we have seen above that the map $f \to f^\circ$ is an algebra homomorphism $A \to \mathscr{R}(S)$, and that the image A° of A in $\mathscr{R}(S)$ is an S-submodule of $\mathscr{R}(S)$. Moreover, one sees easily that μ, u, γ, c induce maps $\mu^\circ, u^\circ, \gamma^\circ, c^\circ$ in the canonical fashion such that $(A^\circ, \mu^\circ, u^\circ, \gamma^\circ, c^\circ)$ is a sub Hopf algebra of the Hopf algebra attached to S and the homomorphism $A \to A^\circ$ is part of a homomorphism of Hopf algebras of (A, μ, u, γ, c) onto $(A^\circ, \mu^\circ, u^\circ, \gamma^\circ, c^\circ)$. We shall say that $(A^\circ, \mu^\circ, u^\circ, \gamma^\circ, c^\circ)$ is the *reduction* of (A, μ, u, γ, c). Generally, we shall say that a Hopf algebra (A, μ, u, γ, c) is *reduced* if the algebra homomorphisms of A into the base ring separate the elements of A, and we note that the above reduction process yields a reduced Hopf algebra even in the absence of a symmetry, provided that the base ring is a field.

Now suppose that S is compact. Then, since A° separates the points of S, it is uniformly dense in the algebra of all continuous real-valued functions on S, and hence is uniformly dense in $\mathscr{R}(S)$. Hence we conclude from Theorem 2.6 that $A^\circ = \mathscr{R}(S)$. Together with Lemma 3.3, this amounts to the following result.

THEOREM 3.4. *Let (A, μ, u, γ, c) be a Hopf algebra over R having a symmetry and a gauge. Let S be the group of the algebra homomorphisms $A \to R$. Then S is* *compact, and the reduction* $(A^\circ, \mu^\circ, u^\circ, \gamma^\circ, c^\circ)$ *is the Hopf algebra attached to S in the canonical fashion.*

Now let us begin with a compact group G, and let S be the group of the algebra homomorphisms $\mathscr{R}(G) \to R$, as constructed from the Hopf algebra $(\mathscr{R}(G), \mu, u, \gamma, c)$ attached to G. Let δ denote the continuous group homomorphism $G \to S$ that we have already discussed above; $\delta(x) = x^\circ$, $x^\circ(f) = f(x)$. Since $\mathscr{R}(G)$ separates the points of G, it is clear that δ is injective. Since G is compact, δ is therefore a topological group isomorphism of G onto the closed subgroup G° of S. We claim that $G^\circ = S$. From Theorem 3.4, we know that the map $f \to f^\circ$ is an isomorphism of $\mathscr{R}(G)$ onto $\mathscr{R}(S)$. This implies that if the restriction f_{G° to G° of an element f of $\mathscr{R}(S)$ is constant then f is constant. By decomposing the S-module generated by f, we may write $f = f_0 + f_1$, where f_0 is constant and f_1 lies in an S-submodule V of $\mathscr{R}(S)$ such that $V^S = (0)$. Our above remark evidently implies that V^{G° must also be (0). Let I_S and I_{G° denote the normalized Haar integrals for S and G°. Then $I_S(f_1) = 0$ and $I_{G^\circ}((f_1)_{G^\circ}) = 0$, whence $I_S(f) = I_{G^\circ}(f_{G^\circ})$ for every element f in $\mathscr{R}(S)$. Since $\mathscr{R}(S)$ is uniformly dense in the space of all continuous real-valued functions on S (by the Peter-Weyl Theorem) it follows that $I_S(f) = I_{G^\circ}(f_{G^\circ})$ for every continuous real-valued function f. Now if $G^\circ \neq S$ we can find a non-negative f such that $f_{G^\circ} = 0$ but $f \neq 0$. Then $I_S(f) > 0$ and $I_{G^\circ}(f_{G^\circ}) = 0$, which contradicts what we have just proved. Thus $G^\circ = S$, so that the canonical map $G \to S$ is an isomorphism of topological groups.

This last result is essentially the *Tannaka Duality Theorem*. We may summarize the most important part of the above as follows.

THEOREM 3.5. *For a compact group G, let $\mathscr{H}(G)$ denote the Hopf algebra attached to G in the canonical fashion. Then $\mathscr{H}(G)$ is a reduced Hopf algebra with symmetry and gauge. For a reduced Hopf algebra H having a symmetry and a gauge, let $\mathscr{G}(H)$ denote the topological group of homomorphisms attached to H in the canonical fashion. Then $\mathscr{G}(H)$ is compact. The canonical maps $G \to \mathscr{G}(\mathscr{H}(G))$ and $H \to \mathscr{H}(\mathscr{G}(H))$ are isomorphisms.*

EXERCISES

1. If U and V are modules for a group G over a field F, one defines the structure of a G-module on the tensor product $U \otimes V$ such that $x \cdot (u \otimes v) = (x \cdot u) \otimes (x \cdot v)$. In the notation of Lemma 2.3, and

assuming that U and V are finite-dimensional, show that $S(U \otimes V) = S(U)S(V)$.

2. Let G be a compact group. Prove that if there is a neighborhood of 1 in G containing no non-trivial normal subgroup of G then $\mathscr{R}(G)$ is finitely generated. Conversely, show that if $\mathscr{R}(G)$ is finitely generated then there is a neighborhood of 1 in G containing no non-trivial subgroup of G. [For the first part, consider the kernels of the representations of G on the finite-dimensional submodules of $\mathscr{R}(G)$. For the converse, show first that there is an injective continuous representation of G by linear automorphisms of a finite-dimensional complex vector space V that are unitary with respect to a positive definite Hermitian inner product on V. Given an element $x \neq 1$ of G, there is an element v_x in V such that $[v_x] = 1$ and $x \cdot v_x = cv_x$, where c is a complex number, different from 1 but necessarily of absolute value 1. Now show that there is a positive integer n such that $[x^n \cdot v_x - v_x] \geq \sqrt{3}$.]

3. For a finite group G, determine the Hopf algebra attached to G explicitly in terms of the multiplication table of G.

4. Let (A, μ, u, γ, c) be a Hopf algebra over K, as in Proposition 3.2, and let S be the monoid of the algebra homomorphisms $A \to K$. Let T be the set of all algebra endomorphisms (leaving the identity element fixed) $\alpha : A \to A$ such that $(i \otimes \alpha) \circ \gamma = \gamma \circ \alpha$. Show that the map $\alpha \to c \circ \alpha$ is an isomorphism of the monoid T (with the usual composition of maps) onto the monoid S, its inverse being the map $s \to (i \otimes s) \circ \gamma$. In the case of the algebra $\mathscr{R}(G)$ of the representative functions on a group G, deduce that every algebra endomorphism of $\mathscr{R}(G)$ that commutes with the G-operations $f \to f \cdot x$, $x \in G$, is actually an automorphism of $\mathscr{R}(G)$ and, in the case where G is compact, is a group operation $f \to x \cdot f$.

5. Let G be a compact group, and let A be a subalgebra of $\mathscr{R}(G)$ containing the constants and such that $x \cdot A \subset A$ for every x in G. Let ${}^A G$ denote the group consisting of all x in G such that $f \cdot x = f$ for every f in A. Show that every element f of $\mathscr{R}(G)$ such that $f \cdot x = f$ for every x in ${}^A G$ belongs to A. [Apply the Stone-Weierstrass Theorem to the space of the cosets $({}^A G)x$, and use Theorem 2.6.]

6. Let G be a compact group, K a closed subgroup of G. By using the result of the last exercise for K, show that every representative function

on K is the restriction to K of a representative function on G. Next, in the notation of the last exercise, show that $K = {}^T G$, where T is the algebra of all f in $\mathscr{R}(G)$ such that $f \cdot x = f$ for every x in K. [Show that every representative function on ${}^T G$ that is constant on K is a constant.]

III. ELEMENTARY
STRUCTURE THEORY [8, 9]

1

If V is a finite-dimensional vector space over the field R of the real numbers we may regard V as a topological group, the group operation being addition and the topology being the topology of V as a real vector space. Such a topological group is called a vector group. Evidently, every linear map of a vector group V into a vector group W is a continuous homomorphism. The converse of this is almost trivial, but we record it for later reference.

PROPOSITION 1.1. *Every continuous homomorphism of a vector group V into a vector group W is a linear map.*

Proof. Let f be a continuous homomorphism $V \to W$. Let p and q be integers, with $q \neq 0$. Then we have, for every v in V, $qf((p/q)v) = f(pv) = pf(v)$, so that $f(\alpha v) = \alpha f(v)$ for every rational number α. By continuity, this extends to all real numbers α, so that f is indeed a linear map.

PROPOSITION 1.2. *Let A be a closed subgroup of the vector group V. Then there is a direct vector space decomposition $V = X + Y + Z$ such that $A = X + (A \cap Y)$ and $A \cap Y$ is the free abelian group generated by an R-basis of Y.*

Proof. We show first that if A is not discrete then it contains a line. Choose a metric on V, and let $[v]$ denote the distance of v from 0. If A is not discrete, it contains a sequence (a_n) such that $0 < [a_n] < 1/n$ for every positive integer n. Put $b_n = [a_n]^{-1}a_n$. Then $[b_n] = 1$, and by taking a subsequence, if necessary, we may arrange that the sequence (b_n) converges to a point b in V. We claim that $Rb \subset A$. In order to show this, let r

be any real number, and, for each n, choose the integer t_n so that $t_n[a_n]$ is as close as possible to r. Then $t_n a_n$ belongs to A, and we have

$$[t_n a_n - rb] = [t_n[a_n]b_n - rb] \leqq |t_n|[a_n][b_n - b] + |t_n[a_n] - r|[b]$$
$$< \left(r + \frac{1}{n}\right)[b_n - b] + \frac{1}{n}.$$

The expression on the right converges to 0 as n becomes large, so that $t_n a_n$ converges to rb. Since A is closed, we have therefore $rb \in A$, and so A contains the line Rb.

Now it is clear that if A is any closed subgroup of V we may apply the above result repeatedly to obtain a vector space decomposition $V = X + W$ where $X \subset A$ and $A \cap W$ is discrete. Let Y be a vector subspace of W of maximal dimension p such that $A \cap Y$ is the free abelian group generated by some basis $(y_1, \cdots, y_p)$ of Y. It suffices to show that then $A \cap W \subset Y$. Suppose this is not the case, and choose an element a in $A \cap W$ that does not lie in Y. Consider the subset T of W consisting of the points

$$r_1 y_1 + \cdots + r_p y_p + ra, \text{ where } 0 \leqq r_q < 1 \text{ and } 0 < r \leqq 1.$$

This bounded set can contain only a finite number of elements of the discrete group $A \cap W$, because the distances between pairs of distinct points of $A \cap W$ have a positive minimum (namely, the distance from 0 of the set of non-zero elements of $A \cap W$). Hence there is a point z in $T \cap A$ such that the coefficient r of a in z is minimal. Then we see easily that $A \cap (Y + Ra) = (A \cap Y) + (z)$, where (z) is the additive group generated by z. Since $(y_1, \cdots, y_p, z)$ is a basis for $Y + Ra$ and $A \cap (Y + Ra)$ is the free abelian group generated by this basis, this contradicts the maximality of p. Thus $A \cap W \subset Y$, which completes the proof of Proposition 1.2.

If V is a vector group and B is the free abelian group generated by an R-basis of V then V/B is called a *toroid*; it is evidently a direct product of a finite number of copies of R/Z, where Z is the additive group of the integers. Proposition 1.2 immediately implies that *every factor group of a vector group mod. a closed subgroup is a direct product of a vector group and a toroid.*

In order to determine the closed subgroups of such direct products, we require the following addition to Proposition 1.2.

PROPOSITION 1.3. *Let A and B be closed subgroups of a vector group such that $B \subset A$. Suppose that a decomposition $B = V + Q$ is given, where V is a* *vector group and Q is a discrete free abelian group of finite rank. Then there is a decomposition $A = U + P$, where U is a vector group containing V, P is a discrete free abelian group of finite rank, and $Q = (Q \cap U) + (Q \cap P)$.*

Proof. Note first that the vector components of A and B are necessarily the connected components A_0 and B_0 of 0 in A or B, respectively, so that $V \subset U$. We must merely prove that P can be chosen so as to satisfy the requirements of the proposition. From Proposition 1.2, we know that A is of the form $U + T$, where T is a discrete free abelian group of finite rank and $U \cap T = (0)$. Let τ denote the projection $A \to T$ with kernel U. Then $\tau(Q)$ is a subgroup of T, and it follows from the standard theory of discrete finitely generated abelian groups that there is a free basis $(t_1, \cdots, t_n)$ of T and positive integers $z_1, \cdots, z_r$ $(r \leq n)$ such that $(z_1 t_1, \cdots, z_r t_r)$ is a free basis for $\tau(Q)$. For each i, choose an element q_i in Q such that $\tau(q_i) = z_i t_i$. Now put $p_i = (1/z_i)q_i = t_i + (1/z_i)(q_i - \tau(q_i))$ for $i \leq r$, and $p_i = t_i$ for $i > r$. Let P be the group generated by $(p_1, \cdots, p_n)$. Evidently, we have $A = U + P$, and $U \cap P = (0)$. Moreover, $q_i = z_i p_i$ and, given an element q in Q, there is an integral linear combination of the q_i's whose image under τ is $\tau(q)$. Hence it is clear that $Q = (Q \cap U) + (Q \cap P)$, and Proposition 1.3 is proved.

Let us call a group *elementary* if it is a direct product of a vector group, a toroid and a discrete finitely generated abelian group. Then it is clear that every elementary group is a factor group A/B with A and B as in Proposition 1.3. Conversely, the proposition evidently implies that *every* group A/B, where A and B are closed subgroups of a vector group, is elementary. Clearly, every subgroup and every factor group of a group of the type A/B is again of this type. Thus we have the following result.

THEOREM 1.4. *If E is an elementary group and S is a closed subgroup of E then both S and E/S are elementary groups.*

An important property of vector groups is the following.

PROPOSITION 1.5. *Let N be a connected neighborhood of 0 in the vector group V and let g be a continuous map of N into a topological group G such that $g(x + y) = g(x)g(y)$ whenever x, y and $x + y$ all lie in N. Then there is one and only one homomorphism $f: V \to G$ such that f coincides with g on N.*

Proof. Let x be any element of V. Then there is a positive integer p such that $(1/n)x$ lies in N for all integers $n \geq p$. Let q be a positive integer with the same property as p. Then we have $g(p^{-1}x)^p = g((pq)^{-1}x)^{pq} = g(q^{-1}x)^q$. Thus there is a map $f: V \to G$ such that $f(x) = g(p^{-1}x)^p$ for every positive integer p such that $n^{-1}x \in N$ for all integers $n \geq p$. One verifies immediately that f is a homomorphism. Let T denote the set of all points x in N such that $f(x) = g(x)$. Then T contains the set of all points x such that $n^{-1}x \in N$ for every positive integer n. Hence T is a neighborhood of 0 in V, from which we conclude, in particular, that f is continuous. Hence T is a closed subset of N. Moreover, it is clear that $(T + T) \cap N \subset T$, so that T is also an open subset of N. Since N is connected, we have therefore $T = N$, which completes the proof.

A simple application is the following.

PROPOSITION 1.6. *Let T be a toroid. Then there is an element t in T such that the closure of the subgroup generated by t coincides with T.*

Proof. We have $T = V/F$, where V is a vector group and F is the group generated by a basis $(v_1, \cdots, v_n)$ of V. Let v be an element of the form $\sum_{i=1}^{n} r_i v_i$, where the r_i's are real numbers such that the set $(1, r_1, \cdots, r_n)$ is linearly independent over the field of the rational numbers. Let A denote the closure in V of the group generated by $v_1, \cdots, v_n, v$. In order to prove the proposition, it suffices to show that $A = V$.

Since A contains F, V/A is compact. Evidently, V/A is connected. Since the only compact connected elementary groups are the toroids, we conclude that V/A is a toroid, and thus a direct product of a finite number of copies of R/Z. Hence, in order to prove that V/A is trivial, it suffices to show that every continuous homomorphism $\gamma: V/A \to R/Z$ is trivial. Let π denote the canonical homomorphism $V \to V/A$. Then $\gamma \circ \pi$ is a continuous homomorphism $V \to R/Z$. Evidently, there is a neighborhood U of the neutral element of R/Z and a homeomorphism μ of U onto a neighborhood U_0 of 0 in R such that $\rho \circ \mu$ is the identity map on U, where ρ is the canonical map $R \to R/Z$. By following up $\gamma \circ \pi$ with μ, we clearly obtain a map g of a connected neighborhood N of 0 in V into R that satisfies the requirements of Proposition 1.5. Hence there is a continuous homomorphism $f: V \to R$ such that $\rho \circ f = \gamma \circ \pi$, and we know from Proposition 1.1 that f is a linear map.

Now we have $\rho(f(v_i)) = \gamma(\pi(v_i)) = 0$, so that $f(v_i)$ is an integer z_i for each i. Hence $f(v) = \sum_{i=1}^{n} r_i z_i$. But $v \in A$, so that we find, as just now for v_i, that $f(v)$ is also an integer z. Now $z = \sum_{i=1}^{n} r_i z_i$ and, since $(1, r_1, \cdots, r_n)$

is linearly independent over the field of the rational numbers, this implies that each z_i is 0, whence $f = 0$, which evidently gives $\gamma = 0$, q.e.d.

2

We need the following purely technical lemma.

LEMMA 2.1.   *Let G be a locally compact topological group, and let K be a closed subgroup of G such that the coset space G/K is compact.   Then there is a continuous non-negative real-valued function w with compact support on G such that, for every x in G, $I_K((x \cdot w)_K) = 1$, where I_K is a Haar integral for K.*

Proof.   Let C be a compact neighborhood of 1 in G.   Then a finite set of translates of the canonical image of C in G/K covers G/K, whence we see that there is a compact subset D of G (a union of a finite family of translates of C) such that $G = DK$.   Now we can find a non-negative real-valued continuous function g with compact support on G such that $g(x) = 1$ for every x in D^{-1}.   For x in G, $(x \cdot g)_K$ is evidently a continuous function with compact support on K.   Define the function f on G by setting $f(x) = I_K((x \cdot g)_K)$. Clearly, f is continuous.   Now $G = KD^{-1}$, so that every x in G may be written yz with y in K and z in D^{-1}.   We have $(x \cdot g)_K(y^{-1}) = g(y^{-1}x) = g(z) = 1$.   Thus the non-negative real-valued function $(x \cdot g)_K$ on K is not identically 0, whence $f(x) > 0$ for every x in G.   Hence we may define a continuous non-negative real-valued function w on G by setting $w(x) = g(x)/f(x)$ for every x in G.   Since g has compact support, so has w.

For y in K, we have

$$(x \cdot f)(y) = f(yx) = I_K((yx \cdot g)_K) = I_K(y \cdot (x \cdot g)_K) = I_K((x \cdot g)_K) = f(x).$$

Thus $(x \cdot f)_K$ is the constant function on K with value $f(x)$.   Hence $I_K((x \cdot w)_K) = f(x)^{-1}I_K((x \cdot g)_K) = 1$, and the lemma is proved.

PROPOSITION 2.2.   *Let G be a locally compact topological group, and let K be a closed normal subgroup of G such that G/K is compact.   Let V be a continuous G-module of finite dimension over R such that the induced representation of K on V is trivial.   Let f be a continuous homomorphism $K \to V$ such that $x \cdot f(y) = f(xyx^{-1})$ for every y in K and every x in G.   Then f is the restriction to K of a continuous map f^* of G into V such that $f^*(xy) = x \cdot f^*(y) + f^*(x)$ for all x and y in G.*

Proof.   Let I_K be a Haar integral for K and extend I_K to continuous V-valued functions f with compact support such that $I_K(f) \in V$ and $\alpha(I_K(f)) = I_K(\alpha \circ f)$ for every element α of the dual space V° to V.   For y in K, we have evidently $y \cdot f = f + f(y)$, where $f(y)$ is identified with the constant function

37

with value $f(y)$. Let w be a function on G such as is provided by Lemma 2.1. Then our above identity yields, for every x in G,

$$I_K((x \cdot w)_K(y \cdot f)) = I_K((x \cdot w)_K f) + f(y),$$

so that
$$\begin{aligned} f(y) &= I_K((x \cdot w)_K(y \cdot f)) - I_K((x \cdot w)_K f) \\ &= I_K((y^{-1}x \cdot w)_K f) - I_K((x \cdot w)_K f). \end{aligned}$$

Now define the map f_1 of G into V by setting

$$f_1(x) = I_K((x \cdot w)_K f) - x \cdot I_K(w_K f).$$

Clearly, f_1 is continuous, and the above gives $f(y) = f_1(y^{-1}x) - f_1(x)$. For each x in G, define the map g_x of G into V by setting

$$g_x(t) = t^{-1} \cdot (f_1(t) - f_1(tx)).$$

Clearly, g_x is continuous. We claim that, for every y in K, $g_x(yt) = g_x(t)$. The verification is as follows:

$$\begin{aligned} g_x(yt) &= t^{-1}y^{-1} \cdot (f_1(yt) - f_1(ytx)) \\ &= t^{-1} \cdot (f(y^{-1}) + f_1(t) - f(y^{-1}) - f_1(tx)) = g_x(t). \end{aligned}$$

Hence, for every x in G, there is a continuous map $g_x{}^\circ$ of G/K into V such that $g_x{}^\circ(tK) = g_x(t)$ for every t in G. Now let $I_{G/K}$ be the normalized Haar integral for G/K, extended as above. Define the map f^* of G into V by $f^*(x) = I_{G/K}(g_x{}^\circ)$. Clearly, f^* is continuous. If y is in K, we have

$$\begin{aligned} g_y(t) &= t^{-1} \cdot (f_1(t) - f_1(ty)) = t^{-1} \cdot (f_1(t) - f_1((tyt^{-1})t)) \\ &= t^{-1} \cdot (-f(ty^{-1}t^{-1})) = -f(y^{-1}) = f(y). \end{aligned}$$

Thus the restriction of f^* to K coincides with f.

Now observe that, for all x, t, u in G,

$$\begin{aligned} g_{xt}(u) &= u^{-1} \cdot (f_1(u) - f_1(uxt)) \\ &= u^{-1} \cdot ((f_1(u) - f_1(ux)) + (f_1(ux) - f_1(uxt))) \\ &= g_x(u) + x \cdot g_t(ux). \end{aligned}$$

Write ρ for the given representation of G on V, and x° for the coset xK. Then the last result yields

$$g_{xt}{}^\circ = g_x{}^\circ + \rho(x) \circ (x^\circ \cdot g_t{}^\circ).$$

Hence we obtain

$$f^*(xt) = f^*(x) + \rho(x)(I_{G/K}(x^\circ \cdot g_t{}^\circ)) = f^*(x) + x \cdot f^*(t),$$

which is the identity required by our proposition. This completes the proof.

Let G be a topological group, and let N be a closed normal subgroup of G. We say that N is a *semidirect factor* of G if there is a subgroup H of G such that the map of the Cartesian product space $N \times H$ into the space G that sends each pair (n, h) onto nh is a homeomorphism. It is readily seen that N is a semidirect factor of G if and only if there is a continuous homomorphism $\sigma: G/N \to G$ such that $\pi \circ \sigma$ is the identity map on G/N, where π is the canonical homomorphism $G \to G/N$; one may then take $H = \sigma(G/N)$.

THEOREM 2.3. *Let G be a topological group containing a vector group V as a closed normal subgroup. If G/V is compact then V is a semidirect factor of G.*

Proof. If we associate with each element x of G the conjugation $v \to xvx^{-1}$ of V we have evidently the structure of a continuous G-module on V, and the restriction to V of this representation of G is trivial. Hence we may apply Proposition 2.2 to the identity map on V and conclude that there is a continuous projection $g: G \to V$ such that, using the multiplicative notation also for the group composition in V, $g(xy) = xg(y)x^{-1}g(x)$ for all x and y in G. Define the map γ of G into G by $\gamma(x) = g(x)^{-1}x$. Then γ is evidently continuous, and we have

$$\gamma(x)\gamma(y) = g(x)^{-1}xg(y)^{-1}y = g(x)^{-1}(xg(y^{-1})x^{-1})xy = g(xy)^{-1}xy = \gamma(xy),$$

i.e., γ is a homomorphism. Since V is evidently in the kernel of γ, we have an induced continuous homomorphism $\sigma: G/V \to G$, and one sees immediately that $\pi \circ \sigma$ is the identity map on G/V, where π is the canonical map $G \to G/V$. Thus V is a semidirect factor of G.

Proposition 2.2 has another striking application in a very different direction. This is the following.

THEOREM 2.4. *Let G be a connected topological group, and let D be a discrete central subgroup of G such that G/D is compact and the commutator subgroup of G/D is dense in G/D. Then D is finite.*

Proof. We know from Theorem 2.6 of Chapter I that G is locally compact. In Exercise 2 of Chapter I, we have sketched a proof showing that D is finitely generated. It is clear from the elementary structure theorem for finitely generated discrete abelian groups that if D is not finite there exists a surjective homomorphism of D onto the additive group Z of the integers. We may regard this as a continuous homomorphism f of D into the one-dimensional vector group R, and we may view R as a trivial representation space for G. Now we may apply Proposition 2.2 and conclude that f can be extended to a continuous homomorphism f^* of G into R.

39

Since $f^*(G)$ must be connected, it cannot coincide with Z. Hence, following up f^* with the canonical homomorphism $R \to R/Z$, we obtain a non-trivial continuous homomorphism of G/D into R/Z. Since the commutator subgroup of G/D is dense in G/D, this is evidently impossible. Thus D must be finite.

3

Let G be a locally compact topological group, and let $\mathscr{A}(G)$ denote the group of all topological group automorphisms of G. We wish to define the structure of a topological group on $\mathscr{A}(G)$. We do this by prescribing a fundamental system of neighborhoods of the identity in $\mathscr{A}(G)$. If K is a compact subset of G and V is a neighborhood of 1 in G we denote by $N(K, V)$ the set of all elements α of $\mathscr{A}(G)$ such that $\alpha(x)x^{-1}$ and $\alpha^{-1}(x)x^{-1}$ belong to V for every x in K. We claim that the family of these sets $N(K, V)$ satisfies the conditions $N_1, \cdots, N_4$ characterizing a fundamental system of neighborhoods of the neutral element of a topological group that we listed in Section 2 of Chapter I. Conditions N_1, N_2 and N_4 are evidently satisfied, even if we do not assume that G is locally compact. Condition N_3 demands that, given K and V, there should be K' and V' such that

$$N(K', V') \, N(K', V')^{-1} \subset N(K, V).$$

Now, since G is locally compact, we can find a compact neighborhood V' of 1 in G such that $V'V'V' \subset V$. Put $K' = K \cup V'$. Since our sets $N(K, V)$ and $N(K', V')$ are stable under the involution $\alpha \to \alpha^{-1}$, it suffices to show that if α and β are elements of $N(K', V')$ and x belongs to K then $\alpha(\beta(x))x^{-1}$ belongs to V. We have

$$\alpha(\beta(x))x^{-1} = [\alpha(\beta(x)x^{-1})(\beta(x)x^{-1})^{-1}][\beta(x)x^{-1}][\alpha(x)x^{-1}],$$

and each of the three bracketed elements belongs to V'. Hence $\alpha(\beta(x))x^{-1}$ belongs to V, and we have shown that N_3 is satisfied.

Thus we have the structure of a topological group on $\mathscr{A}(G)$ for which the sets $N(K, V)$ constitute a fundamental system of neighborhoods of the identity. An important property is the following.

PROPOSITION 3.1. *If G is a locally compact group then the canonical map $\mathscr{A}(G) \times G \to G$ sending each pair (α, x) onto $\alpha(x)$ is continuous and open.*

Proof. Let U be an open set in G, and let (α, x) be a point of its inverse image in $\mathscr{A}(G) \times G$. Then we can find a compact neighborhood W of 1 in G such that $\alpha(WWx) \subset U$. Let β be an element of $N(Wx, W)$ and let y

be an element of W. Then we have $(\alpha\beta)(yx) = \alpha(\beta(yx))$, and $\beta(yx) \in Wyx \subset WWx$, whence $(\alpha\beta)(yx) \in U$. Thus $(\alpha N(Wx, W)) \times Wx$ lies in the inverse image of U, and we have shown that the map $\mathscr{A}(G) \times G \to G$ is continuous. It is evident that this map is an open map, so that Proposition 3.1 is proved.

It is very easy to see that if V is a vector group then the topology of $\mathscr{A}(V)$ as introduced above coincides with the topology induced on $\mathscr{A}(V)$ by the standard vector group topology on $E(V) = \mathrm{Hom}_R(V, V)$. The group $\mathscr{A}(V)$ is usually called the *full linear group on V*. Note that $\mathscr{A}(V)$ is an open subset of $E(V)$.

Let G be a locally compact topological group, and let H be an arbitrary topological group. Suppose we are given a homomorphism $\eta : H \to \mathscr{A}(G)$. We claim that η *is continuous if and only if the map of $H \times G$ into G that sends each (α, x) onto $\eta(\alpha)(x)$ is continuous*. This condition is evidently necessary, by Proposition 3.1. Now suppose that it is satisfied. In order to prove that η is continuous, it suffices to show that it is continuous at the identity element of H. Let U be a neighborhood of the identity in $\mathscr{A}(G)$. Then there is a compact subset K of G and a neighborhood V of 1 in G such that $N(K, V) \subset U$. Our assumption evidently implies that the maps of $H \times G$ into G that send each (α, x) onto $\eta(\alpha)(x)x^{-1}$ or onto $\eta(\alpha^{-1})(x)x^{-1}$, respectively, are also continuous. Since K is compact, we can therefore find a neighborhood W of the neutral element of H such that each of these maps sends $W \times K$ into V, which means that $\eta(W) \subset N(K, V)$. This completes the proof of our assertion.

In particular, if G is a vector group, this means that η defines the structure of a continuous H-module on G if and only if it is a *continuous* homomorphism of H into the full linear group on G. In other words, the continuous finite-dimensional representations of a topological group H are the continuous homomorphisms of H into automorphism groups $\mathscr{A}(V)$, where V is a vector group.

Now let G and H be arbitrary topological groups, and let η be a homomorphism of H into the (untopologized) group $\mathscr{A}(G)$ of the topological group automorphisms of G. Then we can define a group structure on $G \times H$ such that the product is given by the formula

$$(g_1, h_1)(g_2, h_2) = (g_1\eta(h_1)(g_2), h_1h_2).$$

This gives

$$(g_1, h_1)(g_2, h_2)^{-1} = (g_1\eta(h_1h_2^{-1})(g_2^{-1}), h_1h_2^{-1}).$$

41

Hence we see that our group is a topological group with the Cartesian product topology if and only if η has the continuity property we discussed above, i.e., if and only if the map of $H \times G$ into G that sends each (α, x) onto $\eta(\alpha)(x)$ is continuous. In that case, we shall call our group the *semidirect product of G by H that is determined by* η, and we shall denote it by $G \times_\eta H$. If G is locally compact then we know from the above that η defines a semidirect product if and only if it is a continuous homomorphism of H into $\mathscr{A}(G)$.

The following proposition is a simple application of some of our above results.

PROPOSITION 3.2. *Let T be the toroid V/F, where V is a vector group and F is the discrete free abelian subgroup generated by a basis of V. Then $\mathscr{A}(T)$ is discrete and isomorphic with $\mathscr{A}(F)$.*

Proof. Let π denote the canonical homomorphism $V \to V/F$. Then, for each α in $\mathscr{A}(T)$, the map $\alpha \circ \pi$ is a continuous homomorphism of V into V/F. It follows from Proposition 1.5 (as we have seen in proving Proposition 1.6) that there is one and only one continuous homomorphism α^* of V into V such that $\pi \circ \alpha^* = \alpha \circ \pi$. It is clear that the map $\alpha \to \alpha^*$ is actually an injective homomorphism of $\mathscr{A}(T)$ into $\mathscr{A}(V)$. Moreover, one sees immediately that the image of $\mathscr{A}(T)$ in $\mathscr{A}(V)$ consists precisely of those automorphisms that map F onto itself. Let $\mathscr{A}(V)_F$ denote this subgroup of $\mathscr{A}(V)$, so that our map $\alpha \to \alpha^*$ is a bijective homomorphism of $\mathscr{A}(T)$ onto $\mathscr{A}(V)_F$. Since F is generated by a basis of V, the restriction of the elements of $\mathscr{A}(V)_F$ to F is evidently a bijective homomorphism of $\mathscr{A}(V)_F$ onto $\mathscr{A}(F)$. Thus we have a bijective homomorphism $\mathscr{A}(T) \to \mathscr{A}(F)$ sending each α onto $(\alpha^*)_F$. Since F is finitely generated and discrete, it is clear that $\mathscr{A}(F)$ is discrete. Hence it suffices to show that our map $\alpha \to (\alpha^*)_F$ is continuous. Since the restriction map $\mathscr{A}(V)_F \to \mathscr{A}(F)$ is evidently continuous, it suffices to see that the map $\alpha \to \alpha^*$ is continuous. But this is almost evident from the definition of this map, so that Proposition 3.2 is proved.

EXERCISES

1. Let A and B be toroids, written explicitly as direct products of copies of the multiplicative group of the complex numbers of absolute value 1. Let α be any continuous homomorphism of A into B. Show that there

are integers e_{ij} such that, for every element $(a_1, \cdots, a_m)$ of A, one has $\alpha(a_1, \cdots, a_m) = (b_1, \cdots, b_n)$, with $b_j = \prod_{i=1}^{m} a_i{}^{e_{ij}}$.

2. Let G be a topological group having a discrete free abelian group D as a closed central subgroup such that G/D is compact. Show that every homomorphism of D into a toroid T can be extended to a continuous homomorphism of G into T.

3. Let G be a locally compact topological group, N a closed connected normal subgroup of G, and H a closed connected subgroup of G such that $G = NH$ and $N \cap H = (1)$. Prove that the multiplication induces a topological group isomorphism of the appropriately defined semidirect product $N \times_\eta H$ onto G. [See Exercise 1 of Chapter I.]

4. Let G be a compact topological group. Let $\mathscr{S}$ denote the set of all neighborhoods U of the neutral element in G such that $U = U^{-1}$. Let $M(U)$ be the set of all topological group automorphisms α of G such that $\alpha(x)x^{-1} \in U$ for every element x of G. Show that the $M(U)$'s, as U ranges over $\mathscr{S}$, constitute a fundamental system of neighborhoods of the identity in $\mathscr{A}(G)$.

IV. COVERINGS [1, 8]

1

Let f be a continuous map of a space S into a space T. We say that a subset E of T is *evenly covered* by f if f maps every connected component of $f^{-1}(E)$ homeomorphically onto E. One sees immediately that if F is any connected subset of an evenly covered set E then the connected components of $f^{-1}(F)$ are precisely its intersections with the connected components of $f^{-1}(E)$, so that F is also evenly covered. A *covering* of a space T is a continuous map of a connected and locally connected space S onto T such that every point of T has a neighborhood that is evenly covered by f. Let $f: S \to T$ be a covering, and let s be a point of S. Let V be an evenly covered neighborhood of $f(s)$, and let U be the connected component of $f^{-1}(V)$ that contains s. Since $f^{-1}(V)$ is a neighborhood of s and since S is locally connected, U is still a neighborhood of s. Since f maps U homeomorphically onto V, we have shown that *a covering map is a local homeomorphism*. If we start with an arbitrary neighborhood V of a point t of T, choose a connected neighborhood U of a point s such that $f(s) = t$ and $U \subset f^{-1}(V)$, then we obtain a connected neighborhood $f(U)$ of t such that $f(U) \subset V$. Thus *if a space T has a covering then it is connected and locally connected*.

PROPOSITION 1.1.   *Let $f: S \to T$ be a covering, and let g_1 and g_2 be continuous maps of a connected space P into S such that $f \circ g_1 = f \circ g_2$.   Then if g_1 and g_2 agree at one point of P it follows that $g_1 = g_2$.*

Proof.   Let A be the set of all points p of P such that $g_1(p) = g_2(p)$. By assumption, A is non-empty. Since P is connected, it suffices therefore to show that A is both open and closed in P. Evidently, A is closed. In order to see that A is open, let p be any point in A. Let V be an evenly covered neighborhood of $f(g_1(p))$. Let U be the connected component of $f^{-1}(V)$ that contains $g_1(p) = g_2(p)$. Then U is a neighborhood of this point, so that we can find a neighborhood Q of p in P such that $g_i(Q) \subset U$ for $i = 1, 2$. Now f maps U injectively into T, whence it is clear that $Q \subset A$. This completes the proof of Proposition 1.1.

LEMMA 1.2. *Let f be a surjective continuous map of a locally connected space S onto a space T such that every point of T has an evenly covered neighborhood. Let A be a connected and locally connected subspace of T. Then $f^{-1}(A)$ is locally connected, and the restriction of f to any connected component of $f^{-1}(A)$ is a covering of A.*

Proof. Let p be any point in $f^{-1}(A)$. The assumptions imply that T is locally connected, so that every neighborhood of $f(p)$ in T contains an open connected neighborhood of $f(p)$. Hence, since a connected subset of an evenly covered set is evenly covered, there is an open neighborhood V of $f(p)$ in T that is evenly covered by f. Let W be the connected component of $V \cap A$ that contains $f(p)$. Since A is locally connected, W is open in A. Let W' be the connected component of $f^{-1}(W)$ that contains p, and let V' be the connected component of $f^{-1}(V)$ that contains p. Since V' is a neighborhood of p in S and $W' = f^{-1}(W) \cap V'$, it is clear that W' is a neighborhood of p in $f^{-1}(A)$. But f maps W' homeomorphically onto the open subset W of the locally connected space A. Hence W' is locally connected. Thus we have shown that $f^{-1}(A)$ is locally connected. Moreover, it is clear that W is evenly covered by f.

Now let A' be any connected component of $f^{-1}(A)$. Let a be a point in the closure of $f(A')$ in A. Take the point p in the above so that $f(p) = a$. Now $W \cap f(A')$ is non-empty, so that $f^{-1}(W)$ meets A'. Hence A' contains a connected component of $f^{-1}(W)$, which implies that $f(A')$ contains W. Thus $f(A')$ is both open and closed in A. Since A is connected, we have therefore $f(A') = A$. The connected components of $f^{-1}(W) \cap A'$ are precisely those components of $f^{-1}(W)$ which meet A'. Hence it is clear that W is evenly covered by the restriction of f to A', so that Lemma 1.2 is proved.

LEMMA 1.3. *Let $f: S \to T$ be a covering, and let A and B be closed connected and locally connected subsets of T that are evenly covered by f. Then, if $A \cap B$ is non-empty and connected, $A \cup B$ is evenly covered by f.*

Proof. We show first that $A \cup B$ is locally connected. Evidently, every point in $A - B$ and every point in $B - A$ has the property that every neighborhood of it in $A \cup B$ contains a connected neighborhood. Now let p be a point of $A \cap B$, and let V be a neighborhood of p in $A \cup B$. Then there are neighborhoods V_A and V_B that are contained in V and such that $A \cap V_A$ and $B \cap V_B$ are connected. Hence also $(A \cap V_A) \cup (B \cap V_B)$ is connected. Since this set contains $V_A \cap V_B$, it is a neighborhood of p. Thus $A \cup B$ is locally connected.

Now let A'_σ denote the components of $f^{-1}(A)$. We know that the components of $f^{-1}(A \cap B)$ are the intersections $A'_\sigma \cap f^{-1}(A \cap B)$. Since the same holds for the components of $f^{-1}(B)$ in the place of the components of $f^{-1}(A)$, it is clear that we may label the components of $f^{-1}(B)$ such that $A'_\sigma \cap f^{-1}(A \cap B) = B'_\sigma \cap f^{-1}(A \cap B)$ for each σ. Put $K_\sigma = A'_\sigma \cup B'_\sigma$ and $L_\sigma = \bigcup_{\tau \neq \sigma} K_\tau$. Clearly, K_σ is closed in S. By Lemma 1.2, A'_σ is open in $f^{-1}(A)$, whence $\bigcup_{\tau \neq \sigma} A'_\tau$ is closed in $f^{-1}(A)$ and therefore also in S. Similarly, $\bigcup_{\tau \neq \sigma} B'_\tau$ is closed in S, whence L_σ is closed in S. Now $K_\sigma \cup L_\sigma = f^{-1}(A \cup B)$ and $K_\sigma \cap L_\sigma = \varnothing$. Hence K_σ is both closed and open in $f^{-1}(A \cup B)$. Since K_σ is connected, it follows that the K_σ's are the connected components of $f^{-1}(A \cup B)$.

Now let f_σ be the restriction of f to K_σ. Since $A \cup B$ is connected and locally connected, we know from Lemma 1.2 that $f_\sigma : K_\sigma \to A \cup B$ is a covering. Moreover, one sees immediately from the fact that the restrictions of f to A'_σ and B'_σ are injective that f_σ is injective. Hence f_σ is a homeomorphism, so that $A \cup B$ is evenly covered by f.

We shall say that a space P is *simply connected* if it satisfies the following conditions. (1) P is connected and locally connected; (2) if $f : S \to T$ is a covering, g a continuous map of P into T, p_0 a point of P, and s_0 a point of S such that $g(p_0) = f(s_0)$ then there is one and only one continuous map h of P into S such that $g = f \circ h$ and $h(p_0) = s_0$.

THEOREM 1.4. *Let P be a connected and locally connected space. Then P is simply connected if and only if every covering of P is a homeomorphism.*

Proof. Suppose first that P is simply connected, and let $f : S \to P$ be a covering of P. Then there exists a continuous map h of P into S such that $f \circ h$ is the identity map on P. Let s be a point of the closure of $h(P)$ in S, and let V be an evenly covered neighborhood of $f(s)$. Let V' be the connected component of $f^{-1}(V)$ that contains s. Then V' meets $h(P)$ and therefore $h(V)$. Since $h(V)$ is connected, we must therefore have $h(V) \subset V'$. Since f maps both V' and $h(V)$ bijectively onto V, it follows that $h(V) = V'$. Thus $V' \subset h(P)$. Since V' is a neighborhood of s, this shows that $h(P)$ is both open and closed in S and thus coincides with S. Hence it is clear that f is a homeomorphism.

Now suppose that P is connected and locally connected and that every covering of P is a homeomorphism. Let f, S, T, g, p_0, s_0 be as in the definition of a simply connected space. Let C be the subspace of $P \times S$ consisting of all the points (p, s) such that $g(p) = f(s)$. Let π denote the restriction to C of the projection map of $P \times S$ onto P. We show first that every point p of P has a neighborhood that is evenly covered by π. Let V be a neighborhood of $g(p)$ that is evenly covered by f, and let U be a connected neighborhood of p such that $g(U) \subset V$. Let V'_σ be the connected components of $f^{-1}(V)$, and let f_σ be the restriction of f to V'_σ. Let U'_σ be the subset of C consisting of the points $(u, f_\sigma{}^{-1}(g(u)))$, with u in U. Clearly, π maps U'_σ homeomorphically onto U. We have $\pi^{-1}(U) = \bigcup_\sigma U'_\sigma$. The projection of $P \times S$ onto S maps every connected subset of $\pi^{-1}(U)$ into one of the components V'_σ, so that every connected subset of $\pi^{-1}(U)$ is contained in one of the sets U'_σ. Hence the U'_σ's are the connected components of $\pi^{-1}(U)$, and U is evenly covered by π.

Next we show that C is locally connected. Let (p, s) be a point of C, and let N be a neighborhood of (p, s) in $P \times S$. Then N contains a neighborhood of the form $U \times V'_\sigma$, where U and V'_σ are as above. Then we have $U'_\sigma \subset N$ and $(U \times V'_\sigma) \cap C = U'_\sigma$, so that U'_σ is a neighborhood of (p, s) in C. Since U'_σ is connected, we have shown that C is locally connected.

Now let C' be the connected component of C that contains the given point (p_0, s_0), and let π' be the restriction of π to C'. Since C is locally connected and every point of P has a neighborhood that is evenly covered by π, Lemma 1.2 applies and shows that $\pi': C' \to P$ is a covering. By our assumption on P, π' is therefore a homeomorphism. For p in P, write $(\pi')^{-1}(p) = (p, h(p))$. Then h is a continuous map of P into S, $f \circ h = g$ and $h(p_0) = s_0$. By Proposition 1.1, there is only one map h satisfying these conditions. Hence we have shown that P is simply connected, which completes the proof of Theorem 1.4.

THEOREM 1.5. *Let P be a Cartesian product of a finite family of finite closed intervals on the real line. Then P is simply connected.*

Proof. Since P is connected and locally connected, it suffices, by virtue of Theorem 1.4, to show that every covering of P is a homeomorphism. For this purpose, we recall the well-known Lebesgue Lemma, which says the following.   Let (V_α) be a family of open subsets of P whose union is P. Then there is a positive real number d such that every subset of P having diameter less than d is contained in one of the V_α's.   Indeed, if this were false then, for every positive integer n, we could find a subset A_n of P of diameter less than $1/n$ that is not contained in any V_α.   Since P is compact, there is a point p in P such that every neighborhood of p meets A_n for infinitely many n's.   There is an α such that p lies in V_α, and hence there is a positive real number r such that every point q of P whose distance from p is less than r belongs to V_α.   By our choice of p, there is a point q whose distance from p is less than $r/2$ and that belongs to an A_n with $n > 2/r$. But then every point of A_n has distance less than r from p, so that $A_n \subset V_\alpha$, which is a contradiction.

Now let $f \colon S \to P$ be any covering of P.   We know that every point p of P has an open neighborhood V_p that is evenly covered by f.   The Lebesgue Lemma gives us a positive real number d such that every subset of P having diameter less than d is contained in one of the V_p's.   By slicing up P with hyperplanes orthogonal to the coordinate axis, we represent P as the union of a finite family of closed congruent "boxes", each of diameter less than d, so that each is evenly covered by f.   Clearly, we can stack these boxes one by one to build up P in such a way that the requirements of Lemma 1.3 are fulfilled at each stage, where, in the notation of Lemma 1.3, A is the stack already constructed and B is the box adjoined to A to form the new stack. Thus Lemma 1.3 shows inductively that each stack is evenly covered by f, so that finally P is seen to be evenly covered by f.   But this means that f is a homeomorphism, which proves Theorem 1.5.

THEOREM 1.6.   *If P and Q are simply connected then $P \times Q$ is simply connected.*

Proof.   By virtue of Theorem 1.4, it suffices to show that every covering $f \colon S \to P \times Q$ is a homeomorphism.   For a point s of S, write $f(s) = (p_s, q_s)$.   Let $P(s)$ denote the connected component of $f^{-1}(P \times (q_s))$ that contains s, and define $Q(s)$ analogously.   It is clear from Lemma 1.2 that f maps $P(s)$ homeomorphically onto $P \times (q_s)$ and $Q(s)$ homeomorphically onto $(p_s) \times Q$.   Let us fix a point a of S, and let A denote the union of the family of sets $Q(s)$ with s ranging over $P(a)$.   Clearly, f induces a bijection of A onto $P \times Q$.   We wish to show that A is open in S.

Let s be any point of S, and let V and W be connected subsets of P and Q respectively such that $V \times W$ is evenly covered and contains $f(s)$.   Let

$(V \times W)(s)$ denote the connected component of $f^{-1}(V \times W)$ that contains s. If T is any subset of S, let T_s denote the subset of T consisting of the points t of T for which $q_t = q_s$. We claim that if $(V \times W)(s)_s$ is contained in A then $(V \times W)(s)$ is contained in A. In order to show this, let c be any point of $(V \times W)(s)$. Let d be the point of $(V \times W)(s)$ such that $p_d = p_c$ and $q_d = q_s$. Then d lies in $(V \times W)(s)_s$ and hence in A. By the definition of A, this means that $Q(d)$ lies in A. Let e be the point of $Q(d)$ such that $q_e = q_c$. Then $f(e) = (p_d, q_c) = (p_c, q_c) = f(c)$. On the other hand, $e \in Q(d) \cap f^{-1}(V \times W)$, which is mapped homeomorphically onto $(p_d) \times W$ by f and therefore connected. Since $d \in (V \times W)(s) \cap Q(d)$, it follows that $e \in (V \times W)(s)$. The restriction of f to $(V \times W)(s)$ being injective, we must therefore have $e = c$, whence $c \in A$.

Now suppose that $s \in P(a)$, and choose the above sets V and W so that $V \times W$ is a neighborhood of $f(s)$. Then $(V \times W)(s)$ is a neighborhood of s, and evidently $(V \times W)(s)_s \subset P(a) \subset A$. Since, by the above, this implies that $(V \times W)(s) \subset A$, we conclude that s is an interior point of A. Thus every point of $P(a)$ is an interior point of A.

Now consider a set $Q(s)$ with s in $P(a)$. Let E be the set of all points of $Q(s)$ that lie in the interior of A. Then E is non-empty, because it contains s. Let t be a point of $Q(s)$ that lies in the closure of E. Choose connected subsets V and W of P and Q, respectively, such that $V \times W$ is an evenly covered neighborhood of $f(t)$. Then $(V \times W)(t)$ contains a point e of E, so that, replacing V with a smaller connected set if necessary, we may arrange to have $(V \times W)(t)_e \subset A$. But $(V \times W)(t) = (V \times W)(e)$, and we know from the above that we must therefore have $(V \times W)(t) \subset A$, so that $t \in E$. Thus E is both open and closed in $Q(s)$, whence $E = Q(s)$. We have therefore shown that every point of A is an interior point, i.e., that A is open in S.

Hence the restriction of f to A is an open map. Since it is also a continuous bijection of A onto $P \times Q$, it is therefore a homeomorphism of A onto $P \times Q$. Its inverse is a continuous map h of $P \times Q$ into S such that $f \circ h$ is the identity map on $P \times Q$. By the first part of the proof of Theorem 1.4, this implies that f is a homeomorphism, so that Theorem 1.6 is proved.

We conclude this Section with an important property of simply connected spaces, which is expressed by the following *Monodromy Theorem*.

THEOREM 1.7. *Let S be a simply connected space, and let D be an open* *connected neighborhood of the diagonal in $S \times S$. Suppose there is given a map δ of D into a group G such that $\delta(p, q)\delta(q, r) = \delta(p, r)$ whenever (p, q), (q, r) and (p, r) belong to D. Then there is a map σ of S into G such that $\delta(p, q) = \sigma(p)\sigma(q)^{-1}$ for all (p, q) in D. Moreover, if τ is any other such map of S into G there is an element x in G such that $\tau(p) = \sigma(p)x$ for every point p of S.*

Proof. We define a family T of subsets of $S \times G$ by saying that a subset U of $S \times G$ should belong to T if, and only if, for every point (p, x) of U, there is a neighborhood N of p in S such that $N \times N \subset D$ and $(q, \delta(q, p)x) \in U$ for every point q of N. Clearly, $\varnothing$ and $S \times G$ belong to T, and arbitrary unions and finite intersections of subfamilies of T belong to T. If V is any subset of S such that $V \times V \subset D$ and if (p, x) is a point of $V \times G$ then we denote by $V(p, x)$ the set of all points $(q, \delta(q, p)x)$ with q in V. If V is open in S then $V(p, x) \in T$. For suppose that (q, y) belongs to $V(p, x)$. Then q lies in V and $y = \delta(q, p)x$. Now let r be a point of V. Then (r, q), (q, p) and (r, p) lie in D, and $(r, \delta(r, q)y) = (r, \delta(r, q)\delta(q, p)x) = (r, \delta(r, p)x) \in V(p, x)$, which proves our assertion. Now let (p, x) and (q, y) be distinct points of $S \times G$. If $p \neq q$ then there are disjoint open sets V and W in S such that $p \in V$, $q \in W$, and both $V \times V$ and $W \times W$ lie in D. Then the sets $V(p, x)$ and $W(q, y)$ belong to T and are evidently disjoint. If $p = q$ then $x \neq y$ and again the sets $V(p, x)$ and $V(p, y)$ are disjoint, for if (r, z) were a common point we would have $\delta(r, p)x = \delta(r, p)y$, which would give $x = y$, contrary to assumption. Thus we have shown, in particular, that T is a Hausdorff topology on $S \times G$. We shall now regard $S \times G$ as a space with the topology T.

Clearly, the projection map $\pi : S \times G \to S$ is continuous and open. Since S is locally connected, every point p of S has an open connected neighborhood V_p such that $V_p \times V_p \subset D$. The set $\pi^{-1}(V_p)$ is the union of the family of open sets $V_p(p, x)$, where x ranges over G. We have seen above that these sets are mutually disjoint. Moreover, π maps $V_p(p, x)$ homeomorphically onto V_p. Hence, since V_p is connected, the sets $V_p(p, x)$ are precisely the connected components of $\pi^{-1}(V_p)$, and V_p is evenly covered by π. Since every open set of $S \times G$ contains such a set $V_p(p, x)$ for each of its points (p, x), it is clear also that $S \times G$ is locally connected. Hence we may apply Lemma 1.2 to conclude that if S^* is any connected component of $S \times G$ and π^* is the restriction of π to S^* then $\pi^* : S^* \to S$ is a covering. Since S is simply connected, π^* is therefore a homeomorphism. Now we define the map $\sigma : S \to G$ by $(\pi^*)^{-1}(p) = (p, \sigma(p))$. We show that σ satisfies the requirement of Theorem 1.7.

Let E denote the set of all points (p, q) in D for which $\delta(p, q) = \sigma(p)\sigma(q)^{-1}$. Since δ maps the diagonal of $S \times S$ onto the neutral element of G, E is non-empty. Now let (p, q) be a point of D that lies in the closure of E. Choose connected neighborhoods U and V of p and q respectively such that $U \times U$, $V \times V$ and $U \times V$ all lie in D. The set $U \times V$ contains a point (p', q') of E. Let (u, v) be any point of $U \times V$. Since U is connected, the set $U(p, \sigma(p))$ is connected and therefore contained in S^*. Hence $(u, \delta(u, p)\sigma(p)) \in S^*$, so that $\delta(u, p)\sigma(p) = \sigma(u)$, which means precisely that (u, p) belongs to E. In the same way, we show that (p, p'), (q', q) and (q, v) belong to E. Hence we have

$$\delta(u, v) = \delta(u, p)\delta(p, p')\delta(p', q')\delta(q', q)\delta(q, v) = \sigma(u)\sigma(v)^{-1},$$

i.e., $(u, v) \in E$. Thus we have shown that E is both open and closed in D, whence $E = D$, which means that σ satisfies the requirement of Theorem 1.7.

Finally, let τ be another map of S into G satisfying the requirement of Theorem 1.7. Then we have, for every point (p, q) of D,

$$\tau(q)^{-1}\sigma(q) = [\tau(p)^{-1}\delta(p, q)][\delta(p, q)^{-1}\sigma(p)] = \tau(p)^{-1}\sigma(p).$$

This shows that the sets A_x of the points p of S for which $\tau(p)^{-1}\sigma(p) = x$ are open in S. Since S is connected, it follows that $S = A_x$ for some x in G, which completes the proof.

2

An *arc* in a space S is a continuous map α of the closed interval $[0, 1]$ into S. We shall call such an arc α a *closed arc* if $\alpha(0) = \alpha(1)$. We say that a closed arc α can be *shrunk to a point* if there is a continuous map β of $[0, 1] \times [0, 1]$ into S such that $\beta(0, r) = \alpha(r)$ for every r in $[0, 1]$, $\beta(1, r)$ is a fixed point p of S not depending on r, and $\beta(t, 0) = \beta(t, 1)$ for every t in $[0, 1]$. We shall say that a space S is *arcwise simply connected* if S is connected and locally arcwise connected, and if every closed arc in S can be shrunk to a point. It is easy to see that this implies the following property: let α and β be arcs in S such that $\alpha(0) = \beta(0)$ and $\alpha(1) = \beta(1)$. Then α and β are *homotopic*, in the sense that there is a continuous map η of $[0, 1] \times [0, 1]$ into S such that $\eta(0, r) = \alpha(r)$, $\eta(1, r) = \beta(r)$, $\eta(t, 0) = \alpha(0)$ and $\eta(t, 1) = \alpha(1)$ for all r and t in $[0, 1]$. In other words, α can be continuously deformed into β, keeping the endpoints fixed under the deformation.

THEOREM 2.1. *If P is arcwise simply connected then P is simply connected.*

Proof. Let $f\colon S \to T$ be a covering, p_0 a point of P, s_0 a point of S, g a continuous map of P into T such that $g(p_0) = f(s_0)$. We must construct a continuous map h of P into S such that $h(p_0) = s_0$ and $f \circ h = g$. Since P is connected and locally arcwise connected, it is clear that P is arcwise connected. Thus, for every point p in P, there is an arc α in P such that $\alpha(0) = p_0$ and $\alpha(1) = p$. Since $[0, 1]$ is simply connected (by Theorem 1.5), there is a continuous map α^* of $[0, 1]$ into S such that $\alpha^*(0) = s_0$ and $f \circ \alpha^* = g \circ \alpha$. Let β be any other arc in P from p_0 to p. We wish to prove that $\beta^*(1) = \alpha^*(1)$.

Let η be a homotopy, as described above, deforming α into β. Since $[0, 1] \times [0, 1]$ is simply connected (again by Theorem 1.5), there is a continuous map π^* of $[0, 1] \times [0, 1]$ into S such that $\pi^*(0, 0) = s_0$ and $f \circ \eta^* = g \circ \eta$. We may apply Proposition 1.1 to the maps α^* and $r \to \eta^*(0, r)$ which take 0 into the same point s_0 of S and whose composites with f coincide. The conclusion is that these two maps must coincide. If we apply Proposition 1.1 to the constant map with value s_0 and the map $t \to \eta^*(t, 0)$, we find that $\eta^*(t, 0) = s_0$ for every t in $[0, 1]$. Hence we may apply Proposition 1.1 to the maps β^* and $r \to \eta^*(1, r)$ and conclude that these two maps coincide. Finally, we may apply Proposition 1.1 to the constant map with value $\eta^*(0, 1)$ and the map $t \to \eta^*(t, 1)$ and conclude that $\eta^*(t, 1) = \eta^*(0, 1)$ for all t. Now we obtain $\alpha^*(1) = \eta^*(0, 1) = \eta^*(1, 1) = \beta^*(1)$.

Thus there is a map h of P into S such that $h(p) = \alpha^*(1)$ for every arc α^* obtained as above from an arc α from p_0 to p. Clearly, we have $f \circ h = g$ and $h(p_0) = s_0$, so that it remains only to show that h is continuous. Let p be a point of P, and let U be any neighborhood of $h(p)$ in S. Since f is a covering, U contains a neighborhood V of $h(p)$ such that $f(V)$ is a neighborhood of $g(p)$ and V is a connected component of $f^{-1}(f(V))$. Let W be an arcwise connected neighborhood of p in P such that $g(W) \subset f(V)$. Let q be a point of W. Then there is an arc α in S that is composed of an arc from p_0 to p, followed by an arc from p to q that lies in W. It follows that $h(p)$ and $h(q)$ are joined by an arc in $h(W)$, so that $h(q)$ must lie in the same component of $f^{-1}(f(V))$ as $h(p)$, i.e., $h(q) \in V \subset U$. Hence h is continuous, and Theorem 2.1 is proved.

We shall say that a space S is *locally arcwise simply connected* if S is locally arcwise connected and every point of S has a neighborhood V such that every closed arc in V can be shrunk to a point (over S).

THEOREM 2.2. *Let S be a connected and locally arcwise simply connected space. Then there is a covering $f: T \to S$ with T arcwise simply connected.*

Proof. Choose a fixed base point s_0 in S. For every point s of S, denote by s'_i (where i runs over some index set) the homotopy classes of arcs from s_0 to s. The points of T will be these homotopy classes s'_i. The map f of T into S is defined by $f(s'_i) = s$. We proceed to defining a topology on T.

If V is any subset of S and v is a point of V we denote by $V(v'_i)$ the set of all those homotopy classes of arcs which contain an arc composed of a member of v'_i, followed by an arc in V issuing from v. The open sets of our topology on T will be the unions of families of such sets $V(v'_i)$, with V open in S. One sees immediately that if s'_k is any point of $V(v'_i) \cap W(w'_j)$ then $(V \cap W)(s'_k) \subset V(v'_i) \cap W(w'_j)$. Thus we have indeed a topology on T. In order to prove that this is a Hausdorff topology, consider distinct points v'_i and w'_j of T. If $v \neq w$ then there are disjoint open neighborhoods V and W of v and w, respectively, and $V(v'_i) \cap W(w'_j) = \varnothing$. If $v = w$ then $i \neq j$. We choose an open neighborhood V of v such that every closed arc in V can be shrunk to a point over S. Then $V(v'_i) \cap V(v'_j)$ must be empty, for if there were a point in this intersection one would find a homotopy deforming a member of v'_i into a member of v'_j. Thus we have a Hausdorff topology on T, and it is clear from its definition that f is a continuous and open map of T onto S.

Given a point v of S, we can evidently find an open arcwise connected neighborhood V of v such that every closed arc in V can be shrunk to a point over S. Let α be an arc in S whose homotopy class belongs to $f^{-1}(V)$. Let β be an arc in V joining the endpoint of α to v. Let v'_i be the homotopy class of the arc composed of α, followed by β. Evidently, the homotopy class of α belongs to $V(v'_i)$. Thus $f^{-1}(V)$ is the union of the family of sets $V(v'_i)$. Since every closed arc in V can be shrunk to a point, the restriction of f to $V(v'_i)$ is injective, so that f maps $V(v'_i)$ homeomorphically onto V. Hence the sets $V(v'_i)$ are arcwise connected. Since they are open and mutually disjoint, they are therefore the connected components of $f^{-1}(V)$, and V is evenly covered by f. This shows also that T is locally arcwise connected.

Next, we show that T is arcwise connected. Let v'_i be a point of T, and let α be an arc belonging to v'_i. For each t in $[0, 1]$, let $\alpha'(t)$ denote the homotopy class of the initial segment of α from $s_0 = \alpha(0)$ to $\alpha(t)$. Then α' is a map of $[0, 1]$ into T, $\alpha'(0)$ is the homotopy class of the trivial arc at s_0 and $\alpha'(1) = v'_i$. Hence it suffices to show that α' is continuous. Clearly, every neighborhood of $\alpha'(t)$ in T contains a neighborhood of the form $V(\alpha'(t))$, where V is an open neighborhood of $\alpha(t)$ in S. We can choose a neighborhood U of t in $[0, 1]$ such that $\alpha(U) \subset V$. Then we have $\alpha'(r) \in V(\alpha'(t))$ for every r in U, which shows that the map α' is indeed continuous, so that T is arcwise connected. In particular, T is connected, and since we have already seen that T is locally arcwise connected (and so locally connected) and that every point of S has an evenly covered neighborhood, we have shown that $f\colon T \to S$ is a covering.

It remains only to show that every closed arc in T can be shrunk to a point, and since T is arcwise connected it suffices to show that every closed arc μ in T that starts and ends at the homotopy class of the trivial arc at s_0 can be shrunk to a point. Put $\alpha = f \circ \mu$, so that α is a closed arc in S starting and ending at s_0. Let α' be as above. We have shown above that α' is continuous, and so an arc in T. Now α' and μ are continuous maps of $[0, 1]$ into T, $\alpha'(0) = \mu(0)$ and $f \circ \alpha' = \alpha = f \circ \mu$. Hence we conclude from Proposition 1.1 that $\alpha' = \mu$. Hence $\alpha'(1)$ is the homotopy class of the trivial arc at s_0, i.e., the homotopy class of α is the homotopy class of the trivial arc at s_0, which means that α can be deformed into the trivial arc at s_0. Since $[0, 1] \times [0, 1]$ is simply connected, a homotopy deforming α into the trivial arc at s_0 can be lifted to yield a homotopy deforming μ into the homotopy class of the trivial arc at s_0 (the argument needed for this has been given in the proof of Theorem 2.1). This completes the proof of Theorem 2.2.

3

We shall now adapt the theory of coverings to the theory of topological groups. The first result below points up the importance of the property of being simply connected for topological groups.

THEOREM 3.1. *Let G be a simply connected topological group, and let η be a map of an open connected neighborhood V of 1 in G into a group H such that $\eta(xy) = \eta(x)\eta(y)$ whenever x, y and xy lie in V. Then η extends to a homomorphism of G into H.*

Proof. Let D be the subset of $G \times G$ consisting of all points (x, y) such that xy^{-1} lies in V. Then D is an open connected neighborhood of the diagonal in $G \times G$. Define the map $\delta\colon D \to H$ by $\delta(x, y) = \eta(xy^{-1})$. Then δ evidently satisfies the conditions of the Monodromy Theorem (Theorem 1.7), so that there is a map σ of G into H such that $\eta(xy^{-1}) =$

$\sigma(x)\sigma(y)^{-1}$ whenever xy^{-1} lies in V. Replacing σ by the map $x \to \sigma(x)\sigma(1)^{-1}$, we can arrange furthermore that $\sigma(1) = 1$, so that σ coincides with η on V.

Let y be an element of V^{-1} and let x be an arbitrary element of G. Then we have $x(yx)^{-1} = y^{-1} \in V$, so that $\sigma(y)^{-1} = \eta(y^{-1}) = \eta(x(yx)^{-1}) = \sigma(x)\sigma(yx)^{-1}$, i.e., $\sigma(yx) = \sigma(y)\sigma(x)$. Since G is connected, every element z of G can be written as a product $y_1 \cdots y_n$ with each y_i in V^{-1}. Hence we have $\sigma(zx) = \sigma(y_1) \cdots \sigma(y_n)\sigma(x) = \sigma(z)\sigma(x)$, showing that σ is a homomorphism and completing the proof of Theorem 3.1.

A *group covering* is a group homomorphism $f: G \to H$ that is also a space covering. Since f is then a local homeomorphism, it is clear that its kernel F is a discrete and hence central subgroup of G, and that the map $G/F \to H$ induced by f is an isomorphism of topological groups.

THEOREM 3.2. *Let G be a topological group, and suppose that there is given a space covering $f: S \twoheadrightarrow G$, with S simply connected. Then S can be endowed with a group structure for which it becomes a topological group such that f is a group covering. If $h: H \to G$ is any group covering then there is one and only one topological group homomorphism $\sigma: S \to H$ such that $h \circ \sigma = f$. Moreover, σ is necessarily a group covering.*

Proof. Choose a point e in S such that $f(e)$ is the neutral element of G. Consider the continuous map of $S \times S$ into G that sends each (x, y) onto $f(x)f(y)^{-1}$. By Theorem 1.6, $S \times S$ is simply connected. Hence there is a continuous map γ of $S \times S$ into S such that $f(\gamma(x, y)) = f(x)f(y)^{-1}$ for all (x, y) in $S \times S$ and $\gamma(e, e) = e$. We define the product of the points x and y of S by $xy = \gamma(x, \gamma(e, y))$.

If $\delta(x) = \gamma(x, e)$ then δ is a continuous map $S \to S$, $\delta(e) = e$ and $f \circ \delta = f$. Hence Proposition 1.1 shows that δ is the identity map on S. Hence we have $xe = \gamma(x, \gamma(e, e)) = \gamma(x, e) = x$. Similarly, we show that $ex = x$. Now we have $xy(e, x) = \gamma(x, \gamma(e, \gamma(e, x))) = \gamma(x, ex) = \gamma(x, x)$. Since $\gamma(e, e) = e$ and $f(\gamma(x, x)) = f(x)f(x)^{-1} = 1$, we see again from Proposition 1.1 that $\gamma(x, x) = e$, so that the above gives $xy(e, x) = e$. Similarly, one shows that $\gamma(e, x)x = e$.

If we apply Proposition 1.1 to the two maps of $S \times S \times S$ into S that send (x, y, z) onto $(xy)z$ or $x(yz)$, respectively, we find that these maps coincide, i.e., that our multiplication on S is associative. We have the neutral element e and the inverse $\gamma(e, x)$ of x. Hence our multiplication is a group structure on S. Since $xy^{-1} = \gamma(x, \gamma(e, y^{-1})) = \gamma(x, y)$, it is clear that S is a topological group. We have $f(y^{-1}) = f(\gamma(e, y)) = f(e)f(y)^{-1} = f(y)^{-1}$ and hence $f(xy) = f(\gamma(x, y^{-1})) = f(x)f(y^{-1})^{-1} = f(x)f(y)$. Thus f is a homomorphism and therefore a group covering.

Now let $h: H \to G$ be any group covering. Then we can find an open neighborhood V of 1 in G that is evenly covered by both f and h. Let V' be the connected component of $f^{-1}(V)$ that contains e and let V° be the connected component of $h^{-1}(V)$ that contains the neutral element of H. Let $f_{V'}$ be the restriction of f to V' and let h_{V° be the restriction of h to V°. Then it is clear that $(h_{V^\circ})^{-1} \circ f_{V'}$ is a homeomorphism η of V' onto V° such that $\eta(xy) = \eta(x)\eta(y)$ whenever x, y and xy lie in V'. By Theorem 3.1, η extends to a homomorphism σ of S into H. We have $(h \circ \sigma)_{V'} = f_{V'}$ and, since V' generates the connected group S, it follows that $h \circ \sigma = f$. Since η is a homeomorphism, it is clear that σ is a local homeomorphism. It follows that $\sigma(S)$ is an open subgroup of H and therefore coincides with H. It follows also that the kernel of σ is discrete, whence it is clear that σ is a covering. Finally, the uniqueness of σ is evident from Proposition 1.1.

EXERCISES

1. Let f be a surjective continuous and open map of a simply connected space T onto a space S such that $f^{-1}(s)$ is connected for every point s of S. Show that S is simply connected. [Consider a covering $\pi: U \to S$, lift f to a continuous map $g: T \to U$ such that $\pi \circ g = f$; show that g is surjective and that $g(f^{-1}(s))$ is a single point, from which it follows that π is injective.]

2. The *mobility* group of a covering $f: T \to S$ is defined as the group of all homeomorphisms α of T onto T such that $f \circ \alpha = f$. In the situation of Theorem 2.2, produce an isomorphism of the mobility group onto the group of the homotopy classes of closed arcs starting and ending at the fixed base point s_0 of S, where the composition of homotopy classes is that obtained in the natural way from the composition of closed arcs (following up one with the other).

3. If $f: G \to H$ is a group covering, show that the mobility group is isomorphic with the kernel of f.

V. POWER SERIES MAPS

1

We consider formal power series in n variables with complex coefficients. If

$$A(X_1, \cdots, X_n) = \sum_{e_i \geq 0} a(e_1, \cdots, e_n) X_1^{e_1} \cdots X_n^{e_n}$$

is such a power series then we shall say that $A(X_1, \cdots, X_n)$ is *usable* with an n-tuple $(b_1, \cdots, b_n)$ of positive real numbers if $\sum |a(e_1, \cdots, e_n)| b_1^{e_1} \cdots b_n^{e_n}$ is convergent in the usual sense as a series of non-negative real numbers. If B is the closed box in C^n defined by the set of inequalities $|c_i| \leq b_i$ ($i = 1, \cdots, n$) then our power series $A(X_1, \cdots, X_n)$ defines a complex-valued function A_B on B, the value $A_B(c_1, \cdots, c_n)$ at the point $(c_1, \cdots, c_n)$ of B being the sum of the series $\sum a(e_1, \cdots, e_n) c_1^{e_1} \cdots c_n^{e_n}$. If f is a complex-valued function on a subset S of C^n then we say that f is a *power series function* if there is a power series $A(X_1, \cdots, X_n)$ such that, for every point $(c_1, \cdots, c_n)$ of S, $A(X_1, \cdots, X_n)$ is usable with some n-tuple $(b_1, \cdots, b_n)$ of real numbers $b_i > |c_i|$ and $f(c_1, \cdots, c_n) = A_B(c_1, \cdots, c_n)$. We shall then say that f is *represented* by the power series $A(X_1, \cdots, X_n)$.

Let $P(X_1, \cdots, X_m)$ be a polynomial, i.e., a finite power series. Let $f_1, \cdots, f_m$ be power series functions defined on a subset S of C^n. Then the composite function $P(f_1, \cdots, f_m)$ is easily seen to be a power series function. In fact, if f_i is represented by the power series $F_i(X_1, \cdots, X_n)$ then $P(f_1, \cdots, f_n)$ is represented by the power series

$$P(F_1(X_1, \cdots, X_n), \cdots, F_m(X_1, \cdots, X_n)).$$

For each integer $k = 1, \cdots, n$, we denote by D_k the derivation of the algebra of power series that is given by

$$D_k(\sum a(e_1, \cdots, e_n) X_1^{e_1} \cdots X_n^{e_n}) = \sum e_k a(e_1, \cdots, e_n) X_1^{e_1} \cdots X_k^{e_k - 1} \cdots X_n^{e_n}.$$

Then, if f is any power series function on an open subset S of C^n and f is represented by the power series $F(X_1, \cdots, X_n)$, the partial derivative $\delta_k(f)$ of f with respect to the k-th argument exists as a power series function on S and is represented by $D_k(F(X_1, \cdots, X_n))$. It follows, incidentally, that there is only one power series representing f.

We define the operator D_k^{-1} on the space of power series by

$$D_k^{-1}(\sum a(e_1, \cdots, e_n)X_1^{e_1} \cdots X_n^{e_n})$$
$$= \sum (e_k + 1)^{-1}a(e_1, \cdots, e_n)X_1^{e_1} \cdots X_k^{e_k+1} \cdots X_n^{e_n}.$$

Then, if f is a power series function on the open subset S of C^n, represented by $F(X_1, \cdots, X_n)$, we have a partial anti-derivative $\delta_k^{-1}(f)$, which is the power series function on S represented by $D_k^{-1}(F(X_1, \cdots, X_n))$.

While the above facts are easily established by simple estimates performed on series of complex numbers, the following result requires a little analysis and makes essential use of *complex* numbers.

LEMMA 1.1. *Let f be a power series function on the closed box B in C^n defined by the system of inequalities $|c_i| \leqq b_i$, where $(b_1, \cdots, b_n)$ is an n-tuple of positive real numbers, and suppose that f is represented by the power series*

$$\sum a(e_1, \cdots, e_n)X_1^{e_1} \cdots X_n^{e_n}.$$

Let $M = \max_{|c_i| = b_i}(|f(c_1, \cdots, c_n)|)$. Then

$$|a(e_1, \cdots, e_n)| \leqq M(b_1^{e_1} \cdots b_n^{e_n})^{-1}.$$

Proof. Let T denote the Cartesian product of n copies of the closed real interval $[0, 1]$. Define the map g of T into C by

$$g(t_1, \cdots, t_n) = f(b_1 \exp (2\pi i t_1), \cdots, b_n \exp(2\pi i t_n))$$
$$= \sum a(e_1, \cdots, e_n)b_1^{e_1} \cdots b_n^{e_n} \exp(2\pi i(e_1 t_1 + \cdots + e_n t_n)).$$

Now multiply each side by $\exp(-2\pi i(p_1 t_1 + \cdots + p_n t_n))$, where the p_i's are non-negative integers. The resulting expression on the right is a series that converges uniformly on T. Hence we may compute its integral over T by integrating it term by term. The integrals of the individual terms are evidently all 0, except for the term in which each e_i is equal to p_i, in which case the integral is $a(e_1, \cdots, e_n)b_1^{e_1} \cdots b_n^{e_n}$. The integral of the function on the left is evidently of absolute value at most M. Hence we obtain the inequality of Lemma 1.1 by comparing the two sides.

If S is any subset of C^n we define a norm $\| \; \|_S$ on the space of all bounded complex-valued functions on S by putting $\|f\|_S = \sup_{x \in S}(|f(x)|)$. The *distinguished boundary* of a closed box B: $|c_i| \leqq b_i$ is the subset of the points for which each $|c_i| = b_i$.

LEMMA 1.2. *Let B be as in Lemma 1.1, and let (f_k) be a sequence of power series functions on B. Suppose that the restrictions $(f_k)_{B'}$ to the distinguished boundary B' of B constitute a Cauchy sequence with respect to the norm $\| \ \|_{B'}$. Then, for every compact subset K of the interior of B, the sequence of the restrictions $(f_k)_K$ converges uniformly to a power series function on K.*

Proof. Denote the coefficients of the power series representing f_k by $a^{(k)}(e_1, \cdots, e_n)$. By hypothesis, given $\varepsilon > 0$, there is a natural number $t(\varepsilon)$ such that $\|f_p - f_q\|_{B'} \leqq \varepsilon$ whenever $p \geqq t(\varepsilon)$ and $q \geqq t(\varepsilon)$. By Lemma 1.1, this implies that

$$|a^{(p)}(e_1, \cdots, e_n) - a^{(q)}(e_1, \cdots, e_n)| \leqq \varepsilon(b_1^{e_1} \cdots b_n^{e_n})^{-1}.$$

Hence, as $k \to \infty$, $a^{(k)}(e_1, \cdots, e_n)$ converges to a complex number $a(e_1, \cdots, e_n)$, and $|a(e_1, \cdots, e_n) - a^{(k)}(e_1, \cdots, e_n)| \leqq \varepsilon(b_1^{e_1} \cdots b_n^{e_n})^{-1}$ as soon as $k \geqq t(\varepsilon)$. First, by comparison with the series for $f_{t(\varepsilon)}$, one sees easily from this that the power series with coefficients $a(e_1, \cdots, e_n)$ is usable with the n-tuple $(b_1, \cdots, b_n)$, and therefore represents a power series function f on the interior of B.

Now let K be a compact subset of the interior of B. Then there are real numbers r_i such that $0 < r_i < b_i$ and $|c_i| \leqq r_i$ for all points $(c_1, \cdots, c_n)$ of K. We have then

$$|a(e_1, \cdots, e_n)c_1^{e_1} \cdots c_n^{e_n} - a^{(k)}(e_1, \cdots, e_n)c_1^{e_1} \cdots c_n^{e_n}|$$
$$\leqq \varepsilon(r_1 b_1^{-1})^{e_1} \cdots (r_n b_n^{-1})^{e_n}$$

whenever $k \geqq t(\varepsilon)$, whence

$$|f(c_1, \cdots, c_n) - f_k(c_1, \cdots, c_n)| \leqq \varepsilon \prod_{i=1}^n \left(1 - \frac{r_i}{b_i}\right)^{-1}.$$

This completes the proof of Lemma 1.2.

PROPOSITION 1.3. *Let g be a power series function on the closed box U in C^m defined by an m-tuple $(u_1, \cdots, u_m)$ of positive real numbers. Let $h_1, \cdots, h_m$ be power series functions on the open box V in C^n defined by an n-tuple $(v_1, \cdots, v_n)$ of positive real numbers. Suppose that, for every point $(c_1, \cdots, c_n)$ of V, the point $(h_1(c_1, \cdots, c_n), \cdots, h_m(c_1, \cdots, c_n))$ lies in U. Then the composite function $g(h_1, \cdots, h_m)$ is a power series function on V.*

Proof. Let G be the power series representing g and, for every non-negative integer k, let G_k be the sum of the terms of G whose total degrees do not exceed k. Let H_p denote the power series representing h_p. Since G_k is a polynomial, we may form the power series $G_k(H_1, \cdots, H_m)$, and it is clear that this represents a power series function s_k on V. Now let $0 < b_i < v_i$, and let B be the closed box in C^n defined by $(b_1, \cdots, b_n)$. Our assumptions evidently imply that the sequence of the restrictions $f_k = (s_k)_B$ satisfies the conditions of Lemma 1.2. Hence, for every compact subset K of the interior of B, the sequence of the restrictions $(s_k)_K$ converges to a power series function on K. On the other hand, it is clear that this sequence converges to the restriction $g(h_1, \cdots, h_m)_K$ of $g(h_1, \cdots, h_m)$ to K. Since every compact subset of V lies in the interior of some closed box B such as we have used here, this shows that $g(h_1, \cdots, h_m)_K$ is a power series function for every compact subset K of V, and this evidently means that $g(h_1, \cdots, h_m)$ is a power series function on V.

2

If $f_1, \cdots, f_n$ are power series functions on a subset S of C^m then we shall call the map of S into C^n that sends each point $(c_1, \cdots, c_m)$ of S onto the point $(f_1(c_1, \cdots, c_m), \cdots, f_n(c_1, \cdots, c_m))$ a *power series map*. We define a norm $[\ ]$ on C^m by $[(c_1, \cdots, c_m)] = \max_i(|c_i|)$, and we shall denote the open box defined by the inequality $[x] < t$ by $C^m(t)$. The closure of a set S will be denoted S^*.

THEOREM 2.1. *Let r and s be positive real numbers, and let f be a power series map of $C(r)^* \times C^n(s)^*$ into C^n. As is evidently possible, choose real numbers $L \geq 1$ and $K \geq 1$ such that $[f(t, x)] \leq L$ and $[f(t, x) - f(t, y)] \leq K[x - y]$ for all t in $C(r)^*$ and all x and y in $C^n(s)^*$. Let $0 < b < \min(K^{-1}, s(2KL)^{-1}, r)$. Then there is a power series map $\alpha: C(b) \times C^n(s/2) \to C^n(s)^*$ satisfying*

(1): $\alpha(0, x) = x$ *for every x in $C^n(s/2)$*

(2): $\alpha'(t, x) = f(t, \alpha(t, x))$ *for every t in $C(b)$ and every x in $C^n(s/2)$, where α' denotes the partial derivative of α with respect to the first variable.*

Moreover, if $x \in C^n(s/2)$, $0 < b^\circ \leq b$, and β_x is a map of $C(b^\circ)$ into $C^n(s)^*$ such that $\beta_x(0) = x$ and β_x has a derivative β'_x such that $\beta'_x(t) = f(t, \beta_x(t))$ for all t in $C(b^\circ)$ then $\beta_x(t) = \alpha(t, x)$ for all t in $C(b^\circ)$.

Proof. Let M denote the set of maps $\mu: C(b)^* \times C^n(s/2)^* \to C^n(s)^*$ such that $\mu(0, x) = x$ and the map $t \to \mu(t, x)$ is continuous for every x. Define a metric d on M by putting $d(\sigma, \tau) = \sup_u[\sigma(u) - \tau(u)]$. It is easy to see that M is complete with respect to this metric. We define a map S of M

into the set of all maps of $C(b)^* \times C^n(s/2)^*$ into C^n by putting $S(\mu)(t, x) = x + \int_0^t f(c, \mu(c, x))dc$, where the integration is along the straight line from 0 to t in C.

Evidently, $S(\mu)(0, x) = x$ and the map $t \to S(\mu)(t, x)$ is continuous. Moreover, the straightforward estimate of the integral gives

$$[S(\mu)(t, x) - x] \leqq |t|L \leqq bL < s/2,$$

so that $[S(\mu)(t, x)] < [x] + s/2 \leqq s$. Thus S maps M into M. Furthermore, the evident estimation of the integral yields

$$[S(\sigma)(t, x) - S(\tau)(t, x)] \leqq b \sup_c [f(c, \sigma(c, x)) - f(c, \tau(c, x))]$$
$$\leqq bK \sup_c [\sigma(c, x) - \tau(c, x)],$$

whence $d(S(\sigma), S(\tau)) \leqq bKd(\sigma, \tau)$.

Now let μ be any element of M, and consider the sequence of the iterated transforms $S^n(\mu)$. If $n \geqq m$ we have

$$d(S^n(\mu), S^m(\mu)) \leqq (bK)^m d(S^{n-m}(\mu), \mu) \leqq (bK)^m 2s.$$

Since $bK < 1$, this shows that our sequence is a Cauchy sequence in M and hence converges to an element γ of M. We have

$$d(S(\gamma), \gamma) \leqq d(S(\gamma), S^{n+1}(\mu)) + d(S^{n+1}(\mu), \gamma)$$
$$\leqq bKd(\gamma, S^n(\mu)) + d(S^{n+1}(\mu), \gamma).$$

Making n large, we see from this that $d(S(\gamma), \gamma) = 0$, i.e., that $S(\gamma) = \gamma$. If β is any fixed point of S in M we have $d(\gamma, \beta) = d(S(\gamma), S(\beta)) \leqq bKd(\gamma, \beta)$. Since $bK < 1$, this gives $d(\gamma, \beta) = 0$, so that $\gamma = \beta$. Thus S has one and only one fixed point γ in M, and γ is the limit of the sequence $S^n(\mu)$, for any element μ of M.

Let P denote the subset of M consisting of those elements whose restrictions to $C(b) \times C^n(s/2)$ are power series maps. It is clear from Proposition 1.3 that if μ belongs to P then the map $(t, x) \to f(t, \mu(t, x))$ is a power series map h on $C(b) \times C^n(s/2)$. The partial anti-derivative $\delta_1^{-1}(h)$ is again a power series map on $C(b) \times C^n(s/2)$. If μ_0 denotes the element of P defined by $\mu_0(t, x) = x$ then the restriction of $S(\mu)$ to $C(b) \times C^n(s/2)$ is the sum of $\delta_1^{-1}(h)$ and the restriction of μ_0. Hence $S(\mu) \in P$.

Now γ is the uniform limit of the sequence of elements $S^n(\mu_0)$ of P. Hence it follows from Lemma 1.2 that γ still belongs to P. Let α be the restriction of γ to $C(b) \times C^n(s/2)$. Then α is a power series map. From $S(\gamma) = \gamma$, it is clear that $\alpha'(t, x) = f(t, \alpha(t, x))$.

Finally, let x and β_x be as in the last statement of our theorem. Define

$\alpha_x(t) = \alpha(t, x)$. Choose b' such that $0 < b' < b°$, and let M' denote the set of all continuous maps σ of $C(b')^*$ into $C^n(s)^*$ such that $\sigma(0) = x$. Let S' be defined on M' as S was defined on M, i.e.,

$$S'(\sigma)(t) = x + \int_0^t f(c, \sigma(c))dc.$$

Then it is clear that, like S, the map S' has only one fixed point in M'. Clearly, the restrictions to $C(b')^*$ of β_x and α_x are fixed points of S'. Hence they must coincide. Since every point of $C(b°)$ lies in some $C(b')^*$, it follows that $\beta_x(t) = \alpha_x(t)$ for all t in $C(b°)$, so that Theorem 2.1 is proved.

3

Let U be an open box in C^m and V an open box in C^n (defined as before by an m-tuple and an n-tuple of positive real numbers). Let h be a power series map of $U \times V$ into C^n. We define the *Jacobian* $J(h)$ as a power series function on $U \times V$ as follows. Let $h_1, \cdots, h_n$ be the coordinate functions associated with h, i.e., for (x, y) in $U \times V$,

$$h(x, y) = (h_1(x, y), \cdots, h_n(x, y)).$$

Let $\delta_{m+1}, \cdots, \delta_{m+n}$ denote the partial differentiation operators with respect to the n complex arguments making up y. Then $J(h)$ is the determinant of the matrix whose entries are the functions $\delta_{m+p}(h_q)$.

THEOREM 3.1. *Let U be a neighborhood of 0 in C^n, and let f be a power series map of U into C^n such that $f(0) = 0$ and the Jacobian $J(f)$ does not vanish at 0. Then U contains an open neighborhood V of 0 in C^n such that $f(V)$ is an open neighborhood of 0 in C^n, and there is a power series map g of $f(V)$ onto V such that $f \circ g$ is the identity map on $f(V)$ and $g \circ f$ is the identity map on V.*

Proof. We may write $f = t + h$, where t is the restriction to U of a linear endomorphism τ of C^n and h is a power series map of U into C^n such that the terms of total degree not exceeding 1 in the coordinate functions associated with h are 0. Since $J(f)(0) \neq 0$, it is clear that τ is actually a linear *automorphism* of C^n. Replacing f with $\tau^{-1} \circ f$, we reduce Theorem 3.1 to the case where t is the identity map on U, i.e., where $f(x) = x + h(x)$, with h as described above. Then we can evidently find a positive real number r such that, in the notation of Section 2, $C^n(2r)^*$ lies in the interior of U and $[h(x) - h(y)] \leq s[x - y]$, with a fixed positive real number $s \leq \frac{1}{2}$, for all points x and y of $C^n(2r)^*$.

Corresponding to each point y of $C^n(r)^*$, let us define a map k_y of

$C^n(2r)^*$ into C^n by putting $k_y(x) = y - h(x)$. Evidently, k_y sends $C^n(2r)^*$ into itself. Moreover, we have

$$[k_y(x_1) - k_y(x_2)] = [h(x_2) - h(x_1)] \leqq s[x_2 - x_1].$$

Since $s < 1$, we may apply the same reasoning to k_y that we used in dealing with "S" in the proof of Theorem 2.1 to conclude that k_y has one and only one fixed point $g(y)$ in $C^n(2r)^*$, and that $g(y)$ is actually the limit of the sequence of iterated transforms $g_p(y) = k_y{}^p(0)$. Clearly, $f(g(y)) = y$.

Now observe that

$$[g_{p+1}(y) - g_p(y)] = [h(g_{p-1}(y)) - h(g_p(y))] \leqq s[g_p(y) - g_{p-1}(y)]$$
$$\leqq \cdots \leqq s^p[g_1(y) - 0] \leqq 2rs^p.$$

Hence it is clear that the sequence (g_p) is a uniform Cauchy sequence of maps of $C^n(r)^*$ into $C^n(2r)^*$. By Proposition 1.3, each g_p is a power series map. Hence we conclude from Lemma 1.2 that g is a power series map on $C^n(r)$. By construction, $f \circ g$ is the identity map on $C^n(r)^*$.

Let u and v be points of $C^n(2r)^*$. Then

$$[u - v] = [f(u) - h(u) - f(v) + h(v)] \leqq [f(u) - f(v)] + [h(v) - h(u)]$$
$$\leqq [f(u) - f(v)] + s[u - v].$$

Hence it is clear that if $f(u) = f(v)$ then $u = v$. Thus f is injective on $C^n(2r)^*$. Now if V is an open neighborhood of 0 in C^n such that $V \subset C^n(2r)$ and $f(V) \subset C_n(r)$ then, since $f \circ (g \circ f)$ coincides with f on V and f is injective on V, we may conclude that $g \circ f$ is the identity map on V, so that (V, g) satisfies the requirements of Theorem 3.1; $f(V)$ is open because it coincides with $g^{-1}(V)$.

Let R denote the field of the real numbers. We obtain the notion of power series maps of subsets of R^m into R^n by replacing the formal power series used above with formal power series whose coefficients are real. The results of this chapter are valid also for power series maps based on R, and the proofs are identical, except for the following: (1) in Lemma 1.1, the bound M must be defined in terms of the complexified power series function that is obtained from the given real power series function simply by allowing substitutions of complex numbers for the variables in the representing formal power series; (2) in Lemma 1.2, the norm $\| \ \|$ must be taken with respect to the complexified power series functions and the distinguished boundary of the box in C^n defined by $(b_1, \cdots, b_n)$. After this, the proofs can be copied word for word, merely replacing C with R. In particular, the real analogues of Proposition 1.3 and Theorems 2.1 and 3.1 are now considered to be available for future use.

EXERCISES

1. Let f be a power series function defined on a neighborhood of 0 in C^n. Show that if $|f|$ takes its maximum at 0 then f must be a constant. [Express $f(0)$ as an integral as in the proof of Lemma 1.1, and deduce from this that f must be constant and equal to $f(0)$ on the distinguished boundary of every closed box around 0 in C^n on which it is defined.]

2. Let A be a finite-dimensional associative algebra with identity over C or over R. Let α be a homomorphism of C or of R, respectively, into the multiplicative group of the units of A. Assume that, as $t \to 0$, $(1/t)(\alpha(t) - \alpha(0))$ converges to an element a of A. Prove that then $\alpha(t) = \mathrm{Exp}(ta) = \sum_{n=0}^{\infty} \dfrac{t^n}{n!} a^n$ for every t.

VI. ANALYTIC MANIFOLDS [1, 4]

1

Let X be a topological space. A *functional structure* on X is a function $\mathscr{F}$ (denoted also $\mathscr{F}_X$ if the space is to be kept in sight) assigning to each open set U of X a subalgebra $\mathscr{F}(U)$ of the algebra of the real-valued continuous functions on U such that the following conditions are satisfied.

(1) If $U \neq \varnothing$ then $\mathscr{F}(U)$ contains all the constant functions on U; $\mathscr{F}(\varnothing)$ is the algebra consisting of 0 alone.

(2) If U and V are open sets with $U \subset V$ and if f is an element of $\mathscr{F}(V)$ then the restriction f_U of f to U belongs to $\mathscr{F}(U)$; we agree that $f_\varnothing$ is the only element 0 of $\mathscr{F}(\varnothing)$.

(3) If S is any family of open sets of X and U is its union and f is a function on U such that f_V belongs to $\mathscr{F}(V)$ for every member V of S, then f belongs to $\mathscr{F}(U)$.

A *structured space* $(X, \mathscr{F}_X)$ is a space X that is equipped with a functional structure $\mathscr{F}_X$. A *morphism* of structured spaces $(X, \mathscr{F}_X) \to (Y, \mathscr{F}_Y)$ is a continuous map $\gamma: X \to Y$ such that, for every open set V of Y and every element f of $\mathscr{F}_Y(V)$, the composite function $f \circ \gamma$ belongs to $\mathscr{F}_X(\gamma^{-1}(V))$. It is evident that a composite of morphisms is a morphism. If the morphism γ is bijective and γ^{-1} is a morphism $(Y, \mathscr{F}_Y) \to (X, \mathscr{F}_X)$ then γ is called an isomorphism of structured spaces. If U is an open set of X then a functional structure $\mathscr{F}$ on X evidently yields a functional structure $\mathscr{F}_U$ on U simply by restricting $\mathscr{F}$ to the set of open sets that are contained in U. We say that $\mathscr{F}_U$ is the functional structure *induced* on U by $\mathscr{F}$, and it is evident that the injection map $U \to X$ is a morphism $(U, \mathscr{F}_U) \to (X, \mathscr{F})$.

Let U be an open subset of Euclidean space R^n. A real-valued function f on U is called an *analytic function* if, for every point u of U, there is a neighborhood $N(u)$ of u in U and a power series function $f^{(u)}$ on $N(u) - u$ such that $f(v) = f^{(u)}(v - u)$ for every point v of $N(u)$. We evidently obtain a functional structure $\mathscr{A}_U$ on U by making $\mathscr{A}_U(V)$ the algebra of all analytic functions on V, for every open subset V of U.

We define an *analytic manifold* as a connected space X, equipped with a functional structure $\mathscr{F}$, in which every point p has an open neighborhood $U(p)$ such that the structured space $(U(p), \mathscr{F}_{U(p)})$ is isomorphic with $(B, \mathscr{A}_B)$, where B is an open box in an R^n. An isomorphism γ: $(U(p), \mathscr{F}_{U(p)}) \to (B, \mathscr{A}_B)$ is called a *chart* of X at p, and $U(p)$ is called a *coordinate neighborhood* of p.

Clearly, if U is a connected open subset of an analytic manifold X then the induced functional structure on U makes U into an analytic manifold, called an *open submanifold* of X. If X and Y are analytic manifolds then a morphism of structured spaces $(X, \mathscr{F}_X) \to (Y, \mathscr{F}_Y)$ will simply be called an *analytic map* of X into Y. If such a morphism is an isomorphism then it will simply be called an *analytic isomorphism*.

If X and Y are analytic manifolds we wish to define the structure of an analytic manifold on the Cartesian product space $X \times Y$ such that the following basic properties are satisfied: (i) the canonical projections of $X \times Y$ onto X and Y should be analytic maps; (ii) if T is any analytic manifold and α, β are analytic maps of T into X and Y, respectively, then the map $\alpha \times \beta$ of T into $X \times Y$, where $(\alpha \times \beta)(t) = (\alpha(t), \beta(t))$, should be an analytic map. It is easy to see that there can be at most one such structure on $X \times Y$.

Let us first consider the case where X and Y are open boxes in R^m and R^n, respectively, with the structures $\mathscr{A}_X$ and $\mathscr{A}_Y$ defined above. Then $X \times Y$ is an open box in R^{m+n}, so that we already have an analytic manifold structure $\mathscr{A}_{X \times Y}$ on $X \times Y$. Evidently, this structure satisfies condition (i) above. Now let T, α, β be as in condition (ii). Let W be an open set of $X \times Y$, and let f be an element of $\mathscr{A}_{X \times Y}(W)$. We must show that $f \circ (\alpha \times \beta)$ belongs to $\mathscr{F}_T((\alpha \times \beta)^{-1}(W))$. By condition (3) of the definition of a functional structure, it suffices to show that every point t of $(\alpha \times \beta)^{-1}(W)$ has a coordinate neighborhood $U(t) \subset (\alpha \times \beta)^{-1}(W)$ such that $(f \circ (\alpha \times \beta))_{U(t)}$ belongs to $\mathscr{F}_T(U(t))$. Hence it suffices to deal with the case where T is an open box in an R^p and $t = 0$. Moreover, since the map $u \to u + (\alpha(0), \beta(0))$ is an analytic isomorphism of R^{m+n} onto itself, we may assume without loss of generality that $(\alpha(0), \beta(0)) = (0, 0)$. Replacing T with a smaller open box, if necessary, we may assume, furthermore, that $(\alpha \times \beta)(T)$ lies in a closed box on which f is a power series map. Let $x_1, \cdots, x_m$ be the coordinate functions on X, and let $y_1, \cdots, y_n$ be the coordinate functions on Y. Since α and β are analytic maps, we can ensure, by taking T small enough, that the composites $x_i \circ \alpha$ and $y_j \circ \beta$ are power series functions on T. But then it is clear from Proposition 1.3 of Chapter V that $f \circ (\alpha \times \beta)$ is a power series function on T. For the original situation, this means that $\alpha \times \beta$ is indeed an analytic map of T into $X \times Y$, so that the manifold structure $\mathscr{A}_{X \times Y}$ satisfies condition (ii).

Now let X and Y be arbitrary analytic manifolds. We define a functional structure $\mathscr{F}_{X \times Y}$ as follows. Let W be an open set of $X \times Y$. Then we define $\mathscr{F}_{X \times Y}(W)$ as the algebra of all functions f on W for which the following holds: for every point (p, q) of W, there are charts

$$\alpha: (U(p), \mathscr{F}_{U(p)}) \to (K, \mathscr{A}_K) \quad \text{and} \quad \beta: (V(q), \mathscr{F}_{V(q)}) \to (L, \mathscr{A}_L)$$

of X at p and of Y at q, respectively, such that $U(p) \times V(q) \subset W$ and $f_{U(p) \times V(q)} = g \circ (\alpha \times \beta)$, where $g \in \mathscr{A}_{K \times L}(K \times L)$. It is clear that this makes $(X \times Y, \mathscr{F}_{X \times Y})$ an analytic manifold and that the above condition (i) is satisfied. From the special case we have dealt with above, it follows easily that condition (ii) is also satisfied. The analytic manifold $X \times Y$ so defined is called the *Cartesian product* of the analytic manifolds X and Y.

Let X be an analytic manifold, and let p be a point of X. Let A_p denote the algebra of all real-valued functions f on X for which there is an open neighborhood $U(p)$ of p such that $f_{U(p)}$ belongs to $\mathscr{F}(U(p))$. Let I_p denote the ideal of A_p consisting of those functions f which vanish on some neighborhood of p. We write $\mathscr{F}(p)$ for the algebra A_p/I_p, and we call this the *stalk* at p. The elements of $\mathscr{F}(p)$ are called the *germs of analytic functions* at p. One may view the algebra $\mathscr{F}(p)$ as the direct limit of the system of the algebras $\mathscr{F}(U(p))$ and the restriction maps $\mathscr{F}(U(p)) \to \mathscr{F}(V(p))$ for $V(p) \subset U(p)$. In particular, for every open neighborhood $U(p)$ of p, there is a canonical algebra homomorphism of $\mathscr{F}(U(p))$ into $\mathscr{F}(p)$, which we indicate by $f \to f_p$, and which is compatible with the restriction homomorphisms, in the sense that, if $V(p) \subset U(p)$, then $(f_{V(p)})_p = f_p$. The evaluation map $f \to f(p)$ evidently induces a surjective algebra homomorphism of $\mathscr{F}(p)$ onto R, which we shall again indicate by $u \to u(p)$. Thus we have $f_p(p) = f(p)$, for every f in $\mathscr{F}(U(p))$.

A *tangent* to X at p is a *differentiation* of $\mathscr{F}(p)$ into R, i.e., an R-linear map $\tau: \mathscr{F}(p) \to R$ such that $\tau(uv) = u(p)\tau(v) + v(p)\tau(u)$ for all elements u and

v of $\mathscr{F}(p)$. The tangents to X at p evidently constitute a vector space over R in the natural fashion. We denote this vector space by X_p and call it the *tangent space* to X at p.

Let $\gamma : X \to Y$ be an analytic map of an analytic manifold X into an analytic manifold Y. Then the composition of functions on Y with γ evidently induces an algebra homomorphism of $\mathscr{F}(\gamma(p))$ into $\mathscr{F}(p)$, which we indicate by $v \to v \circ \gamma$. Dualization of this map yields an R-linear map of X_p into $Y_{\gamma(p)}$, which we denote by γ_p°, and which we call the *differential* of γ at p. Explicitly, we have, if τ is in X_p and v in $\mathscr{F}(\gamma(p))$, $\gamma_p^{\circ}(\tau)(v) = \tau(v \circ \gamma)$. If $\delta : Y \to Z$ is an analytic map of Y into an analytic manifold Z then we see immediately that $(\delta \circ \gamma)_p^{\circ} = \delta_{\gamma(p)}^{\circ} \circ \gamma_p^{b}$.

In particular, let us compute the tangent space at 0 to an open box B in R^n. Every element of $\mathscr{A}_B(0)$ is the canonical image f_0 of a power series function f on a neighborhood $U(0)$ of 0 in B. If g is a power series function on a neighborhood $V(0)$ of 0 in B, and if $g_0 = f_0$, then f and g coincide on some neighborhood of 0. Hence the partial derivatives $\delta_i(f)$ and $\delta_i(g)$ coincide on some neighborhood of 0. Hence, for each $i = 1, \cdots, n$, there is a map τ_i of $\mathscr{A}_B(0)$ into R such that, if f and f_0 are as above, we have $\tau_i(f_0) = \delta_i(f)(0)$. One verifies immediately from this that τ_i is a tangent to B at 0. We shall show that $(\tau_1, \cdots, \tau_n)$ is an R-basis of B_0. Let f be a power series function on a neighborhood $U(0)$ of 0, and let $x_1, \cdots, x_n$ denote the restrictions to $U(0)$ of the coordinate functions on R^n. Then there are power series functions f_{ij} on $U(0)$ such that

$$f = f(0) + \sum_i x_i \delta_i(f) + \sum_{i,j} x_i x_j f_{ij}.$$

Hence we have

$$f_0 = f(0) + \sum_i (x_i)_0 \delta_i(f)_0 + \sum_{i,j} (x_i)_0 (x_j)_0 (f_{ij})_0.$$

Now let τ be any element of X_0. Then, since $(x_k)_0(0) = 0$ for each k, and since τ annihilates the constant $f(0)$, the above yields

$$\tau(f_0) = \sum_i \tau((x_i)_0) \delta_i(f)_0(0) = \sum_i \tau((x_i)_0) \tau_i(f_0).$$

We conclude that $\tau = \sum_i \tau(u_i)\tau_i$, where u_i is the germ at 0 of the i-th coordinate function on B. Since $\tau_i(u_j)$ is equal to 1 or 0 according to whether $i = j$ or $i \neq j$, the τ_i's are linearly independent and hence constitute an R-basis of B_0.

Now let X be an analytic manifold, p a point of X and $\gamma : (U(p), \mathscr{F}_{U(p)}) \to (B, \mathscr{A}_B)$ a chart of X at p. Evidently, we may identify the tangent space $U(p)_p$ to $U(p)$ at p with the tangent space X_p to X at p. Hence γ_p° may be regarded as an isomorphism of X_p onto B_0. If B is an open box in $R^{n(p)}$ the dimension of X_p over R is therefore $n(p)$. Clearly, for every point b of B, there is an open box $B^{(b)}$ in $R^{n(p)}$ such that $B^{(b)}$ and $b + B^{(b)}$ are contained in B, and the map $x \to x - b$ is an isomorphism of the analytic manifold $b + B^{(b)}$ onto the analytic manifold $B^{(b)}$. Composing this with γ, we obtain a chart of X at $\gamma^{-1}(b)$ whose image lies in $B^{(b)}$. Hence it is clear that, for every point q in $U(p)$, the dimension of X_q is still equal to $n(p)$. It follows that the set of points p of X such that the dimension of X_p has a given value is both open and closed in X. Since X is connected, one of these sets must therefore be X. Thus the dimension of X_p is the same for all points p, and we shall call it the *dimension of X*.

2

Let X be an analytic manifold, p a point of X, $\alpha: U(p) \to A$ a chart of X at p. If A_1 is an open box contained in A and $U_1(p) = \alpha^{-1}(A_1)$ then the map $\alpha_{U_1(p)}$ is evidently a chart of X at p. We shall call it a *subchart* of the given chart α. If B is an open box in R^n and $s = (s_1, \cdots, s_m)$ is an ordered subset of $(1, \cdots, n)$ we define a map π_s of B onto an open box in R^m by putting $\pi_s(r_1, \cdots, r_n) = (r_{s_1}, \cdots, r_{s_m})$. We shall call such a map π_s a *coordinate projection* of B. It is evidently an analytic map.

PROPOSITION 2.1. *Let $\eta: X \to Y$ be an analytic map, let p be a point of X, and suppose that $\eta_p^\circ: X_p \to Y_{\eta(p)}$ is injective. Then, given any chart $\beta: V(\eta(p)) \to B$ of Y at $\eta(p)$, there is a coordinate projection π_s of B and a neighborhood $N(p)$ of p in X such that $\eta(N(p)) \subset V(\eta(p))$ and $(\pi_s \circ \beta \circ \eta)_{N(p)}$ is a chart of X at p. Moreover, given any chart of X at p, there is a subchart $\alpha: U(p) \to A$ of it, a chart $\beta^*: V^*(\eta(p)) \to B^*$ of Y at $\eta(p)$ and a coordinate projection π_s of B^* such that $\eta(U(p)) \subset V^*(\eta(p))$, $(\pi_s \circ \beta^* \circ \eta)_{U(p)} = \alpha$, and $(\pi_{s'} \circ \beta^*)(\eta(U(p))) = (0)$, where s' denotes the complement of s.*

Proof. Suppose first that $\beta: V(\eta(p)) \to B$ is a given chart of Y at $\eta(p)$. We can evidently find a chart $\alpha: U(p) \to A$ of X at p satisfying the following conditions: (1) $\alpha(U(p)) \subset V(\eta(p))$; (2) if $\mu = \beta \circ \eta \circ \alpha^{-1}$ then μ is a power series map of A into B. Let $\mu_1, \cdots, \mu_n$ be the coordinate functions associated with μ, i.e., let $\mu_j = y_j \circ \mu$, where $y_1, \cdots, y_n$ are the coordinate functions on B. Let $\delta_1, \cdots, \delta_m$ be the partial differentiations with respect to the coordinates of A.

Now suppose that $r_1, \cdots, r_m$ are real numbers such that $\sum_{i=1}^m r_i \delta_i(\mu_j)(0) = 0$ for each j. Let $\sigma_1, \cdots, \sigma_m$ be the tangents to A at 0 that correspond to $\delta_1, \cdots, \delta_m$, and let σ be the tangent $\sum_{i=1}^m r_i \sigma_i$. The above relations mean precisely that σ annihilates each $(\mu_j)_0$. Since $\mu_j = y_j \circ \mu$, it is clear from the definition of the differential of an analytic map that $\sigma((\mu_j)_0) = \mu_0^\circ(\sigma)((y_j)_0)$. Thus the above relations mean that $\mu_0^\circ(\sigma)$ annihilates each $(y_j)_0$, which implies that $\mu_0^\circ(\sigma) = 0$. Since η_p° is injective, so is μ_0°, so that we must have $\sigma = 0$, whence each $r_i = 0$. Our conclusion is that the m vectors $\delta_i(\mu)(0)$ in R^n are linearly independent. Hence there must be a subset $s = (s_1, \cdots, s_m)$ of $(1, \cdots, n)$ such that the determinant of the matrix with entries $\delta_i(\mu_{s_j})(0)$ is different from 0. Now this determinant is precisely the Jacobian $J(\pi_s \circ \mu)(0)$. Hence it follows from Theorem 3.1 of Chapter V that there is a neighborhood U of 0 in A such that $(\pi_s \circ \mu)_U$ is a chart of A at 0. Hence, if $N(p) = \alpha^{-1}(U)$, we have $\eta(N(p)) \subset V(\eta(p))$, and $(\pi_s \circ \beta \circ \eta)_{N(p)}$ is a chart of X at p.

Now suppose we are given a chart of X at p. From the above proof, it is clear that we may choose the above chart α to be a subchart of the given chart and, furthermore, such that $\pi_s(\mu(A))$ is an open connected neighborhood of 0 in $\pi_s(B)$ and $\pi_s \circ \mu$ is an analytic isomorphism of A onto $\pi_s(\mu(A))$. For simplicity of notation, let us assume, without loss of generality, that $s = (1, \cdots, m)$, and let us abbreviate $\pi_s \circ \mu$ by ν. Define an analytic map ρ of $\pi_s^{-1}(\nu(A))$ into R^n by

$$\rho(\nu(a), r_{m+1}, \cdots, r_n) = (a, r_{m+1} - \mu_{m+1}(a), \cdots, r_n - \mu_n(a)),$$

where a ranges over A. Clearly, if A is chosen sufficiently small, there is an open box D in R^{n-m} such that $A \times D \subset \rho(\pi_s^{-1}(\nu(A)))$. Define the analytic map σ of $A \times D$ into R^n by

$$\sigma(a, r_{m+1}, \cdots, r_n) = (\nu(a), r_{m+1} + \mu_{m+1}(a), \cdots, r_n + \mu_n(a)).$$

By choosing D small enough, we may evidently ensure that $\sigma(A \times D) \subset B$. Then $\rho \circ \sigma$ is the identity map on $A \times D$ and $\sigma \circ \rho$ is the identity map on $\rho^{-1}(A \times D)$. Now let $V^*(\eta(p)) = (\beta^{-1} \circ \sigma)(A \times D)$ and

$$\beta^* = (\rho \circ \beta)_{V^*(\eta(p))}.$$

Then it is seen immediately from the definitions that the requirements of the second part of Proposition 2.1 are satisfied, with $B^* = A \times D$.

PROPOSITION 2.2. *Let $\eta \colon X \to Y$ be an analytic map, let p be a point of X, and suppose that $\eta_p^\circ \colon X_p \to Y_{\eta(p)}$ is surjective. Let $\beta \colon V(\eta(p)) \to B$ be a chart of Y at $\eta(p)$. Then there is a chart $\alpha \colon U(p) \to A$ of X at p and a coordinate projection π_s of A such that $\eta(U(p)) \subset V(\eta(p))$ and $\pi_s \circ \alpha = (\beta \circ \eta)_{U(p)}$.*

Proof. Choose a chart $\alpha_1 \colon U_1(p) \to A_1$ of X at p such that $\eta(U_1(p)) \subset V(\eta(p))$ and $\mu = \beta \circ \eta \circ \alpha_1^{-1}$ is a power series map of A_1 into B. Using the same notation as in the proof of Proposition 2.1, let $t_1, \cdots, t_n$ be real numbers such that $\sum_{j=1}^{n} t_j \delta_i(\mu_j)(0) = 0$ for each $i = 1, \cdots, m$. Let $\tau_1, \cdots, \tau_n$ be the canonical basis for B_0. Since η_p° is surjective, so is μ_0°, whence there is a tangent ρ_k to A_1 at 0 such that $\mu_0^\circ(\rho_k) = \tau_k$. Then, if $y_1, \cdots, y_n$ are the coordinate functions on B, so that $\mu_j = y_j \circ \mu$, we have $\rho_k((\mu_j)_0) = \mu_0^\circ(\rho_k)((y_j)_0) = \tau_k((y_j)_0) = \delta_{jk}$, where δ_{jk} is equal to 1 or 0 according to whether $j = k$ or $j \neq k$. If $x_1, \cdots, x_m$ are the coordinate functions on A_1, we have $\rho_k = \sum_{i=1}^{m} \rho_k((x_i)_0)\sigma_i$, where $\sigma_1, \cdots, \sigma_m$ is the canonical basis for $(A_1)_0$. Now $\sigma_i((\mu_j)_0) = \delta_i(\mu_j)(0)$, and our above result concerning ρ_k may be written $\sum_{i=1}^{m} \rho_k((x_i)_0)\delta_i(\mu_j)(0) = \delta_{jk}$. Multiplying this by t_j and summing over j, we obtain $t_k = 0$. Thus we have shown that the n vectors $(\delta_1(\mu_j)(0), \cdots, \delta_m(\mu_j)(0))$ in R^m are linearly independent. Hence there must be a subset $s = (s_1, \cdots, s_n)$ of $(1, \cdots, m)$ such that the determinant of the matrix with entries $\delta_{s_k}(\mu_j)(0)$ is different from 0. Let γ be the map of A_1 into R^m such that $\pi_s \circ \gamma = \mu$ while $\gamma(a)_i = x_i(a)$ for the indices i that do not belong to s. Our last result evidently implies that the Jacobian $J(\gamma)(0)$ is different from 0. Hence it follows from Theorem 3.1 of Chapter V that there is a neighborhood N of 0 in A_1 such that γ_N is a chart of A_1 at 0. Now put $U(p) = \alpha_1^{-1}(N)$ and $\alpha = (\gamma \circ \alpha_1)_{U(p)}$. Then it is clear that α is a chart of X at p and that $\pi_s \circ \alpha = (\beta \circ \eta)_{U(p)}$, so that Proposition 2.2 is proved.

PROPOSITION 2.3. *Let $\eta: X \to Y$ be an analytic map, let p be a point of X, and suppose that $\eta_p^\circ: X_p \to Y_{\eta(p)}$ is bijective. Then there is an open connected neighborhood $U(p)$ of p in X such that η induces an analytic manifold isomorphism of $U(p)$ onto an open connected neighborhood of $\eta(p)$ in Y.*

Proof. Choose a chart $\beta: V(\eta(p)) \to B$ of Y at $\eta(p)$, and let $U(p)$, α, π_s be as in Proposition 2.2. Since η_p° is bijective, it is clear that we must now have $m = n$, so that π_s is the identity map on A. Thus $\alpha = (\beta \circ \eta)_{U(p)}$. Since α and β are analytic isomorphisms, this shows that $\eta_{U(p)}$ is an analytic isomorphism of $U(p)$ onto the open connected neighborhood $\beta^{-1}(\alpha(U(p)))$ of $\eta(p)$ in Y.

3

By a *derivation* of an R-algebra A, we mean a linear endomorphism δ of A such that $\delta(x,y) = x\delta(y) + \delta(x)y$ for all elements x and y of A. An *analytic tangent vector field* on an analytic manifold X is a function τ on the set of open sets of X associating with each open set U a derivation τ_U of the

R-algebra $\mathscr{F}(U)$ such that, if V is an open set containing U and $\rho_{U,V}$ is the restriction homomorphism $\mathscr{F}(V) \to \mathscr{F}(U)$, one has $\tau_U \circ \rho_{U,V} = \rho_{U,V} \circ \tau_V$. It follows that, for every point p of X, τ defines a tangent τ_p to X at p such that, whenever U is an open set containing p and f is an element of $\mathscr{F}(U)$, one has $\tau_p(f_p) = \tau_U(f)(p)$.

The simplest non-trivial example of an analytic tangent vector field, which has already been used implicitly before, is the following. Let X be an open submanifold of R^n. Then for each $i = 1, \cdots, n$ there is an analytic tangent vector field $\tau^{(i)}$ on X, defined by making $\tau^{(i)}{}_U$ the partial differentiation δ_i with respect to the i-th variable on the algebra $\mathscr{A}_X(U)$ of the analytic functions on U.

An analytic map $\eta: X \to Y$ is said to be *regular at the point p of X* if η_p° is injective. If η is regular at every point then we shall simply say that η is *regular*.

PROPOSITION 3.1. *Let η be a regular analytic map of an analytic manifold X into an analytic manifold Y. Let τ be an analytic tangent vector field on Y such that, for every point p of X, the tangent $\tau_{\eta(p)}$ belongs to $\eta_p^\circ(X_p)$. Then there is one and only one analytic tangent vector field σ on X such that $\eta_p^\circ(\sigma_p) = \tau_{\eta(p)}$ for every point p of X.*

Proof. Let U be an open set of X, and let f be an element of $\mathscr{F}_X(U)$. Then we define the function $\sigma_U(f)$ on U by putting

$$\sigma_U(f)(p) = (\eta_p^\circ)^{-1}(\tau_{\eta(p)})(f_p).$$

We must show that $\sigma_U(f)$ belongs to $\mathscr{F}_X(U)$. Choose a chart $\beta: V(\eta(p)) \to B$ of Y at $\eta(p)$. By Proposition 2.1, there is a coordinate projection π_s of B and a neighborhood $N(p)$ of p in U such that $\eta(N(p)) \subset V(\eta(p))$ and $(\pi_s \circ \beta \circ \eta)_{N(p)}$ is a chart of X at p. We have $\sigma_U(f)_{N(p)} = \sigma_{N(p)}(f_{N(p)})$, and it suffices to show that, for every p in U, $\sigma_U(f)_{N(p)}$ belongs to $\mathscr{F}_X(N(p))$. Hence we may assume without loss of generality that $U = N(p)$. Then we may write $f = g \circ \eta$, where g is an element of $\mathscr{F}_Y(V^*(\eta(p)))$, with $V^*(\eta(p)) = (\pi_s \circ \beta)^{-1}(\pi_s \circ \beta \circ \eta)(U) \subset V(\eta(p))$. Hence, if q is any point of U,

$$\sigma_U(f)(q) = (\eta_q^\circ)^{-1}(\tau_{\eta(q)})(f_q) = \tau_{\eta(q)}(g_{\eta(q)}) = \tau_{V^*(\eta(p))}(g)(\eta(q)),$$

so that $\sigma_U(f) = \tau_{V^*(\eta(p))}(g) \circ \eta \in \mathscr{F}_Y(V^*(\eta(p))) \circ \eta \subset \mathscr{F}_X(U)$.

Thus σ_U maps $\mathscr{F}_X(U)$ into itself. It is clear from the definition that σ_U

is a derivation and that, for $U \subset V$, $\sigma_U \circ \rho_{U,V} = \rho_{U,V} \circ \sigma_V$. Thus σ is an analytic tangent vector field on X. It follows immediately from the definition that $\eta_p^\circ(\sigma_p) = \tau_{\eta(p)}$. Finally, since σ is evidently determined uniquely by the map $p \rightarrow \sigma_p$ and since η_p° is injective for each p, there can be only one analytic tangent vector field σ on X that satisfies $\eta_p^\circ(\sigma_p) = \tau_{\eta(p)}$ for each p. This completes the proof of Proposition 3.1.

Generally, if $\eta : X \rightarrow Y$ is an analytic map, we say that an analytic tangent vector field τ on Y is *traceable* to an analytic tangent vector field σ on X if, for every point p of X, $\tau_{\eta(p)} = \eta_p^\circ(\sigma_p)$. Note that, if η is not regular, τ may be traceable to more than one analytic tangent vector field on X.

The analytic tangent vector fields on an analytic manifold X evidently constitute a vector space over the field R of the real numbers, in the natural fashion. Moreover, there is a composition of analytic tangent vector fields, called *commutation* and defined as follows: let α and β be two analytic tangent vector fields on X. Then their *commutator* $[\alpha, \beta]$ is defined by $[\alpha, \beta]_U = \alpha_U \circ \beta_U - \beta_U \circ \alpha_U$, for every open set U of X. With this composition, the space of the analytic tangent vector fields on X becomes a *Lie algebra* over R, i.e., the composition $(\alpha, \beta) \rightarrow [\alpha, \beta]$ is bilinear, $[\alpha, \alpha] = 0$ for all α's, and $[[\alpha, \beta], \gamma] + [[\beta, \gamma], \alpha] + [[\gamma, \alpha], \beta] = 0$ for all α, β, γ. This last is called the *Jacobi identity*; it is an immediate consequence of the definition. The next proposition says that the property of traceability is compatible with the Lie algebra structure.

PROPOSITION 3.2. *Let $\eta : X \rightarrow Y$ be an analytic map, and suppose that α and β are analytic tangent vector fields on Y that are traceable to analytic tangent vector fields ρ and σ on X, respectively. Then $[\alpha, \beta]$ is traceable to $[\rho, \sigma]$ and, for arbitrary real numbers r and s, $r\alpha + s\beta$ is traceable to $r\rho + s\sigma$.*

Proof. The last statement is obvious, so that we have to show only that $[\alpha, \beta]$ is traceable to $[\rho, \sigma]$. Let p be a point of X, let V be an open neighborhood of $\eta(p)$ in Y, and let g be an element of $\mathscr{F}_Y(V)$. Then we have, for every point q of $\eta^{-1}(V)$,

$$(\alpha_V(g) \circ \eta)(q) = \alpha_V(g)(\eta(q)) = \alpha_{\eta(q)}(g_{\eta(q)}) = \eta_p^\circ(\rho_q)(g_{\eta(q)})$$
$$= \rho_q((g \circ \eta)_q) = \rho_U(g \circ \eta)(q),$$

where $U = \eta^{-1}(V)$. Thus $\alpha_V(g) \circ \eta = \rho_U(g \circ \eta)$ and similarly $\beta_V(g) \circ \eta = \sigma_U(g \circ \eta)$. Using this, we obtain

$$\eta_p^\circ([\rho, \sigma]_p)(g_{\eta(p)}) = [\rho, \sigma]_p((g \circ \eta)_p) = [\rho, \sigma]_U(g \circ \eta)(p)$$
$$= \rho_p((\sigma_U(g \circ \eta))_p) - \sigma_p((\rho_U(g \circ \eta))_p)$$
$$= \rho_p((\beta_V(g) \circ \eta)_p) - \sigma_p((\alpha_V(g) \circ \eta)_p)$$
$$= \alpha_{\eta(p)}(\beta_V(g)_{\eta(p)}) - \beta_{\eta(p)}(\alpha_V(g)_{\eta(p)})$$
$$= (\alpha_V(\beta_V(g)) - \beta_V(\alpha_V(g)))(\eta(p))$$
$$= [\alpha, \beta]_V(g)(\eta(p)) = [\alpha, \beta]_{\eta(p)}(g_{\eta(p)}).$$

Hence $\eta_p^\circ([\rho, \sigma]_p) = [\alpha, \beta]_{\eta(p)}$, as we had to prove.

EXERCISES

1. Let X and Y be analytic manifolds, (p, q) a point of their Cartesian product $X \times Y$. Show that the projections of $X \times Y$ onto X and onto Y yield an isomorphism of the tangent space $(X \times Y)_{(p,q)}$ onto the direct sum of the tangent spaces X_p and Y_q. Also, show that every analytic tangent vector field on X is traceable to an analytic tangent vector field on $X \times Y$.

2. Let η be the map of R into R given by $\eta(r) = r^3$. Show that η is an analytic map and a homeomorphism, but that its inverse is not analytic.

3. Determine the totality of all analytic tangent vector fields on R^n.

VII. ANALYTIC GROUPS AND THEIR LIE ALGEBRAS [1]

1

An *analytic group* is a group G that is equipped with the structure of an analytic manifold such that the map $G \times G \to G$ that sends each (x, y) onto xy^{-1} is an analytic map. As in the case of the definition of a topological group (Chapter I, Section 2), it follows immediately that the inversion $x \to x^{-1}$ and the multiplication $(x, y) \to xy$ are also analytic maps, and that the right and left translations effected by an element of G on G are analytic manifold isomorphisms of G onto G. If x is an element of G, we shall denote by t_x the left translation effected on G by x; $t_x(y) = xy$.

PROPOSITION 1.1. *Let τ be a tangent to the analytic group G at the neutral element 1 of G. Then there is one and only one analytic tangent vector field τ^* on G such that $\tau_x^* = (t_x)_1^\circ(\tau)$ for every element x of G.*

Proof. Let U be an open set of G, and let f be an element of $\mathscr{F}_G(U)$. Define the function $\tau^*_U(f)$ on U by $\tau^*_U(f)(x) = (t_x)_1^\circ(\tau)(f_x)$. In order to prove Proposition 1.1, it is evidently sufficient to show that $\tau^*_U(f)$ belongs to $\mathscr{F}_G(U)$. Let z be a point of U, and choose charts $\alpha\colon U(z) \to A$, $\beta\colon V \to B$ of G at z and at 1, respectively, such that $U(z)V \subset U$. Consider the map $\eta\colon U(z) \times V \to R$ given by $\eta(x, y) = f(xy)$. Then η is evidently an analytic map. Hence, if $U(z)$ and V are chosen sufficiently small, $\eta \circ (\alpha^{-1} \times \beta^{-1})$ is a power series function on $A \times B$, i.e., we have $f(xy) = p(\alpha(x), \beta(y))$, where p is a power series function on $A \times B$. Thus, for every x in $U(z)$, we have $f \circ t_x = p(\alpha(x), \beta)$. Now $(t_x)_1^\circ(\tau)(f_x) = \tau((f \circ t_x)_1) = \tau(p(\alpha(x), \beta)_1)$. Let i denote the identity map on B. Then $p(\alpha(x), \beta) = p(\alpha(x), i) \circ \beta$, so that the above gives $(t_x)_1^\circ(\tau)(f_x) = \beta_1^\circ(\tau)(p(\alpha(x), i)_0)$. If we write out $\beta_1^\circ(\tau)$ in terms of the canonical basis of the tangent space B_0 we see immediately that the map $x \to \beta_1^\circ(\tau)(p(\alpha(x), i)_0)$ is an analytic map of $U(z)$ into R. Hence $\tau^*_U(f) \in \mathscr{F}_G(U)$, and Proposition 1.1 is proved.

Let μ be any analytic tangent vector field on G, and let x be an element of G. If U is an open set of G and f is an element of $\mathscr{F}_G(U)$ we define the function $(x \cdot \mu)_U(f)$ on U as follows: $(x \cdot \mu)_U(f) = \mu_{x^{-1}U}(f \circ t_x) \circ t_x^{-1}$. One verifies immediately from this definition that the map $U \to (x \cdot \mu)_U$ is an analytic tangent vector field $x \cdot \mu$ on G. Evidently, the map $\mu \to x \cdot \mu$ is a linear endomorphism of the space of the analytic tangent vector fields on G, and we have $x \cdot (y \cdot \mu) = (xy) \cdot \mu$ for all elements x, y of G and all analytic tangent vector fields μ. Moreover, we have, for all analytic tangent vector fields α and β, $x \cdot [\alpha, \beta] = [x \cdot \alpha, x \cdot \beta]$. In order to verify this, let U and f be as above. Then

$$(x \cdot \alpha)_U((x \cdot \beta)_U(f)) = (x \cdot \alpha)_U(\beta_{x^{-1}U}(f \circ t_x) \circ t_x^{-1})$$
$$= \alpha_{x^{-1}U}(\beta_{x^{-1}U}(f \circ t_x)) \circ t_x^{-1}.$$

Hence

$$[x \cdot \alpha, x \cdot \beta]_U(f) = [\alpha, \beta]_{x^{-1}U}(f \circ t_x) \circ t_x^{-1} = (x \cdot [\alpha, \beta])_U(f),$$

which proves our assertion. Thus G acts by Lie algebra automorphisms on the Lie algebra of all analytic tangent vector fields. It follows that *the G-fixed analytic tangent vector fields on G constitute a Lie subalgebra of the Lie algebra of all analytic tangent vector fields on G.* We call this the *Lie algebra of G* and denote it by $\mathscr{L}(G)$.

THEOREM 1.2. *The map $\tau \to \tau^*$ of Proposition 1.1 is a linear isomorphism of the tangent space G_1 onto $\mathscr{L}(G)$.*

Proof. In order to show that τ^* belongs to $\mathscr{L}(G)$, it suffices to show that $(x \cdot \tau^*)_y = \tau_y^*$ for all elements x and y of G. Let U be an open neighborhood of y in G, and let f be an element of $\mathscr{F}_G(U)$. Then we have

$$(x \cdot \tau^*)_y(f_y) = (x \cdot \tau^*)_U(f)(y) = ((\tau_{x^{-1}U}^*)(f \circ t_x) \circ t_x^{-1})(y)$$
$$= \tau_{x^{-1}U}^*(f \circ t_x)(x^{-1}y) = \tau_{x^{-1}y}^*((f \circ t_x)_{x^{-1}y})$$
$$= (t_{x^{-1}y})_1^\circ(\tau)((f \circ t_x)_{x^{-1}y})$$
$$= (t_{x^{-1}})_y^\circ((t_y)_1^\circ(\tau))((f \circ t_x)_{x^{-1}y})$$
$$= (t_{x^{-1}})_y^\circ(\tau_y^*)((f \circ t_x)_{x^{-1}y}) = \tau_y^*(f_y).$$

Hence we have indeed $x \cdot \tau^* = \tau^*$. The map $\tau \to \tau^*$ is evidently linear and injective. Finally, let μ be any element of $\mathscr{L}(G)$. Then, if y, U and f are as above,

$$(t_y)_1^\circ(\mu_1)(f_y) = \mu_1((f \circ t_y)_1) = \mu_{y^{-1}U}(f \circ t_y)(1)$$
$$= (y \cdot \mu)_U(f)(y) = \mu_U(f)(y) = \mu_y(f_y),$$

whence $(t_y)_1^\circ(\mu_1) = \mu_y$. Thus $\mu = (\mu_1)^*$, so that Theorem 1.2 is proved.

Let η be an analytic group homomorphism of an analytic group G into an analytic group H. Then η induces a linear map of $\mathscr{L}(G)$ into $\mathscr{L}(H)$, which we denote by η° and which we call the (global) *differential* of η. This is defined from the differential η_1° of η at 1 by putting $\eta^\circ(\alpha) = \eta_1^\circ(\alpha_1)^*$.

THEOREM 1.3. *Let* $\eta: G \to H$ *be an analytic homomorphism of the analytic group* G *into the analytic group* H. *Then, for every element* α *of* $\mathscr{L}(G)$ *and every point* x *of* G, *we have* $\eta^\circ(\alpha)_{\eta(x)} = \eta_x^\circ(\alpha_x)$, *and* η° *is a Lie algebra homomorphism of* $\mathscr{L}(G)$ *into* $\mathscr{L}(H)$.

Proof. By definition, we have $\eta^\circ(\alpha)_{\eta(x)} = (t_{\eta(x)})_1^\circ(\eta_1^\circ(\alpha_1))$. Now let V be an open neighborhood of $\eta(x)$ in H, and let g be an element of $\mathscr{F}_H(V)$. Then we have

$$(t_{\eta(x)})_1^\circ(\eta_1^\circ(\alpha_1))(g_{\eta(x)}) = \eta_1^\circ(\alpha_1)((g \circ t_{\eta(x)})_1) = \alpha_1((g \circ t_{\eta(x)} \circ \eta)_1)$$
$$= \alpha_1((g \circ \eta \circ t_x)_1) = (t_x)_1^\circ(\alpha_1)((g \circ \eta)_x).$$

By the last part of the proof of Theorem 1.2, we have $(t_x)_1^\circ(\alpha_1) = \alpha_x$. Hence the last expression above is equal to $\alpha_x((g \circ \eta)_x) = \eta_x^\circ(\alpha_x)(g)$. Thus the first part of Theorem 1.3 is proved. It means that $\eta^\circ(\alpha)$ is traceable to α. Hence, if α and β are elements of $\mathscr{L}(G)$, it follows from Proposition 3.2 of Chapter VI that $[\eta^\circ(\alpha), \eta^\circ(\beta)]$ is traceable to $[\alpha, \beta]$, whence $\eta^\circ([\alpha, \beta]) = [\eta^\circ(\alpha), \eta^\circ(\beta)]$. Thus η° is a Lie algebra homomorphism, and Theorem 1.3 is proved.

2

We discuss a particularly important type of analytic group, for which we shall be able to compute the Lie algebra explicitly. Let A be any finite-dimensional associative R-algebra with identity. We topologize A by the coarsest topology making all linear functionals on A continuous. Let A° denote the space dual to A. We define a functional structure $\mathscr{F}_A$ on A as follows. If U is an open set of A then a real-valued function f on A is to belong to $\mathscr{F}_A(U)$ if and only if, for every point u of U, there is a power series function $f^{(u)}$ on an open box in an $R^{n(u)}$ and elements $\alpha_1^{(u)}, \cdots, \alpha_{n(u)}^{(u)}$ of A°

77

such that $f(v) = f^{(u)}(\alpha_1^{(u)}(v) - \alpha_1^{(u)}(u), \cdots, \alpha_{n(u)}^{(u)}(v) - \alpha_{n(u)}^{(u)}(u))$ for all points v in some neighborhood of u in U. By choosing a basis for A°, one sees easily that one may then actually take $n(u)$ to be equal to the dimension n of A°, and $(\alpha_1^{(u)}, \cdots, \alpha_n^{(u)})$ to be this fixed basis $(\alpha_1, \cdots, \alpha_n)$ of A°, for all points u. At the same time, one sees that $\mathscr{F}_A$ is the structure of an analytic manifold, for which A is isomorphic with the analytic manifold R^n (an isomorphism $A \rightarrow R^n$ being obtained from any basis of A in the usual way).

Let U_A denote the multiplicative group of the units of A. An element of A is a unit if and only if the determinants of the left and right multiplications effected on A by that element are different from 0. Hence it is clear that U_A is open in A. Let G_A denote the connected component of the identity in U_A. Since A is locally connected, and since U_A is open in A, it follows that G_A is open in A, and thus is an open submanifold of A. Evidently, G_A is an analytic group, with the manifold structure that is induced from that of A.

Now we shall determine the Lie algebra of G_A. Let τ be any element of the tangent space $(G_A)_1$. Then the map of A° into R that sends each element α of A° onto $\tau((\alpha_{G_A})_1)$ is evidently a linear map. Hence there is one and only one element τ° in A such that $\tau((\alpha_{G_A})_1) = \alpha(\tau^\circ)$ for every element α of A°. Clearly, the map $\tau \rightarrow \tau^\circ$ is an injective linear map of $(G_A)_1$ into A. Since the dimension of $(G_A)_1$ is equal to the dimension of A, this map is therefore a linear isomorphism of $(G_A)_1$ onto A. On the other hand, we know from Theorem 1.2 that the map $\mu \rightarrow \mu_1$ is a linear isomorphism of $\mathscr{L}(G_A)$ onto $(G_A)_1$. Hence the map $\mu \rightarrow (\mu_1)^\circ$ is a linear isomorphism of $\mathscr{L}(G_A)$ onto A. From now on, we shall write μ° for $(\mu_1)^\circ$.

It remains to express $[\rho, \sigma]^\circ$ in terms of ρ° and σ°. For any element a of A denote by l_a and r_a the left and right multiplications effected by a on A, respectively. As before, for x in G_A, t_x denotes the left translation effected by x on G_A, so that $t_x = (l_x)_{G_A}$. Now let ρ and σ be elements of $\mathscr{L}(G_A)$, f an element of A° and x an element of G_A. Then we have

$$\rho_x((f_{G_A})_x) = (t_x)_1^\circ(\rho_1)((f_{G_A})_x) = \rho_1((f_{G_A} \circ t_x)_1)$$
$$= \rho_1(((f \circ l_x)_{G_A})_1) = (f \circ l_x)(\rho^\circ) = f(x\rho^\circ) = (f \circ r_{\rho^\circ})(x).$$

Hence, if U is an open set of G_A, $\rho_U(f_U) = (f \circ r_{\rho^\circ})_U$. Now let U be an open neighborhood of 1 in G_A. Then, noting that $f \circ r_{\rho^\circ}$ belongs to A°, we obtain from the last result

$$\sigma_1(\rho_U(f_U)_1) = \sigma_1((f \circ r_{\rho^\circ})_1) = (f \circ r_{\rho^\circ})(\sigma^\circ) = f(\sigma^\circ \rho^\circ).$$

Hence we have $[\rho, \sigma]_1(f_1) = f(\rho^\circ \sigma^\circ) - f(\sigma^\circ \rho^\circ) = f(\rho^\circ \sigma^\circ - \sigma^\circ \rho^\circ)$, whence $[\rho, \sigma]^\circ = \rho^\circ \sigma^\circ - \sigma^\circ \rho^\circ$.

Let us denote by $\mathscr{L}(A)$ the Lie algebra whose underlying vector space is that of A and where the commutation is defined by $[x, y] = xy - yx$. Then we may put our result as follows.

THEOREM 2.1. *Let A be a finite-dimensional associative R-algebra with identity, and let G_A be the connected component of 1 in the group of units of A. Then G_A, with its analytic manifold structure as an open submanifold of A, is an analytic group. For each element μ of $\mathscr{L}(G_A)$ there is one and only one element μ° in A such that $\mu_1(f_1) = f(\mu^\circ)$ for every element f of A°. The map $\mu \to \mu^\circ$ is a Lie algebra isomorphism of $\mathscr{L}(G_A)$ onto $\mathscr{L}(A)$.*

3

It is evident that the one-dimensional vector group R is an analytic group. The Lie algebra $\mathscr{L}(R)$ has a canonical basis (ρ), ρ being the analytic tangent vector field corresponding to ordinary differentiation, i.e., if U is an open set of R and f is an element of $\mathscr{A}_R(U)$ then $\rho_U(f)$ is the derivative f' of f. The following proposition is basic for the application of Lie algebra theory to the theory of analytic groups.

PROPOSITION 3.1. *Let G be an analytic group, and let γ be an element of $\mathscr{L}(G)$. Then there is one and only one analytic homomorphism h of R into G such that $h^\circ(\rho) = \gamma$.*

Proof. We can evidently find a chart $\alpha: U \to A$ of G at 1 such that the following condition is satisfied: if $f_1, \cdots, f_n$ are the functions on U given by $\alpha(x) = (f_1(x), \cdots, f_n(x))$ then there are power series functions $p_1, \cdots, p_n$ on A such that $\gamma_U(f_i) = p_i(f_1, \cdots, f_n)$ for each i. Now we can apply Theorem 2.1 of Chapter V to obtain the following result: there is an open interval J around 0 in R on which there is one and only one system $(g_1, \cdots, g_n)$ of differentiable functions such that $(g_1(r), \cdots, g_n(r)) \in A$ for every r in J, $g_i(0) = 0$, and $g_i' = p_i(g_1, \cdots, g_n)$; moreover, these functions g_i are power series functions.

Now define the map u of J into G by setting $u(r) = \alpha^{-1}(g_1(r), \cdots, g_n(r))$. Then $f_i \circ u = g_i$, and $\rho_r((f_i \circ u)_r) = g_i'(r) = p_i(g_1(r), \cdots, g_n(r)) = \gamma_U(f_i)(u(r))$, whence $u_r^\circ(\rho_r) = \gamma_{u(r)}$. Now let s be a point of J, and define, for r in $J - s$, $v(r) = u(s)^{-1}u(r + s)$.

Then we have, on $J - s$, $f_i \circ v = f_i \circ t_{u(s)^{-1}} \circ u \circ t_s$, whence

$$
\begin{aligned}
\rho_r&((f_i \circ v)_r) \\
&= (t_s)_r^{\circ}(\rho_r)((f_i \circ t_{u(s)^{-1}} \circ u)_{r+s}) = \rho_{r+s}((f_i \circ t_{u(s)^{-1}} \circ u)_{r+s}) \\
&= u_{r+s}^{\circ}(\rho_{r+s})((f_i \circ t_{u(s)^{-1}})_{u(r+s)}) = \gamma_{u(r+s)}((f_i \circ t_{u(s)^{-1}})_{u(r+s)}) \\
&= (t_{u(s)^{-1}})_{u(r+s)}^{\circ}(\gamma_{u(r+s)})((f_i)_{u(s)^{-1}u(r+s)}) = \gamma_{v(r)}((f_i)_{v(r)}).
\end{aligned}
$$

Thus we have $(f_i \circ v)'(r) = p_i(f_i \circ v, \cdots, f_n \circ v)(r)$ for all points r of $J - s$. Hence it follows from the uniqueness of the system $(g_1, \cdots, g_n)$ that we must have $f_i(v(r)) = g_i(r) = f_i(u(r))$ for all points r of $J - s$. Hence $v(r) = u(r)$, and we have shown that $u(s + r) = u(s)u(r)$ for all r and s such that r, s and $s + r$ all lie in J. By Proposition 1.5 of Chapter III, u has one and only one extension h that is a homomorphism of R into G. Clearly, h is an analytic homomorphism, so that the existence part of Proposition 3.1 is proved.

Finally, let k be any analytic homomorphism of R into G such that $k^{\circ}(\rho) = \gamma$. Write $\alpha(k(r)) = (k_1(r), \cdots, k_n(r))$. By reversing the relevant computation made above, we see immediately that the system $(k_1, \cdots, k_n)$ satisfies the conditions imposed above on the system $(g_1, \cdots, g_n)$. Hence each k_i coincides with g_i on J, so that k coincides with h on J. But this evidently implies that $k = h$, so that Proposition 3.1 is proved.

The unique analytic homomorphism $R \to G$ whose differential sends the canonical generator ρ of $\mathscr{L}(R)$ onto the element γ of $\mathscr{L}(G)$ will now be denoted by η_γ. The *exponential map* $\exp_G$ (or simply $\exp$) of $\mathscr{L}(G)$ into G is defined by $\exp_G(\gamma) = \eta_\gamma(1)$.

We observe that $\eta_\gamma(r) = \exp_G(r\gamma)$ for every r in R. In order to see this, consider the analytic homomorphism μ of R into G that is defined by $\mu(s) = \eta_\gamma(sr)$. If π denotes the multiplication effected by r on R we have $\mu = \eta_\gamma \circ \pi$. Hence $\mu^{\circ}(\rho) = (\eta_\gamma)^{\circ}(\pi^{\circ}(\rho)) = (\eta_\gamma)^{\circ}(r\rho) = r\gamma$. By the uniqueness part of Proposition 3.1, this gives $\mu = \eta_{r\gamma}$, so that $\exp_G(r\gamma) = \mu(1) = \eta_\gamma(r)$.

THEOREM 3.2. *Let G be an analytic group. Then the exponential map* $\exp \colon \mathscr{L}(G) \to G$ *is analytic and induces an analytic manifold isomorphism of some open connected neighborhood of 0 in $\mathscr{L}(G)$ onto an open connected neighborhood of 1 in G.*

Proof. It is understood here that $\mathscr{L}(G)$ is endowed with its natural structure as an analytic manifold, isomorphic with R^n, as described at the beginning of Section 2. We choose a basis $(\gamma_1, \cdots, \gamma_n)$ for $\mathscr{L}(G)$, and a chart $\alpha \colon U \to A$ of G at 1. Let $f_1, \cdots, f_n$ be the functions on U defined by

$\alpha(x) = (f_1(x), \cdots, f_n(x))$. By taking U sufficiently small, we ensure that there are power series functions p_{ji} on A such that $(\gamma_j)_U(f_i) = p_{ji}(f_1, \cdots, f_n)$.

If $(s_1, \cdots, s_n)$ is any n-tuple of real numbers we define $M(s_1, \cdots, s_n)$ as the supremum of the set of the real numbers s with the property that $\eta_\gamma(r) \in U$ whenever $|r| < s$, where $\gamma = \sum_{i=1}^n s_i\gamma_i$. For $|r| < M(s_1, \cdots, s_n)$, define

$$g_i(r, s_1, \cdots, s_n) = f_i(\exp(r\textstyle\sum_k s_k\gamma_k)).$$

The map $r \to g_i(r, s_1, \cdots, s_n)$ is evidently analytic on the open interval $|r| < M(s_1, \cdots, s_n)$ and, in particular, has a derivative g_i'. Writing γ for $\sum_k s_k\gamma_k$, we find

$$\begin{aligned}
g_i'(r, s_1, \cdots, s_n) &= (f_i \circ \eta_\gamma)'(r) = \rho_r((f_i \circ \eta_\gamma)_r) = (\eta_\gamma)_r^\circ(\rho_r)((f_i)_{\eta_\gamma(r)}) \\
&= \gamma_{\eta_\gamma(r)}((f_i)_{\eta_\gamma(r)}) = \textstyle\sum_k s_k(\gamma_k)_{\eta_\gamma(r)}((f_i)_{\eta_\gamma(r)}) \\
&= \textstyle\sum_k s_k p_{ki}(g_1(r, s_1, \cdots, s_n), \cdots, g_n(r, s_1, \cdots, s_n)).
\end{aligned}$$

Clearly, $g_i(0, s_1, \cdots, s_n) = 0$. If we augment this system of differential equations by adjoining n additional equations $g_{n+j}'(r, s_1, \cdots, s_n) = 0$, and initial conditions $g_{n+j}(0, s_1, \cdots, s_n) = s_j$ for $j = 1, \cdots, n$, and then define functions $h_1, \cdots, h_{2n}$ of $2n + 1$ variables by $h_q(r, s_1, \cdots, s_n, t_1, \cdots, t_n) = g_q(r, s_1, \cdots, s_n)$, we obtain, from the above, a system of differential equations for the h_q's to which we can apply Theorem 2.1 of Chapter V. Hence we may conclude the following: there is an open box B in R^{n+1} and power series functions $p_1, \cdots, p_n$ on B such that $(p_1(b), \cdots, p_n(b))$ lies in A for every b in B, and if $(r, s_1, \cdots, s_n)$ lies in B then $p_i(0, s_1, \cdots, s_n) = 0$ and $p_i'(r, s_1, \cdots, s_n) = \sum_k s_k p_{ki}(p_1(r, s_1, \cdots, s_n), \cdots, p_n(r, s_1, \cdots, s_n))$. Furthermore, by the uniqueness part of Theorem 2.1, we have $g_i(r, s_1, \cdots, s_n) = p_i(r, s_1, \cdots, s_n)$ whenever $(r, s_1, \cdots, s_n) \in B$ and $|r| < M(s_1, \cdots, s_n)$.

Let us fix $s_1, \cdots, s_n$ so that $(0, s_1, \cdots, s_n)$ lies in B. There is a positive real number c such that $(r, s_1, \cdots, s_n) \in B$ if and only if $|r| < c$. For such r's, put $u(r) = \alpha^{-1}(p_1(r, s_1, \cdots, s_n), \cdots, p_n(r, s_1, \cdots, s_n))$, so that $f_i(u(r)) = p_i(r, s_1, \cdots, s_n)$. Then we have $u(r) = \eta_\gamma(r)$ whenever $|r| < M(s_1, \cdots, s_n)$. Since $u(r) \in U$, this shows that $c < M(s_1, \cdots, s_n)$, whence $(g_i)_B = p_i$ and $\eta_\gamma(r) \in U$ whenever $(r, s_1, \cdots, s_n)$ lies in B. Since $\eta_\gamma(r) = \eta_{r\gamma}(1)$, this shows that $g_i(1, rs_1, \cdots, rs_n)$ is defined and equal to $g_i(r, s_1, \cdots, s_n)$ whenever $(r, s_1, \cdots, s_n)$ lies in B. In particular, if t is any non-zero real number, we have therefore $p_i(rt, t^{-1}s_1, \cdots, t^{-1}s_n) = p_i(r, s_1, \cdots, s_n)$ for all sufficiently small $r, s_1, \cdots, s_n$. It follows that, for all $(r, s_1, \cdots, s_n)$ in B, $p_i(r, s_1, \cdots, s_n) = q_i(rs_1, \cdots, rs_n)$, where q_i is a power series function on a neighborhood of 0 in R^n containing all these points $(rs_1, \cdots, rs_n)$. Hence the map $(t_1, \cdots, t_n) \to g_i(1, t_1, \cdots, t_n)$ is a power series map on some neighborhood of 0 in R^n (where we may write $t_i = rs_i$, with $(r, s_1, \cdots, s_n)$ in B). Since $g_i(1, t_1, \cdots, t_n) = (f_i \circ \exp)(\sum_k t_k \gamma_k)$, this shows that the restriction of exp to some open connected neighborhood of 0 in $\mathscr{L}(G)$ is an analytic map. But, if m is any positive integer, we have $\exp(\gamma) = \exp(m^{-1}\gamma)^m$. Taking m large enough, we see from this that exp is analytic on some neighborhood of every point of $\mathscr{L}(G)$, so that exp is an analytic map of $\mathscr{L}(G)$ into G.

Now let us compute the differential of exp at 0. We use the coordinate functions $x_1, \cdots, x_n$ on $\mathscr{L}(G)$, where $x_i(\sum_k s_k \gamma_k) = s_i$. Let $\sigma^{(1)}, \cdots, \sigma^{(n)}$ be the analytic tangent vector fields on $\mathscr{L}(G)$ that correspond to the differentiations with respect to the x_i's. Let W be an open neighborhood of 1 in G, and let f be an element of $\mathscr{F}_G(W)$. Let μ be the map of R into $\mathscr{L}(G)$ that is given by $\mu(r) = r\gamma_i$. Then μ is an analytic homomorphism, and we have $\sigma^{(i)} = \mu^\circ(\rho)$. Hence we obtain

$$
\begin{aligned}
\sigma^{(i)}_{r\gamma_i}((f \circ \exp)_{r\gamma_i}) &= \mu^\circ_r(\rho_r)((f \circ \exp)_{\mu(r)}) \\
&= \rho_r((f \circ \exp \circ \mu)_r) = \rho_r((f \circ \eta_{\gamma_i})_r) = (\eta_{\gamma_i})^\circ_r(\rho_r)(f_{\eta_{\gamma_i}(r)}) \\
&= (\gamma_i)_{\eta_{\gamma_i}(r)}(f_{\eta_{\gamma_i}(r)}).
\end{aligned}
$$

Hence

$$
\exp^\circ_0(\sigma^{(i)}_0)(f_1) = \sigma^{(i)}_0((f \circ \exp)_0) = (\gamma_i)_1(f_1),
$$

so that $\exp^\circ_0(\sigma^{(i)}_0) = (\gamma_i)_1$. Thus $\exp^\circ_0$ sends a basis of $\mathscr{L}(G)_0$ onto a basis of G_1. Hence we may conclude from Proposition 2.3 of Chapter VI that exp induces an analytic manifold isomorphism of some open connected neighborhood of 0 in $\mathscr{L}(G)$ onto an open connected neighborhood of 1 in G. This completes the proof of Theorem 3.2.

THEOREM 3.3. *Let μ be an analytic homomorphism of an analytic group G into an analytic group H. Then $\mu \circ \exp_G = \exp_H \circ \mu^\circ$.*

Proof. Let γ be any element of $\mathscr{L}(G)$. Then we have $(\mu \circ \eta_\gamma)^\circ(\rho) = \mu^\circ((\eta_\gamma)^\circ(\rho)) = \mu^\circ(\gamma)$. On the other hand, $\eta_{\mu^\circ(\gamma)}(\rho) = \mu^\circ(\gamma)$. Hence it follows from the uniqueness part of Proposition 3.1 that $\mu \circ \eta_\gamma = \eta_{\mu^\circ(\gamma)}$. If we evaluate this at 1 in R we obtain $\mu(\exp_G(\gamma)) = \exp_H(\mu^\circ(\gamma))$, which is what was to be proved.

A first application of the exponential map is to the proof of the following important result.

THEOREM 3.4. *Let α and β be two analytic homomorphisms of an analytic* *group G into an analytic group H. Then, if the differentials of α and β at the neutral element of G coincide, we have $\alpha = \beta$.*

Proof. In virtue of Theorem 1.2, the assumption means that $\alpha^\circ = \beta^\circ$. Hence, from Theorem 3.3, we have $\alpha \circ \exp_G = \beta \circ \exp_G$. By Theorem 3.2, this implies that α and β coincide on some neighborhood of 1 in G. Since G is connected and α and β are homomorphisms, this gives $\alpha = \beta$.

Let us return to the analytic group G_A of units of an algebra A that we discussed in Section 2. We wish to determine the exponential map $\exp_{G_A}$; the result we shall obtain will show that $\exp_G$ is indeed a generalization of the ordinary exponential map. Let us define the analytic map Exp of A into A by $\mathrm{Exp}(a) = \sum_{n=0}^{\infty}(n!)^{-1}a^n$, noting that the series on the right actually defines a power series map $A \to A$, when the manifold A is identified with an R^n by means of a choice of an R-basis of A. In these terms, we shall obtain the following result.

THEOREM 3.5. *Let G_A be the group of Theorem 2.1, and let $\gamma \to \gamma^\circ$ denote the canonical isomorphism of $\mathscr{L}(G_A)$ onto A. Then $\exp_{G_A}(\gamma) = \mathrm{Exp}(\gamma^\circ)$ for every γ in $\mathscr{L}(G_A)$.*

Proof. Consider the analytic homomorphism $\eta_\gamma : R \to G_A$, where γ is an element of $\mathscr{L}(G_A)$. We may form its derivative, which is characterized by: $f(\eta_\gamma'(r)) = (f \circ \eta_\gamma)'(r)$ for every element f of the space A° dual to A. Denoting the restriction of f to G_A by f^*, we have

$$\gamma_{\eta_\gamma(r)}(f^*{}_{\eta_\gamma(r)}) = \rho_r((f^* \circ \eta_\gamma)_r) = (f \circ \eta_\gamma)'(r) = f(\eta_\gamma'(r)).$$

On the other hand,

$$\gamma_{\eta_\gamma(r)}(f^*{}_{\eta_\gamma(r)}) = (t_{\eta_\gamma(r)})_1^\circ(\gamma_1)(f^*{}_{\eta_\gamma(r)}) = \gamma_1((f^* \circ t_{\eta_\gamma(r)})_1) = f(\eta_\gamma(r)\gamma^\circ).$$

Hence we conclude that $\eta_\gamma'(r) = \eta_\gamma(r)\gamma^\circ$. Now an evident application of the uniqueness part of Theorem 2.1 of Chapter V shows that we must have $\eta_\gamma(r) = \mathrm{Exp}(r\gamma^\circ)$ for all r in R. In particular, if we put $r = 1$, we obtain $\exp_{G_A}(\gamma) = \mathrm{Exp}(\gamma^\circ)$.

4

Let G be an analytic group. We know from Theorem 3.2 that there is an open connected neighborhood U of 0 in $\mathscr{L}(G)$ such that the exponential map induces an analytic manifold isomorphism of U onto an open connected neighborhood $\exp(U)$ of 1 in G. Let us denote the inverse of this manifold isomorphism by log. We shall require the following slight elaboration of Theorem 3.2.

PROPOSITION 4.1. *Let G be an analytic group, and suppose there is given a decomposition of $\mathscr{L}(G)$ as a direct sum of vector subspaces $S_1, \cdots, S_k$. Let π_i denote the corresponding projection of $\mathscr{L}(G)$ onto S_i. Let U be an open connected neighborhood of 0 in $\mathscr{L}(G)$ such that the exponential map induces an analytic manifold isomorphism of U onto an open connected neighborhood of 1 in G. Let V be an open connected neighborhood of 0 in $\mathscr{L}(G)$ such that $\exp(\pi_1(\gamma)) \cdots \exp(\pi_k(\gamma))$ lies in $\exp(U)$ for every γ in V. Let p denote the analytic map $V \to U$ defined by $p(\gamma) = \log(\exp(\pi_1(\gamma)) \cdots \exp(\pi_k(\gamma)))$. Then p_0° is the identity map on V_0, so that p induces an analytic manifold isomorphism of some open connected neighborhood of 0 in $\mathscr{L}(G)$ onto another such neighborhood.*

Proof. Let σ_i be the injection $S_i \to \mathscr{L}(G)$, and put $T_i = ((\sigma_i)_0^{\circ}(S_i)_0)$. It is easy to see that $\mathscr{L}(G)_0$ is the direct sum of the subspaces T_i. We may evidently identify $\mathscr{L}(G)_0$ with U_0, and it suffices to show that $p_0^{\circ}(\tau) = \tau$ for every τ in T_i, because the last assertion of Proposition 4.1 then follows at once from Proposition 2.3 of Chapter VI. Clearly, $\pi_i \circ p \circ \sigma_i$ is the identity map on S_i, while $\pi_j \circ p \circ \sigma_i$ is the 0-map $S_i \to (0)$ if $j \neq i$. Now let τ be an element of T_i, and write $\tau = (\sigma_i)_0^{\circ}(\gamma)$ with γ in S_i. Then $(\pi_i)_0^{\circ}(p_0^{\circ}(\tau)) = (\pi_i \circ p \circ \sigma_i)_0^{\circ}(\gamma) = \gamma$, and $(\pi_j)_0^{\circ}(p_0^{\circ}(\tau)) = 0$ if $j \neq i$. On the other hand, it is clear that $(\sigma_t)_0^{\circ} \circ (\pi_t)_0^{\circ}$ is the projection of $\mathscr{L}(G)_0$ onto T_t. Hence, applying $(\sigma_i)_0^{\circ}$ and $(\sigma_j)_0^{\circ}$ to the last two results, respectively, we see that $p_0^{\circ}(\tau) = \tau$. Thus Proposition 4.1 is proved.

THEOREM 4.2. *Every continuous homomorphism of an analytic group G into an analytic group H is analytic.*

Proof. The critical case is the case where $G = R$, and we shall dispose of this first. Let us choose a neighborhood V of 0 in $\mathscr{L}(H)$ such that V becomes an open box when $\mathscr{L}(H)$ is identified with R^n by means of a basis, and such that $\exp_H$ induces an analytic manifold isomorphism of V onto an open connected neighborhood of the neutral element in H. Let f be the given continuous homomorphism of R into H. We can choose a positive real number c such that $f(r) \in \exp_H(\frac{1}{2}V)$ whenever $|r| < c$. For such r's, put $\mu(r) = \log(f(r))$. Now fix r so that $|r| < c$, and let k be any positive integer. We claim that, for every integer q such that $0 \leq q \leq k$, we have

$$q\mu(k^{-1}r) = \mu(qk^{-1}r).$$

Evidently, this holds for $q = 0$. Suppose it holds for some $q < k$. Then we have $(q + 1)\mu(k^{-1}r) = \mu(qk^{-1}r) + \mu(k^{-1}r) \in \frac{1}{2}V + \frac{1}{2}V \subset V$. On the other hand, we have

$$\exp((q + 1)\mu(k^{-1}r)) = \exp(\mu(k^{-1}r))^{q+1} = f(k^{-1}r)^{q+1}$$
$$= f((q + 1)k^{-1}r) = \exp(\mu((q + 1)k^{-1}r)).$$

Since exp is injective on V, this gives $(q + 1)\mu(k^{-1}r) = \mu((q + 1)^{-1}kr)$. Thus the above holds for all q such that $0 \leq q \leq k$. Hence we have $qk^{-1}\mu(r) = \mu(qk^{-1}r)$ for all these values of q. Since μ is continuous, it follows that $s\mu(r) = \mu(sr)$ for all real numbers s such that $0 \leq s \leq 1$. Since $\mu(-t) = -\mu(t)$, the same holds for all real numbers s such that $|s| \leq 1$.

Thus $f(sr) = \exp(s\mu(r))$ whenever $|s| \leq 1$. Equivalently, $f(t) = \exp(tr^{-1}\mu(r))$ if $r \neq 0$ and $|t| \leq r$. This shows that f is analytic on some open interval containing 0, which implies (since f is a homomorphism) that f is analytic.

Now let us consider the general case. Let $(\gamma_1, \cdots, \gamma_m)$ be a basis for $\mathscr{L}(G)$. The map $r \to f(\exp_G(r\gamma_i))$, where f is the given continuous homomorphism $G \to H$, is a continuous homomorphism of R into H. By what we have just shown, there are elements η_i in $\mathscr{L}(H)$ such that $f(\exp_G(r\gamma_i)) = \exp_H(r\eta_i)$ for all r in R. Hence

$$f(\exp_G(r_1\gamma_1) \cdots \exp_G(r_m\gamma_m)) = \exp_H(r_1\eta_1) \cdots \exp_H(r_m\eta_m).$$

Let $x_1, \cdots, x_m$ be the coordinate functions on $\mathscr{L}(G)$ given by $x_i(\sum_k r_k\gamma_k) = r_i$. Let p be the analytic map on a suitable neighborhood of 0 in $\mathscr{L}(G)$ that is given by

$$p(\textstyle\sum_k r_k\gamma_k) = \log(\exp_G(r_1\gamma_1) \cdots \exp_G(r_m\gamma_m)).$$

By Proposition 4.1, the restriction of p to some open connected neighborhood of 0 in $\mathscr{L}(G)$ is an analytic manifold isomorphism onto some other such neighborhood. Hence, for g in a sufficiently small neighborhood of 1 in G, we may write $f(g)$ as the ordered product of the m elements

$$\exp_H(x_k(p^{-1}(\log(g)))\eta_k),$$

and this shows that f is analytic on some neighborhood of 1 in G. Hence f is an analytic homomorphism of G into H.

Note that if we apply Theorem 4.2 to the identity map on G we obtain the result that *a connected topological group G can have at most one functional structure with which it becomes an analytic group.*

THEOREM 4.3. *Let G be an analytic group, let $\gamma_1, \cdots, \gamma_q$ be elements of $\mathscr{L}(G)$, and let f be an element of $\mathscr{F}_G(U)$, where U is an open neighborhood of 1 in G. Then* *there is an open box B in R^q satisfying the following conditions: if $(r_1, \cdots, r_q)$ lies in B then $\exp_G(r_1\gamma_1)\cdots\exp_G(r_q\gamma_q)$ lies in U and the map $(r_1, \cdots, r_q) \to f(\exp_G(r_1\gamma_1)\cdots\exp_G(r_q\gamma_q))$ is a power series function on B represented by the power series whose coefficients are*

$$a(e_1, \cdots e_q) = (e_1! \cdots e_q!)^{-1}((\gamma_1)_U{}^{e_1}\cdots(\gamma_q)_U{}^{e_q})(f)(1).$$

Proof. The only statement still requiring proof is the one giving the coefficients $a(e_1, \cdots, e_q)$ of the representing power series. For x near 1 in G and r near 0 in R, and for any element γ of $\mathcal{L}(G)$, put $g(r) = f(x\exp_G(r\gamma))$. Then

$$
\begin{aligned}
g'(r) &= \rho_r(g_r) = \rho_r((f \circ t_x \circ \eta_\gamma)_r) = \gamma_{\exp(r\gamma)}((f \circ t_x)_{\exp(r\gamma)}) \\
&= \gamma_{x\exp(r\gamma)}(f_{x\exp(r\gamma)}) = \gamma_U(f)(x\exp(r\gamma)).
\end{aligned}
$$

Repeating this, with $\gamma_U(f)$ in the place of f, etc., we obtain the following result for the n-th derivative of g:

$$g^{(n)}(r) = (\gamma_U)^n(f)(x\exp(r\gamma)).$$

Hence the power series function g is represented by the power series whose coefficients are $(n!)^{-1}(\gamma_U)^n(f)(x)$. Now write this with

$$x = \exp(r_1\gamma_1)\cdots\exp(r_{q-1}\gamma_{q-1})$$

and $\gamma = \gamma_q$. Next proceed with the coefficients of the power series thus obtained as above. The desired result is obtained at the q-th stage.

EXERCISES

1. For the group G_A of Theorems 2.1 and 3.5, define an inverse, log, of $\exp_{G_A}$ explicitly by a power series on a suitable neighborhood of 1.

2. Let A be the algebra of all 2 by 2 real matrices. Show that the matrices $\begin{pmatrix} r & 0 \\ 0 & r^{-1} \end{pmatrix}$ with $r < 0$ belong to G_A, but that they do not lie in the image of $\exp_{G_A}$, except for $r = -1$, thus showing that, in general, $\exp_G$ is not surjective. [If $x = \mathrm{Exp}(y)$ then the characteristic roots of x are the exponentials of the characteristic roots of y.]

3. Use Theorem 3.2 to show that in every analytic group G there is a neighborhood U of the neutral element having the following property: if x is any element of U other than 1 then there is a positive integer p such that $x^p \notin U$. In particular, U contains no non-trivial subgroup of G.

4. Use Theorem 4.3 to show that an analytic group G is commutative if and only if $[\alpha, \beta] = 0$ for all elements α and β of $\mathcal{L}(G)$.

5. Show that every analytic tangent vector field on an analytic group G can be written in one and only one way in the form $f_1\gamma_1 + \cdots + f_n\gamma_n$, where $(\gamma_1, \cdots, \gamma_n)$ is a given basis of $\mathcal{L}(G)$ and $f_1, \cdots, f_n$ are analytic functions on G.

VIII. CLOSED SUBGROUPS
OF LIE GROUPS [1,7]

1

Let G be a topological group, and let G^* be the connected component of the identity in G. Then G^* is a closed normal subgroup of G. We say that G is a *Lie group* if G^* is open in G and can be endowed with a functional structure making it into an analytic group. As we have noted after the proof of Theorem 4.2, there can be at most one such functional structure on G^*. Hence, when we are given a Lie group G, we may view G^* as a given analytic group. The main result of this chapter is the following.

THEOREM 1.1. *Let G be a locally compact topological group, and suppose there is a continuous homomorphism h of G into a Lie group H such that h is injective on some neighborhood of the neutral element in G. Then G is a Lie group.*

We choose a Euclidean norm $| \ |$ on $\mathscr{L}(H)$ such that if S is the open ball around 0 of radius 1 in $\mathscr{L}(H)$ then $\exp_H$ induces an analytic manifold isomorphism of S onto a neighborhood of 1 in H. By assumption, there is a compact neighborhood U of 1 in G such that h_U is injective and $h(U) \subset \exp(S)$. Let us write μ for the composite map $\log \circ h_U$ of U into S. If α is any non-zero element of $\mathscr{L}(H)$ we shall write α^1 for the corresponding unit vector $|\alpha|^{-1}\alpha$. The boundary of U will be denoted by $\delta(U)$. The following lemma is critical for the proof.

LEMMA. *Let (u_k) be a sequence of elements of U converging to the neutral element 1 of G. Assume that none of the u_k's is equal to 1 and that the sequence of unit vectors $\mu(u_k)^1$ converges to an element γ in $\mathscr{L}(H)$. Then there is a continuous homomorphism f of R in G such that $h(f(r)) = \exp_H(r\gamma)$ for every r in R, and $f(r) \in U$ whenever $|r| < \inf_{u \in \delta(U)}(|\mu(u)|)$.*

Proof. Since h_U is injective and $\delta(U)$ does not contain the neutral element of G, it follows that $h(\delta(U))$ does not contain the neutral element of H, whence $0 \notin \mu(\delta(U))$. Hence $\inf_{u \in \delta(U)}(|\mu(u)|) > 0$. Choose a real number c such that $0 < c < \inf_{u \in \delta(U)}(|\mu(u)|)$. For each index k, let p_k denote the largest integer for which $p_k|\mu(u_k)| < c$ and $u_k^m \in U$ for all integers m such that $0 \leq m \leq p_k$. We claim that, for all sufficiently large k, we have $(p_k + 1)|\mu(u_k)| \geq c$. For suppose this is not the case. Then we must have $u_k^{p_k+1} \notin U$ for infinitely many k's. Since U is compact, there is a point u in U such that every neighborhood of u contains infinitely many points $u_k^{p_k}$ with $u_k^{p_k+1} \notin U$. Since $u_k \to 1$, we have $u \in \delta(U)$, so that $|\mu(u)| > c$. On the other hand, $\mu(u)$ is a limit point of the sequence of points $\mu(u_k^{p_k}) = p_k\mu(u_k)$, whence $|\mu(u)| \leq c$, so that we have a contradiction.

Hence, for all sufficiently large k, we have $p_k|\mu(u_k)| < c \leq (p_k + 1)|\mu(u_k)|$. Since $|\mu(u_k)| \to 0$, it follows that $p_k|\mu(u_k)| \to c$ as $k \to \infty$. Now let t be a real number such that $0 \leq t < c$, and put $q_k = [p_kc^{-1}t]$, where $[r]$ denotes the integral part of r. Then $q_k < p_k$, so that $q_k|\mu(u_k)| < c$ and $u_k^{q_k} \in U$. Now we may write

$$\mu(u_k^{q_k}) = q_k\mu(u_k) = q_k|\mu(u_k)||\mu(u_k)|^1 = (q_kp_k^{-1})(p_k|\mu(u_k)|)\mu(u_k)^1,$$

which shows that $\mu(u_k^{q_k})$ converges to $t\gamma$ as k becomes large (note that $p_k \to \infty$, so that $q_kp_k^{-1} \to c^{-1}t$). Hence $h(u_k^{q_k})$ converges to $\exp(t\gamma)$ as k becomes large. Since h_U is a homeomorphism of U onto $h(U)$, this implies that $u_k^{q_k}$ converges to a point $f(t)$ of U as k becomes large, where $h(f(t)) = \exp(t\gamma)$.

Since $u_k \to 1$, we have $u_k^{-1} \in U$ for all sufficiently large k's. Hence we may apply the above argument to the sequence (u_k^{-1}) and obtain $f(-t) \in U$ such that $h(f(-t)) = \exp(-t\gamma)$. Now $f(r)$ is defined as a point of U whenever $|r| < c$, and $h(f(r)) = \exp(r\gamma)$. Since h_U is a homeomorphism of U onto $h(U)$, it is clear that f is continuous and that $f(r_1 + r_2) = f(r_1)f(r_2)$ whenever $|r_1| < c$, $|r_2| < c$ and $|r_1 + r_2| < c$. By Proposition 1.5 of Chapter III, f extends to a homomorphism $R \to G$, which evidently satisfies the requirements of the lemma.

We proceed to the proof of Theorem 1.1. If α is any continuous homomorphism of R into G then $h \circ \alpha$ is a continuous homomorphism of R into H. By Theorem 4.2 of Chapter VII, $h \circ \alpha$ is therefore an analytic homomorphism. Moreover, it is clear from Theorem 3.4 of Chapter VII that $h \circ \alpha = \eta_{\alpha*}$, where $\alpha* = (h \circ \alpha)^\circ(\rho) \in \mathscr{L}(H)$, i.e., $h(\alpha(r)) = \exp(r\alpha*)$ for every r in R. We shall prove first that these elements α^* of $\mathcal{L}(H)$ make up a vector subspace of $\mathcal{L}(H)$.

If $s \in R$ we may define a continuous homomorphism α_s of R into G by $\alpha_s(r) = \alpha(sr)$. Clearly, we have then $s\alpha^* = (\alpha_s)^*$. It remains to show that if α and β are continuous homomorphisms of R into G then there is a continuous homomorphism γ of R into G such that $\gamma^* = \alpha^* + \beta^*$. In doing this, we may evidently assume that $\alpha^* + \beta^* \neq 0$. Put $u_k = \alpha(k^{-1})\beta(k^{-1})$, for $k = 1, 2, \cdots$. For all sufficiently large k's we have $u_k \in U$, and we may consider $\mu(u_k) = \log(\alpha(k^{-1})\beta(k^{-1})) = \log(\exp(k^{-1}\alpha^*)\exp(k^{-1}\beta^*))$. The map $(r, s) \to \log(\exp(r\alpha^*)\exp(s\beta^*))$ is a power series map of some neighborhood of 0 in R^2 into $\mathcal{L}(H)$, and its first partial derivatives are evidently α^* and β^*. Hence we may write $\mu(u_k) = k^{-1}(\alpha^* + \beta^*) + k^{-2}p(k)$, where $p(k)$ remains bounded as $k \to \infty$. Since $\alpha^* + \beta^* \neq 0$, this shows that $u_k \neq 1$ for all sufficiently large k's, and that $\mu(u_k)^1$ converges to $(\alpha^* + \beta^*)^1$ as k becomes large. Hence we conclude from the above lemma that there is a continuous homomorphism f of R into G such that $h(f(r)) = \exp(r(\alpha^* + \beta^*)^1)$ for all r in R. If $\gamma = f_{|\alpha^* + \beta^*|}$ we have evidently $\gamma^* = \alpha^* + \beta^*$. Thus the elements α^* that correspond to the continuous homomorphisms α of R into G constitute a vector subspace W of $\mathcal{L}(H)$.

Let U_1 be the set of all points u in U for which $\mu(u)$ lies in W. We shall prove that U_1 is still a neighborhood of 1 in G. Choose a subspace W' of $\mathcal{L}(H)$ such that $\mathcal{L}(H)$ is the direct sum of W and W'. One sees immediately from Proposition 4.1 of Chapter VII that there is an open connected neighborhood N of 0 in $\mathcal{L}(H)$ and maps $\sigma: N \to W$, $\sigma': N \to W'$ such that the map $\gamma \to \sigma(\gamma) + \sigma'(\gamma)$ is an analytic manifold isomorphism of N onto another open connected neighborhood of 0 in $\mathcal{L}(H)$ and $\exp(\gamma) = \exp(\sigma(\gamma))\exp(\sigma'(\gamma))$ for every γ in N.

Now suppose that U_1 is not a neighborhood of 1 in G. Then there is a sequence (v_n) in U that converges to 1, while no v_n lies in U_1 (note that U is homeomorphic with a subspace of S, so that there is a countable fundamental system of neighborhoods of 1 in U). For all sufficiently large n's, we have $\mu(v_n) \in N$ and, by the definition of W, a continuous homomorphism α_n of R into G such that $h(\alpha_n(r)) = \exp(r\sigma(\mu(v_n)))$ for every r in R. Put $u_k = \alpha_n(k^{-1})$; $k = 1, 2, \cdots$. Then, for large k, $\mu(u_k) = \log(h(\alpha_n(k^{-1}))) = k^{-1}\sigma(\mu(v_n))$.

Suppose that $\sigma(\mu(v_n)) \neq 0$. Then we can form $\mu(u_k)^1 = \sigma(\mu(v_n))^1$. Since this does not depend on k, we may apply the lemma to the sequence (u_k) and conclude that there is a continuous homomorphism f of R into G

such that $h(f(r)) = \exp(r\sigma(\mu(v_n))^1)$ for every r in R and $f(r) \in U$ whenever $|r| < \inf_{u \in \delta(U)}(|\mu(u)|)$. It follows that $\exp(\sigma(\mu(v_n))) \in h(U)$ as soon as n is large enough to have $|\sigma(\mu(v_n))| < \inf_{u \in \delta(U)}(|\mu(u)|)$. Thus, for all sufficiently large such n's, we may define an element w_n in U by $h(w_n) = \exp(\sigma(\mu(v_n)))$.

On the other hand, if $\sigma(\mu(v_n)) = 0$, we simply put $w_n = 1$. Now consider the sequence of points $z_n = w_n^{-1}v_n$. Clearly, $z_n \to 1$. Since $\mu(w_n) = \sigma(\mu(v_n)) \in W$, we have $w_n \in U_1$. Since $v_n \notin U_1$, it follows that none of the z_n's is 1. We have, for large n, $h(z_n) = h(w_n)^{-1}h(v_n) = \exp(\sigma(\mu(v_n)))^{-1}\exp(\mu(v_n)) = \exp(\sigma'(\mu(v_n)))$. Replacing the sequence (z_n) by a subsequence, if necessary, we can ensure that the associated sequence of the unit vectors $\sigma'(\mu(v_n))^1$ converges to an element τ of W' such that $|\tau| = 1$. However, then the lemma applies to the sequence (z_n) and shows that τ belongs to W. Thus we have arrived at a contradiction, so that U_1 must be a neighborhood of 1 in G.

Now μ maps U_1 homeomorphically onto the subspace $\mu(U_1)$ of W, and it is clear from the lemma that $\mu(U_1)$ contains the open ball of radius $\inf_{u \in \delta(U)}(|\mu(u)|)$ around 0 in W. Hence there is an open neighborhood V of 1 in G such that $V \subset U_1$ and μ maps V homeomorphically onto an open box around 0 in W. In particular, V is connected and therefore contained in G^*, so that G^* is open in G.

We define a functional structure $\mathscr{F}_{G^*}$ on G^* as follows. For x in G^*, let t_x denote the left translation effected by x on G^*. Let T be an open set of G^*. Then a real-valued function f on T is to belong to $\mathscr{F}_{G^*}(T)$ if and only if, for every x in T, there is an open neighborhood T_x of x in T such that $x^{-1}T_x \subset V$ and the restriction of $f \circ t_x$ to $x^{-1}T_x$ belongs to the algebra $\mathscr{A}_{\mu(V)}(\mu(x^{-1}T_x)) \circ \mu$. It is evident that $\mathscr{F}_{G^*}$ is the structure of an analytic manifold on G^*; a chart of G^* at x is the restriction of $\mu \circ t_{x^{-1}}$ to xV.

It remains to show that the map $p: G^* \times G^* \to G^*$ given by $p(x, y) = xy^{-1}$ is analytic. If T is an open connected neighborhood of 1 in G^* such that $TT^{-1} \subset V$ then the restriction of p to $T \times T$ is evidently analytic. By the very definition of $\mathscr{F}_{G^*}$, each t_x is an analytic manifold automorphism of G^*. On the other hand, if s_x denotes the right translation $y \to yx$, it follows from the analyticity of p on $T \times T$ that the restriction of s_x to T is an analytic map of T into V whenever x lies in T^{-1}. Since $s_x(y^{-1}z) = (t_{y^{-1}} \circ s_x)(z)$, it follows that s_x is analytic also on yT, for every y in G^*, provided that x belongs to T^{-1}. Hence s_x is analytic on G^* for every x in T^{-1}. Since G^* is connected, given x in G^*, we have $x = x_1 \cdots x_k$ with each x_i in T^{-1}. Then $s_x = s_{x_k} \circ \cdots \circ s_{x_1}$, so that s_x is analytic. Now we have

$$p(x, y) = xy^{-1} = x_0(x_0^{-1}x)(y_0^{-1}y)^{-1}y_0^{-1} = x_0p(x_0^{-1}x, y_0^{-1}y)y_0^{-1}$$
$$= (t_{x_0} \circ s_{y_0}^{-1} \circ p)(x_0^{-1}x, y_0^{-1}y).$$

This shows that p is analytic on $x_0T \times y_0T$ for every pair (x_0, y_0), whence p is analytic. This completes the proof of Theorem 1.1.

Since every closed subgroup of a Lie group is locally compact, it follows immediately from Theorem 1.1 that *every closed subgroup of a Lie group is a Lie group*.

2

Let H be an analytic group, and let G be a closed subgroup of H. We know from Theorem 1.1 that G is a Lie group. We wish to analyze the position of G in H. Let h denote the injection map of G into H. Then h_{G*} is an analytic homomorphism of G^* into H, and its differential sends $\mathscr{L}(G^*)$ isomorphically onto a subalgebra of $\mathscr{L}(H)$; the fact that this map is injective follows immediately from Theorem 3.3 of Chapter VII. We shall identify $\mathscr{L}(G^*)$ with its image in $\mathscr{L}(H)$. Note that $\mathscr{L}(G^*)$ is precisely the subspace of $\mathscr{L}(H)$ that was denoted by W in the proof of Theorem 1.1. Let W' be a linear complement of $\mathscr{L}(G^*)$ in $\mathscr{L}(H)$. It is clear from the proof of Theorem 1.1 that there are open boxes A and A' around 0 in $\mathscr{L}(G^*)$ and W', respectively, such that the map $(\gamma', \gamma) \to \exp_H(\gamma')\exp_H(\gamma)$ is an analytic manifold isomorphism of $A' \times A$ onto an open connected neighborhood U of 1 in H, and $U \cap G = \exp_H(A) = U \cap G^*$. Let B' be a closed box around 0 in W' such that $B' \subset A'$ and $\exp_H(B')\exp_H(B') \subset U$. Put $K = \exp_H(B')$.

Let π denote the canonical map of H onto the space H/G of the cosets xG. The restrictions we have made on B' ensure that no two distinct elements of K belong to the same coset mod. G. Hence π_K is an injective continuous map of K onto a neighborhood of G in H/G. Since K is compact, π_K is therefore a homeomorphism of K onto $\pi(K)$.

We define a functional structure $\mathscr{F}_{H/G}$ on H/G as follows. Let T be any open set of H/G. Then a function f is to belong to $\mathscr{F}_{H/G}(T)$ if and only if $f \circ \pi$ belongs to $\mathscr{F}_H(\pi^{-1}(T))$. Now we are in a position to prove the following result.

THEOREM 2.1. *Let H be an analytic group, and let G be a closed subgroup of H.*

Then the above functional structure $\mathscr{F}_{H/G}$ makes H/G into an analytic manifold, and the canonical map $q\colon H \times H/G \to H/G$, where $q(x, yG) = xyG$, is analytic.

Proof. Let $\alpha\colon U \to A' \times A$ be the chart of H at 1 given by

$$\alpha(\exp_H(\gamma')\exp_H(\gamma)) = (\gamma', \gamma).$$

Let p denote the projection of $A' \times A$ onto A', and let S denote the interior of $\pi(K)$. Put $\beta = (p \circ \alpha \circ \pi_K^{-1})_S$. Then β is evidently a homeomorphism of S onto the interior of B', which we shall denote by B. We claim that β is actually a chart of H/G at G.

Let us show first that β is a morphism of structured spaces: $(S, \mathscr{F}_S) \to (B, \mathscr{A}_B)$. Let f be an analytic function on an open set V of B. We must show that $f \circ \beta$ belongs to $\mathscr{F}_S(\beta^{-1}(V))$, i.e., that $f \circ \beta \circ \pi$ is an analytic function on $\pi^{-1}(\beta^{-1}(V))$. Now $\pi^{-1}(\beta^{-1}(V))$ is the union of a family of open sets Yg, where $g \in G$ and Y is an open set in $U \cap \pi^{-1}(\beta^{-1}(V))$. It suffices to show that $(f \circ \beta \circ \pi)_{Y_g}$ is analytic for each Yg or, equivalently, that $(g \cdot (f \circ \beta \circ \pi))_Y$ is analytic for each Y. Since $g \cdot (f \circ \beta \circ \pi) = f \circ \beta \circ \pi$ and $(f \circ \beta \circ \pi)_Y = (f \circ p \circ \alpha)_Y$, we may therefore conclude that $f \circ \beta \circ \pi$ is analytic, so that β is indeed a morphism of structured spaces.

Now let t be the map of B into $A' \times A$ that is defined by $t(b) = (b, 0)$. Then we have $\beta^{-1} = \pi \circ \exp_H \circ t$. Since $\exp_H \circ t$ is an analytic map of B into H, it is therefore clear from the definition of the functional structure $\mathscr{F}_{H/G}$ that β^{-1} is a morphism of structured spaces $(B, \mathscr{A}_B) \to (S, \mathscr{F}_S)$. Thus β is an isomorphism of structured spaces, and therefore a chart.

Since the maps $H/G \to H/G$ sending each coset yG onto xyG, where x is a fixed element of H, are evidently automorphisms of the structured space H/G, they may be used to obtain charts of H/G at all points by transporting the above chart β. Hence $(H/G, \mathscr{F}_{H/G})$ is indeed an analytic manifold.

Using the action of H on H/G in a similar way, we see that, in order to prove that q is analytic, it suffices to show that its restriction to $H \times S$ is analytic. Now the restriction of q to $H \times S$ can be factored as follows:

$$H \times S \xrightarrow[i_H \times \pi_K^{-1}]{} H \times H \xrightarrow{\mu} H \xrightarrow{\pi} H/G,$$

where μ is the multiplication and i_H is the identity map on H. This shows that $q_{H \times S}$ is analytic, whence q is analytic. The proof of Theorem 2.1 is now complete.

Note that, by its very definition, the manifold structure on H/G has the following basic property. *For every analytic map f of H into an analytic manifold*

93

X that is constant on each coset of G in H, the corresponding map f^π *of H/G into X,*
where $f^\pi \circ \pi = f$, *is analytic.*

Suppose that H' is another analytic group and G' is a closed subgroup of
H'. The projections of $H \times H'$ onto H and onto H', composed with the
canonical maps $H \to H/G$ and $H' \to H'/G'$, respectively, give analytic maps
$H \times H' \to H/G$ and $H \times H' \to H'/G'$, each of which is constant on the
cosets of $G \times G'$ in $H \times H'$. Hence we have corresponding analytic maps
of $(H \times H')/(G \times G')$ onto H/G and onto H'/G', which yield an analytic
map $\sigma: (H \times H')/(G \times G') \to (H/G) \times (H'/G')$ in the canonical fashion.

On the other hand, the canonical map $H \times H' \to (H \times H')/(G \times G')$
gives rise, in the natural fashion, to a map τ of $(H/G) \times (H'/G')$ into
$(H \times H')/(G \times G')$ such that the diagram

$$H \times H' \longrightarrow (H \times H')/(G \times G')$$

$$\searrow \qquad \nearrow \tau$$

$$(H/G) \times (H'/G')$$

is commutative, from which we see immediately that τ is the inverse of σ.
Furthermore, it is easily seen from the definitions of the manifold structures
on $(H/G) \times (H'/G')$ and $(H \times H')/(G \times G')$ that τ is an analytic map.
Hence σ *is an analytic manifold isomorphism of* $(H \times H')/(G \times G')$ *onto*
$(H/G) \times (H'/G')$.

COROLLARY 2.2. *Let H be an analytic group, and let G be a closed normal*
subgroup of H. Then H/G, with the manifold structure of Theorem 2.1, is an
analytic group.

Proof. Let p be the map of $H \times H$ into H given by $p(x, y) = xy^{-1}$, let
π be the canonical map $H \to H/G$, and let p^G be the map of $(H/G) \times (H/G)$
into H/G analogous to p. Then $\pi \circ p$ is an analytic map of $H \times H$ into
H/G and is constant on the cosets of $G \times G$ in $H \times H$. Let f denote the
corresponding map of $(H \times H)/(G \times G)$ into H/G. Then we have
evidently $p^G = f \circ \tau$, where τ is as above. Hence p^G is analytic, and the
corollary is proved.

3

Let H be an analytic group, V an analytic manifold. Suppose we are given
a map $\mu: H \times V \to V$ making V into a homogeneous H-space, in the sense
of Theorem 2.5 of Chapter I. Abbreviating $\mu(x, v)$ by $x \cdot v$, assume in

addition that all the partial maps $x \to x \cdot v$ and $v \to x \cdot v$ are not only continuous but actually analytic. Then we shall say that V is a *homogeneous H-manifold*.

Let v be a point of V, and let γ be the analytic map $x \to x \cdot v$ of H into V. The analytic group H is generated by any compact neighborhood of the neutral element and is therefore a union of a countable family of compact subsets. Hence we may apply Theorem 2.5 of Chapter I to conclude that γ is an open map. Let G be the closed subgroup of H consisting of all elements x such that $x \cdot v = v$. Then G is called the *isotropy group of v in H*. Let δ denote the analytic map of H/G into V that corresponds to γ. Then δ is evidently a homeomorphism of H/G onto V.

THEOREM 3.1. *Let H be an analytic group, and let V be a homogeneous H-manifold. Let v be a point of V, and let G be the isotropy group of v in H. Then the map δ of H/G into V that corresponds to the map $x \to x \cdot v$ of H into V is an analytic manifold isomorphism of H/G onto V, and the given map $\mu: H \times V \to V$ is analytic.*

Proof. Let γ denote the map $x \to x \cdot v$ of H into V, and consider the differential γ_1° of γ at the neutral element 1 of H. Clearly, if α is any element of $\mathscr{L}(G^*)$ (which we identify with its image in $\mathscr{L}(H)$ as before) then α_1 lies in the kernel of γ_1°. Conversely, let α be any element of $\mathscr{L}(H)$ such that α_1 lies in the kernel of γ_1°. Let $\beta: U \to B$ be a chart of V at v, and let $x_1, \cdots, x_k$ be the coordinate functions on B. Let I be an open interval around 0 in R such that $\gamma(\exp_H((r + s)\alpha))$ lies in U whenever r and s lie in I. Fix s in I and, for r such that $s + r \in I$, put

$$f_i(r) = (x_i \circ \beta \circ \gamma)(\exp_H((r + s)\alpha)) = (x_i \circ \beta \circ \tau_{\exp_H(s\alpha)} \circ \gamma)(\exp_H(r\alpha)),$$

where τ_x, for any x in H, denotes the analytic manifold automorphism $w \to x \cdot w$ of V. Then we have

$$\begin{aligned} f_i'(0) = \rho_0((f_i)_0) &= \alpha_1((x_i \circ \beta \circ \tau_{\exp_H(s\alpha)} \circ \gamma)_1) \\ &= \gamma_1^\circ(\alpha_1)((x_i \circ \beta \circ \tau_{\exp_H(s\alpha)})_v) = 0. \end{aligned}$$

This result evidently means that the derivative of the function $r \to (x_i \circ \beta \circ \gamma)(\exp_H(r\alpha))$ vanishes everywhere on I, whence $\exp_H(r\alpha) \in G$ for every r in I, and hence for every r in R. It is clear from Section 2 that this means that $\alpha \in \mathscr{L}(G^*)$. Thus we have shown that the kernel of γ_1° is precisely $\mathscr{L}(G^*)_1$.

We have $\gamma_1^\circ = \delta_G^\circ \circ \pi_1^\circ$, where π is the canonical map $H \to H/G$. The map q of Theorem 2.1 makes H/G into a homogeneous H-manifold, so that the above proof shows also the kernel of π_1° is $\mathscr{L}(G^*)_1$. It follows that δ_G° is injective, so that we may apply Proposition 2.1 of Chapter VI. Since δ is a homeomorphism, this shows that $\dim(V) = \dim(H/G)$, whence δ_G° is a linear isomorphism of the tangent space to H/G at G onto V_v. We may therefore apply Proposition 2.3 of Chapter VI to conclude that δ^{-1} is analytic on a neighborhood of v in V. Using the actions of H on H/G and V in the familiar fashion, we deduce from this that δ^{-1} is analytic everywhere. Thus δ is an analytic manifold isomorphism of H/G onto V, and the first part of Theorem 3.1 is proved.

In order to prove the second part, note that the map $\mu: H \times V \to V$ can be factored according to the scheme

$$(x, w) \longrightarrow (x, \delta^{-1}(w)) \xrightarrow{\ q\ } x \cdot \delta^{-1}(w) \xrightarrow{\ \delta\ } x \cdot w.$$

The first and the third of these maps are analytic, by what we have just proved. The second map is the canonical map $q: H \times H/G \to H/G$, which is analytic, by Theorem 2.1. Thus μ is analytic, and the proof of Theorem 3.1 is complete.

COROLLARY 3.2. *Let γ be a surjective analytic homomorphism of an analytic group G onto an analytic group H, and let K be the kernel of γ. Then the map $\gamma^K: G/K \to H$ is an isomorphism of analytic groups.*

Proof. This follows immediately from Theorem 3.1 upon viewing H as a homogeneous G-manifold in the natural fashion.

EXERCISES

1. Let B be a finite-dimensional, not necessarily associative, R-algebra. Show that the group of all algebra automorphisms of B, with the topology induced from that of the space of all linear endomorphisms of B, is a Lie group, and that its Lie algebra may be identified with the Lie algebra of all derivations of B.

2. Let H be an analytic group, N a closed normal subgroup of H, and G a closed subgroup of H that contains N. Show that the analytic manifold H/G is isomorphic with the analytic manifold $(H/N)/(G/N)$.

3. Let G be an analytic group, and let K and L be closed subgroups of G such that $KL = G$. Prove that the canonical maps $G \to G/K$ and $G \to G/L$ give rise to an analytic manifold isomorphism of $G/(K \cap L)$ onto $(G/K) \times (G/L)$.

IX. AUTOMORPHISM GROUPS AND SEMIDIRECT PRODUCTS [1]

1

Let G be an analytic group, and let $\mathscr{A}(G)$ denote the group of all topological group automorphisms of G. We regard $\mathscr{A}(G)$ as a topological group, with the topology we defined in Section 3 of Chapter III. By Theorem 4.2 of Chapter VII, the elements of $\mathscr{A}(G)$ are actually analytic group automorphisms of G. Hence every element α of $\mathscr{A}(G)$ defines a Lie algebra automorphism α° of $\mathscr{L}(G)$. These elements α° make up a subgroup $\mathscr{A}^\circ(G)$ of the group of all topological group automorphisms of the vector group $\mathscr{L}(G)$, and we regard $\mathscr{A}^\circ(G)$ as a topological group with the topology induced from that of the full linear group on $\mathscr{L}(G)$. We wish to prove that the map $\alpha \to \alpha^\circ$ is a topological group isomorphism of $\mathscr{A}(G)$ onto $\mathscr{A}^\circ(G)$. For this purpose, we require the following result concerning the topology of $\mathscr{A}(G)$.

LEMMA 1.1. *Let G be a topological group, and suppose that there is a compact neighborhood S of 1 in G such that every element of G is a product of elements of the interior of S. Then, for every compact set K in G and every neighborhood V of 1 in G, there is a neighborhood W of 1 in G such that $N(S, W) \subset N(K, V)$, where $N(A, B)$ denotes the set of all elements α in $\mathscr{A}(G)$ such that $\alpha(a)a^{-1}$ and $\alpha^{-1}(a)a^{-1}$ lie in B for all points a in A.*

Proof. Since K is compact, the assumption on S implies that there is a positive integer m such that $K \subset S^m$, where S^m denotes the set of all products of m elements of S. There is a neighborhood U of 1 in G such that $U^m \subset V$. Put $W = \bigcap_{x \in S^m} x^{-1}Ux$. We claim that W is still a neighborhood of 1 in G. In order to see this, choose a neighborhood T of 1 in G such that

$TTT^{-1} \subset U$. Since S^m is compact, we can find elements $x_1, \cdots, x_p$ in S^m such that $S^m \subset \bigcup_{i=1}^{p} Tx_i$. Now, given $x \in S^m$, we may write $x = tx_i$, with t in T and some i. Then $x^{-1}Ux = x_i^{-1}t^{-1}Utx_i$, whence $x_i^{-1}Tx_i \subset x^{-1}Ux$. Hence W contains $\bigcap_{i=1}^{p} x_i^{-1}Tx_i$ and is therefore a neighborhood of 1 in G.

Now let α be an element of $N(S, W)$, and let y be an element of K. We have $y = s_1 \cdots s_m$, where each s_i is an element of S. Put $y_k = s_1 \cdots s_k$. Then $\alpha(y_1)y_1^{-1} = \alpha(s_1)s_1^{-1} \in W \subset U$. Suppose we have already shown that $\alpha(y_k)y_k^{-1} \in U^k$, for some $k < m$. Then we have

$$\alpha(y_{k+1})y_{k+1}^{-1} = \alpha(y_k)\alpha(s_{k+1})s_{k+1}^{-1}y_k^{-1} \in U^k y_k W y_k^{-1} \subset U^k U = U^{k+1},$$

because $y_k W y_k^{-1} \subset U$. Hence we find eventually that $\alpha(y)y^{-1} \in U^m \subset V$, and similarly $\alpha^{-1}(y)y^{-1} \in V$. Thus $N(S, W) \subset N(K, V)$, and the lemma is proved.

THEOREM 1.2. *Let G be an analytic group. Then the map $\alpha \to \alpha^\circ$ is a topological group isomorphism of $\mathscr{A}(G)$ onto $\mathscr{A}^\circ(G)$.*

Proof. By Theorem 3.4 of Chapter VII, the homomorphism $\alpha \to \alpha^\circ$ is injective, so that all that remains to be shown is that it is continuous, and open to its image.

Choose a Euclidean norm $| \ |$ on $\mathscr{L}(G)$. For any positive real number r, let B_r denote the closed ball of radius r around 0 in $\mathscr{L}(G)$. Let U be an open connected neighborhood of 1 in G on which log is defined and is an analytic manifold isomorphism of U onto an open connected neighborhood of 0 in $\mathscr{L}(G)$. Let γ_1 and γ_2 be two elements of $\mathscr{L}(G)$, and consider the elements $\exp(r_1\gamma_1)\exp(r_2\gamma_2)$, for small real numbers r_1 and r_2. Let us apply Theorem 4.3 of Chapter VII to a function f of the form $g \circ \log$, where g is a linear function on $\mathscr{L}(G)$. We have $f(\exp(r\gamma_i)) = rg(\gamma_i)$, whence $f(1) = 0$, $(\gamma_i)_U(f)(1) = g(\gamma_i)$, and $((\gamma_i)_U)^e(f)(1) = 0$ whenever $e > 1$. Hence, for sufficiently small $r_1, r_2, \gamma_1, \gamma_2$, Theorem 4.3 of Chapter VII gives

$$\log(\exp(r_1\gamma_1)\exp(r_2\gamma_2)) = r_1\gamma_1 + r_2\gamma_2 + r_1r_2 p(r_1, \gamma_1, r_2, \gamma_2),$$

where p is a certain power series map. It is clear from this that there is a positive real number r satisfying the following conditions:

(1) $\exp(B_{3r})\exp(B_{3r}) \subset U$;

(2) if σ and τ belong to B_r then $\exp(\sigma)\exp(\tau) = \exp(\sigma + \tau + \delta(\sigma, \tau))$, where $\delta(\sigma, \tau)$ is an element in B_r and $|\delta(\sigma, \tau)| \leq Q|\sigma||\tau|$, with some constant Q not depending on σ and τ.

Now let s be a real number such that $0 < s < r$, and let α be an element of $N(\exp(B_r), \exp(B_s))$. Then, if σ is an element of B_r, we have $\alpha(\exp(\sigma)) = \exp(\sigma')\exp(\sigma)$, where $\sigma' \in B_s$. By Theorem 3.3 of Chapter VII, we have $\alpha(\exp(\sigma)) = \exp(\alpha^\circ(\sigma))$. Hence the above gives $\exp(\alpha^\circ(\sigma)) = \exp(\sigma' + \sigma + \delta(\sigma', \sigma))$, whence $|\alpha^\circ(\sigma) - \sigma| = |\sigma' + \delta(\sigma', \sigma)| \leqq (1 + Qr)s$. The same estimate is obtained if α is replaced with α^{-1}. Since $N(\exp(B_r), \exp(B_s))$ is a neighborhood of the identity in $\mathscr{A}(G)$, this shows that the map $\alpha \to \alpha^\circ$ is continuous at the identity element. Since it is a homomorphism, it is therefore continuous.

On the other hand, given any neighborhood V of 1 in G, we see easily from the compactness of B_r that there is a real number s such that $0 < s < r$ and $\exp(\sigma + \tau)\exp(-\tau) \in V$ whenever $\sigma \in B_s$ and $\tau \in B_r$. Now suppose that α is an element of $\mathscr{A}(G)$ such that $\alpha^\circ(\tau) - \tau$ and $(\alpha^\circ)^{-1}(\tau) - \tau$ lie in B_s for all elements τ of B_r. Then we have

$$\alpha(\exp(\tau))\exp(\tau)^{-1} = \exp(\alpha^\circ(\tau))\exp(-\tau) \in V,$$

and similarly $\alpha^{-1}(\exp(\tau))\exp(\tau)^{-1} \in V$, so that $\alpha \in N(\exp(B_r), V)$. By Lemma 1.1, the sets $N(\exp(B_r), V)$, with V ranging over a fundamental system of neighborhoods of 1 in G, constitute a fundamental system of neighborhoods of the identity in $\mathscr{A}(G)$. Hence our last result shows that the inverse of the bijective homomorphism $\alpha \to \alpha^\circ$ of $\mathscr{A}(G)$ onto $\mathscr{A}^\circ(G)$ is continuous, which completes the proof of Theorem 1.2.

PROPOSITION 1.3. *Let G and H be analytic groups, and let f be a continuous homomorphism of H into $\mathscr{A}(G)$. Then the map $H \times G \to G$ that sends each (y, x) onto $f(y)(x)$ is analytic.*

Proof. By Theorem 1.2, the map $y \to f(y)^\circ$ is a continuous homomorphism of H into the connected component of the identity in the full linear group on $\mathscr{L}(G)$. By Theorem 4.2 of Chapter VII, this is therefore an analytic homomorphism, when the connected component of the identity in the full linear group on $\mathscr{L}(G)$ is regarded as an analytic group as per Theorem 2.1 of Chapter VII. It follows immediately from this that the map $H \times \mathscr{L}(G) \to \mathscr{L}(G)$ that sends each (y, γ) onto $f(y)^\circ(\gamma)$ is analytic.

Now let U be an open connected neighborhood of 1 in G on which log is defined and analytic. Then, if x lies in U, we have

$$f(y)(x) = \exp(f(y)^\circ(\log(x))).$$

Hence our last result shows that the map $(y, x) \to f(y)(x)$ is analytic on $H \times U$. If x_0 is any given element of G we can find elements $u_1, \cdots, u_p$ in

U such that $x_0 = u_1 \cdots u_p$. Now, for x in Ux_0, we may write $f(y)(x) = f(y)(xx_0{}^{-1})f(y)(u_1)\cdots f(y)(u_p)$, whence we see that our map is analytic also on $H \times Ux_0$. Hence our map is analytic on all of $H \times G$, so that Proposition 1.3 is proved.

2

Let G be a Lie group, G^* the connected component of 1 in G. For each element x of G, let $f(x)$ denote the conjugation $y \to xyx^{-1}$ effected by x on G^*. Then f is evidently a continuous homomorphism of G into $\mathscr{A}(G^*)$, so that Theorem 1.2 implies that the map $x \to f(x)^\circ$ is a continuous homomorphism of G into the full linear group on $\mathscr{L}(G^*)$. This homomorphism is called the *adjoint representation of G*. We shall now assume that $G = G^*$, i.e., that G is an analytic group. Then the adjoint representation of G maps G into the connected component of the identity in the full linear group on $\mathscr{L}(G)$, and, as we have already observed in proving Proposition 1.3, is an analytic homomorphism.

If L is any Lie algebra and γ is an element of L we denote by D_γ the *derivation* of L that is defined by $D_\gamma(\alpha) = [\gamma, \alpha]$. By a derivation of L, we mean a linear endomorphism e of L such that $e([\alpha, \beta]) = [e(\alpha), \beta] + [\alpha, e(\beta)]$ for all elements α and β of L. This identity, with $e = D_\gamma$, is simply the Jacobi identity. The map $\gamma \to D_\gamma$ is called the *adjoint representation of L*. It is easy to see (cf. Exercise 1 of Chapter VIII) that, if the the Lie algebra of the full linear group on $\mathscr{L}(G)$ is identified with the Lie algebra of all linear endomorphisms of $\mathscr{L}(G)$ by Theorem 2.1 of Chapter VII, the differential of the adjoint representation of G sends every element of $\mathscr{L}(G)$ onto a derivation of $\mathscr{L}(G)$. Actually, we shall obtain the following result.

THEOREM 2.1. *Let G be an analytic group. Then the differential of the adjoint representation of G is the adjoint representation of $\mathscr{L}(G)$, where the Lie algebra of the full linear group on $\mathscr{L}(G)$ is identified with the Lie algebra of all linear endomorphisms of $\mathscr{L}(G)$ (by Theorem 2.1 of Chapter VII).*

Proof. Let a denote the adjoint representation of G, and let γ be an element of $\mathscr{L}(G)$. The linear endomorphism of $\mathscr{L}(G)$ that corresponds to γ via the differential a° of a and the identification of Theorem 2.1 of Chapter VII is $a^\circ(\gamma)^\circ$. Thus what we have to prove is that $a^\circ(\gamma)^\circ(\beta) = [\gamma, \beta]$ for every element β of $\mathscr{L}(G)$. By Theorem 3.5 of Chapter VII, we have

100

$\exp(ta°(\gamma)) = \mathrm{Exp}(ta°(\gamma)°)$ for every real number t. Hence $a(\exp(t\gamma)) = \mathrm{Exp}(ta°(\gamma)°)$. Thus, for every element β of $\mathscr{L}(G)$, we have

$$a(\exp(t\gamma))(\beta) = \sum_{n=0}^{\infty}(n!)^{-1}t^n(a°(\gamma)°)^n(\beta).$$

Now replace β by $r\beta$, where r is a small real number, and take t small. Then we have

$$a(\exp(t\gamma))(r\beta) = \log(\exp(a(\exp(t\gamma))(r\beta)))$$
$$= \log(\exp(t\gamma)\exp(r\beta)\exp(-t\gamma)).$$

We apply Theorem 4.3 of Chapter VII to obtain an expression for this as a power series in t and r with coefficients in $\mathscr{L}(G)$. By applying linear functions on $\mathscr{L}(G)$ to this, we see immediately that the coefficient of tr is $[\gamma, \beta]$. By the above, this must be equal to the coefficient of tr in

$$\sum_{n=0}(n!)^{-1}t^n(a°(\gamma)°)^n(r\beta),$$

which is $a°(\gamma)°(\beta)$. This completes the proof of Theorem 2.1.

3

Let G and H be analytic groups, and let f be a continuous homomorphism of H into $\mathscr{A}(G)$. We consider the semidirect product $G \times_f H$, as defined in Section 3 of Chapter III. This is a topological group whose underlying space is the Cartesian product of the spaces of G and H, and the multiplication is given by $(x_1, y_1)(x_2, y_2) = (x_1 f(y_1)(x_2), y_1 y_2)$. We shall show that when $G \times_f H$ is equipped with the analytic manifold structure of the Cartesian product of the manifolds of G and H it becomes an analytic group. This means showing that the map $((x_1, y_1), (x_2, y_2)) \to (x_1, y_1)(x_2, y_2)^{-1}$ is analytic. Now this map may be written as a composite of maps according to the following scheme:

$$((x_1, y_1), (x_2, y_2)) \to ((x_1, y_1), (x_2^{-1}, y_1 y_2^{-1}))$$
$$\to ((x_1, y_1), (f(y_1 y_2^{-1})(x_2^{-1}), y_1 y_2^{-1}))$$
$$\to (x_1 f(y_1 y_2^{-1})(x_2^{-1}), y_1 y_2^{-1}) = (x_1, y_1)(x_2, y_2)^{-1}.$$

It is evident that the first and the third of these maps are analytic. The second map is analytic in virtue of Proposition 1.3. Hence the composite map is analytic, and we have shown that $G \times_f H$ is an analytic group.

Next, we shall determine the Lie algebra of $G \times_f H$. Consider the diagram of analytic group homomorphisms

$$G \xrightarrow[\gamma]{} G \times_f H \xrightarrow[\pi]{} H \xrightarrow[\eta]{} G \times_f H,$$

where
$$\gamma(x) = (x, 1), \qquad \pi(x, y) = y, \qquad \eta(y) = (1, y).$$

This induces a diagram of Lie algebra homomorphisms

$$\mathscr{L}(G) \xrightarrow{\gamma^\circ} \mathscr{L}(G \times_f H) \xrightarrow{\pi^\circ} \mathscr{L}(H) \xrightarrow{\eta^\circ} \mathscr{L}(G \times_f H).$$

Since $\pi \circ \eta$ is the identity map on H, $\pi^\circ \circ \eta^\circ$ is the identity map on $\mathscr{L}(H)$. Since $\pi \circ \gamma$ is the trivial map, $\pi^\circ \circ \gamma^\circ$ is the trivial map. Finally, since γ is injective, we see from Theorem 3.3 of Chapter VII that γ° is injective. Hence we may identify $\mathscr{L}(G)$ with its image $\gamma^\circ(\mathscr{L}(G))$ in $\mathscr{L}(G \times_f H)$, and similarly we may identify $\mathscr{L}(H)$ with $\eta^\circ(\mathscr{L}(H))$. Then π° annihilates $\mathscr{L}(G)$ and coincides with the identity map on $\mathscr{L}(H)$, so that $\mathscr{L}(G) \cap \mathscr{L}(H) = (0)$. Since the dimension of $G \times_f H$ is the sum of the dimensions of G and H, it follows that, as a vector space, $\mathscr{L}(G \times_f H)$ is the direct sum of $\mathscr{L}(G)$ and $\mathscr{L}(H)$, and that π° is simply the corresponding projection of $\mathscr{L}(G \times_f H)$ onto $\mathscr{L}(H)$. Clearly, $\mathscr{L}(H)$ is a Lie subalgebra of $\mathscr{L}(G \times_f H)$, while $\mathscr{L}(G)$ is an *ideal* of $\mathscr{L}(G \times_f H)$, in the sense that

$$[\mathscr{L}(G \times_f H), \mathscr{L}(G)] \subset \mathscr{L}(G).$$

Hence $\mathscr{L}(G \times_f H)$ will be determined as soon as we have computed the commutators $[\alpha, \beta]$ for α in $\mathscr{L}(H)$ and β in $\mathscr{L}(G)$.

Since $\gamma(G)$ and $\eta(H)$ are closed connected subgroups of $G \times_f H$, they are analytic groups, γ is an analytic group isomorphism of G onto $\gamma(G)$ and η an analytic group isomorphism of H onto $\eta(H)$. Hence we shall identify G with $\gamma(G)$ and H with $\eta(H)$, and it is clear that these identifications are compatible with the identifications of Lie algebras we have made above. Let y be an element of H, and let x be an element of G. Then we have $(1, y)(x, 1)(1, y)^{-1} = (f(y)(x), 1)$. After the above identifications, this reads simply $yxy^{-1} = f(y)(x)$. Now put $x = \exp(\beta)$, with β in $\mathscr{L}(G)$. Let a denote the adjoint representation of $G \times_f H$. Then the last equation becomes $\exp(a(y)(\beta)) = \exp(f(y)^\circ(\beta))$, whence $f(y)^\circ = a(y)_{\mathscr{L}(G)}$.

The map $y \to f(y)^\circ$ is an analytic homomorphism of H into the connected component of the identity in the full linear group on $\mathscr{L}(G)$. Its differential may be regarded (by Theorem 2.1 of Chapter VII) as a Lie algebra homomorphism of $\mathscr{L}(H)$ into the Lie algebra of all linear endomorphisms of $\mathscr{L}(G)$. Let us denote this Lie algebra homomorphism by $f^{\circ\circ}$. Then, if α is any element of $\mathscr{L}(H)$, we have $f(\exp(\alpha))^\circ = \mathrm{Exp}(f^{\circ\circ}(\alpha))$. On the other hand, $a(\exp(\alpha)) = \exp(a^\circ(\alpha)) = \mathrm{Exp}(a^\circ(\alpha)^\circ)$. Hence our above result $f(y)^\circ = a(y)_{\mathscr{L}(G)}$ yields $\mathrm{Exp}(f^{\circ\circ}(\alpha)) = \mathrm{Exp}(a^\circ(\alpha)^\circ_{\mathscr{L}(G)})$.

Replacing α by $t\alpha$ and letting t range over all real numbers, we infer from this that $f^{\circ\circ}(\alpha) = a^{\circ}(\alpha)^{\circ}\mathscr{L}_{(G)}$. By Theorem 2.1, this gives $f^{\circ\circ}(\alpha)(\beta) = [\alpha, \beta]$ for every β in $\mathscr{L}(G)$.

We may summarize the results of this section as follows.

THEOREM 3.1. *Let G and H be analytic groups, and let f be a continuous homomorphism of H into $\mathscr{A}(G)$. Then the semidirect product $G \times_f H$, with the manifold structure of the Cartesian product of the manifolds of G and H, is an analytic group. If the Lie algebras of G and H are identified with their canonical isomorphic images in the Lie algebra of $G \times_f H$, the Lie algebra of $G \times_f H$ becomes the semidirect sum of the ideal $\mathscr{L}(G)$ and the subalgebra $\mathscr{L}(H)$ with the following commutation, where $f^{\circ\circ}$ is the differential of the representation $y \to f(y)^{\circ}$ of H:*

$$[(\sigma_1, \tau_1), (\sigma_2, \tau_2)] = ([\sigma_1, \sigma_2] + f^{\circ\circ}(\tau_1)(\sigma_2) - f^{\circ\circ}(\tau_2)(\sigma_1), [\tau_1, \tau_2]).$$

EXERCISES

1. Show that, in general, not every automorphism of the Lie algebra of an analytic group is the differential of an automorphism of the group (see Proposition 3.2 of Chapter III).

2. Let G be the group consisting of all pairs of real numbers and having the multiplication

$$(x_1, y_1)(x_2, y_2) = (x_1 + e^{y_1}x_2, y_1 + y_2).$$

Show that G is an analytic group, and determine its Lie algebra. Also, prove that every element of $\mathscr{A}(G)$ is the conjugation $v \to u\,v\,u^{-1}$ effected by an element u of G.

3. Show that the group of the Euclidean motions of the plane is a Lie group with 2 connected components, and determine its Lie algebra.

103

X. THE CAMPBELL-HAUSDORFF FORMULA [4, 5, 9]

1

We consider Lie algebras over an arbitrary field K, i.e., vector spaces L over K with a bilinear map $L \times L \to L$, denoted $(x, y) \to [x, y]$, satisfying the identities $[x, x] = 0$ and $[x, [y, z]] + [y, [z, x]] + [z, [x, y]] = 0$. Let $\mathcal{T}(L)$ denote the tensor algebra built over the K-space L. This is to be understood as an associative algebra *with identity element*; we include K as the homogeneous component of degree 0 in $\mathcal{T}(L)$, so that the identity element of K is also the identity element of $\mathcal{T}(L)$. Throughout in what follows, all associative algebras will be assumed to have identity elements, and all homomorphisms of associative algebras will be assumed to send identity elements onto identity elements. Let $\mathcal{I}(L)$ denote the two-sided ideal of $\mathcal{T}(L)$ that is generated by the set of elements of the form $x \otimes y - y \otimes x - [x, y]$, with x and y in L. The algebra $\mathcal{U}(L) = \mathcal{T}(L)/\mathcal{I}(L)$ is called the *universal enveloping algebra* of L. The injection $L \to \mathcal{T}(L)$ induces a linear map $\mu: L \to \mathcal{U}(L)$. The definition of $\mathcal{I}(L)$ ensures that μ is a Lie algebra homomorphism when $\mathcal{U}(L)$ is regarded as a Lie algebra with the commutation $[u_1, u_2] = u_1 u_2 - u_2 u_1$. Generally, if A is any associative algebra, let us agree to call a linear map $\alpha: L \to A$ a Lie algebra homomorphism of L into A if $\alpha([x, y]) = \alpha(x)\alpha(y) - \alpha(y)\alpha(x)$ for all elements x and y of L. One sees easily that, to within isomorphisms, $(\mathcal{U}(L), \mu)$ is characterized by the following property. *For every Lie algebra homomorphism α of L into an associative algebra A, there is one and only one homomorphism of associative algebras $\alpha^\mu: \mathcal{U}(L) \to A$ such that $\alpha^\mu \circ \mu = \alpha$.* In fact, the existence of α^μ is clear from the corresponding property of $\mathcal{T}(L)$ with respect to arbitrary linear maps of L into associative algebras. We need some information on $\mathscr{U}(L)$, which is given by the *Poincaré-Birkhoff-Witt Theorem*, as follows.

THEOREM 1.1. *Let L be a Lie algebra over the field K, and let X be a totally ordered K-basis of L. Let $S(X)$ be the set of all finite non-decreasing sequences $x_1 \leq \cdots \leq x_n$ of elements of X (including the empty sequence $\varnothing$). For $(x_1, \cdots, x_n)$ in $S(X)$, define $\mu(x_1, \cdots, x_n) = \mu(x_1) \cdots \mu(x_n)$, and put $\mu(\varnothing) = 1$. Then μ is a bijective map of $S(X)$ onto a K-basis of $\mathscr{U}(L)$.*

Proof. An evident "straightening" procedure, based on the relation $\mu(x)\mu(y) = \mu(y)\mu(x) + \mu([x,y])$, shows that the set $\mu(S(X))$ spans $\mathscr{U}(L)$ over K. Hence it suffices to show that μ maps $S(X)$ injectively into a linearly independent subset of $\mathscr{U}(L)$. This will be done by defining a suitable Lie algebra homomorphism of L into the algebra $E(\mathscr{S}(L))$ of all linear endomorphisms of the symmetric algebra $\mathscr{S}(L)$ built over L, such that the corresponding associative algebra homomorphism of $\mathscr{U}(L)$ into $E(\mathscr{S}(L))$ does not annihilate any *formally* non-trivial linear combination of ordered monomials in the elements $\mu(x)$, with x in X.

We may identify the elements of $S(X)$ with the corresponding monomials $x_1 \cdots x_n$ in $\mathscr{S}(L)$ ($\varnothing$ is identified with the empty monomial 1), and it is clear that $S(X)$ thus becomes a K-basis of $\mathscr{S}(L)$ (notice that this is actually the special case of Theorem 1.1 where $[L, L] = (0)$, in which case $\mathscr{U}(L) = \mathscr{S}(L)$; the difficulty in the general case is caused by the non-homogeneity of the ideal $\mathscr{I}(L)$). Thus we regard $\mathscr{S}(L)$ as the ordinary commutative polynomial algebra in the "variables" $x \in X$. Let S_p denote the subspace of $\mathscr{S}(L)$ consisting of the polynomials of total degree $\leq p$. We wish to define a Lie algebra homomorphism $\rho: L \to E(\mathscr{S}(L))$. If y is an element of L and s an element of $\mathscr{S}(L)$ we shall write $y \cdot s$ for $\rho(y)(s)$. Then, in order to define ρ, it suffices to define the transforms $x \cdot s$ for x in X and s in $S(X)$. The definition of ρ is then obtained simply by enforcing the bilinearity of the map $(y, s) \to \rho(y)(s)$.

If $s = x_1 \cdots x_p$ is an element of $S(X)$ and x is an element of X we shall write $x \leq s$ if and only if $x \leq x_i$ for each factor x_i of s. We make the convention that $x \leq 1$ for every x in X. The conditions we wish to impose on the transforms $x \cdot s$, where $x \in X$ and $s \in S(X)$, are the following:

(1)   if $x \leq s$ then $x \cdot s = xs$;
(2)   if $s \in S_p$ then $x \cdot s - xs \in S_p$.

It is clear that condition (2) will then extend, by bilinearity, to arbitrary elements x of L and arbitrary elements s of S_p. In addition, we must ensure that ρ be a Lie algebra homomorphism, i.e., that the *commutator condition* $y \cdot (z \cdot t) - z \cdot (y \cdot t) = [y, z] \cdot t$ be satisfied for all elements y and z of L and all elements t of $\mathscr{S}(L)$. Again, it suffices to enforce this for the elements of X and $S(X)$.

Now we shall define the transforms $x \cdot s$, where $x \in X$ and $s \in S(X) \cap S_p$ inductively on p. For $p = 0$, (1) forces $x \cdot 1 = x$, and then (2) is trivially satisfied. Now suppose that the transforms $x \cdot s$ have already been defined for all x in L and all s in S_p so that (1) and (2) are satisfied, as well as the commutator condition with t in S_{p-1}. We must define the transforms $x \cdot s$ for x in X and s in $S(X) \cap S_{p+1}$. If $x \leqq s$ we put $x \cdot s = xs$, so as to satisfy (1) and (2). If $x \nleqq s$, we may write, with uniquely determined elements s' in X and s^* in $S(X) \cap S_p$, $s = s's^*$, where $s' \leqq s^*$. By the inductive hypothesis, we have then $x \cdot s^* - xs^* \in S_p$, so that $s' \cdot (x \cdot s^* - xs^*)$ is defined. Enforcing the commutator condition, we define

$$x \cdot s = [x, s'] \cdot s^* + s' \cdot (x \cdot s^* - xs^*) + xs.$$

Then (2) is evidently satisfied. Now that the transforms of the elements of S_{p+1} are defined, we may write the last equation in the form $x \cdot (s' \cdot s^*) - s' \cdot (x \cdot s^*) = [x, s'] \cdot s^*$. Thus we see that the commutator condition $y \cdot (z \cdot t) - z \cdot (y \cdot t) = [y, z] \cdot t$ is satisfied for all t in $S(X) \cap S_p$ and all pairs (y, z) of elements of X such that $z \leqq t$ and $z < y$. Since each side is antisymmetric in (y, z), the condition is satisfied also whenever $y \leqq t$ and $y < z$. It holds trivially for $y = z$. Hence all that remains to be shown is that this commutator condition is satisfied if both $y \nleqq t$ and $z \nleqq t$. Then, as before, $t = t't^*$, and $t' < y$, $t' < z$. Now we have

$$z \cdot t = z \cdot (t' \cdot t^*) = t' \cdot (z \cdot t^*) + [z, t'] \cdot t^*$$
$$= t' \cdot (zt^*) + t' \cdot (z \cdot t^* - zt^*) + [z, t'] \cdot t^*.$$

Hence

$$y \cdot (z \cdot t) = y \cdot (t' \cdot (zt^*)) + y \cdot (t' \cdot (z \cdot t^* - zt^*)) + y \cdot ([z, t'] \cdot t^*).$$

By the inductive hypothesis, the commutator condition is satisfied for the last two terms. Since $t' \leqq zt^*$ and $t' < y$, the commutator condition is satisfied also for the first term. Hence we have

$$y \cdot (z \cdot t) = t' \cdot (y \cdot (zt^*)) + [y, t'] \cdot (zt^*) + t' \cdot (y \cdot (z \cdot t^* - zt^*))$$
$$+ [y, t'] \cdot (z \cdot t^* - zt^*) + [z, t'] \cdot (y \cdot t^*) + [y, [z, t']] \cdot t^*$$
$$= t' \cdot (y \cdot (z \cdot t^*)) + [y, t'] \cdot (z \cdot t^*) + [z, t'] \cdot (y \cdot t^*)$$
$$+ [y, [z, t']] \cdot t^*.$$

Now interchange y and z, and subtract the result. Then we obtain

$$y \cdot (z \cdot t) - z \cdot (y \cdot t)$$
$$= t' \cdot (y \cdot (z \cdot t^*) - z \cdot (y \cdot t^*)) + [y, [z, t']] \cdot t^* - [z, [y, t']] \cdot t^*.$$

Using the inductive hypothesis for rewriting the first term and the Jacobi identity for combining the remaining two terms, we reduce the right-hand side above to $t' \cdot ([y, z] \cdot t^*) - [t', [y, z]] \cdot t^*$. By the inductive hypothesis, this is equal to $[y, z] \cdot (t' \cdot t^*) = [y, z] \cdot t$. Thus we conclude that the commutator condition is satisfied for all elements t in S_p. This completes the induction, so that the existence of a Lie algebra homomorphism $\rho: L \to E(\mathscr{S}(L))$ satisfying the above conditions, and, in particular, condition (1), is established. But this implies that if $(x_1, \cdots, x_n)$ is an element of $S(X)$ then $\rho^\mu(\mu(x_1, \cdots, x_n))(1)$ is the corresponding monomial $x_1 \cdots x_n$ in $\mathscr{S}(L)$. Evidently, this gives the conclusion of Theorem 1.1.

2

Let V be any vector space over the field K. Then a Lie algebra L over K containing V as a vector subspace is called the *free Lie algebra generated by* V if it has the following property, which evidently characterizes it to within an isomorphism leaving the elements of V fixed: if γ is any linear map of V into a Lie algebra M over K then there is one and only one extension of γ to a Lie algebra homomorphism of L into M.

A model for the free Lie algebra generated by V is easily obtained as follows. Let $\mathscr{T}(V)$ denote the tensor algebra built over V, and let L be the Lie subalgebra of $\mathscr{T}(V)$ that is generated by V. In order to show that L has the above property, let γ be any linear map of V into a Lie algebra M. Let $\mu: M \to \mathscr{U}(M)$ be the canonical Lie algebra homomorphism of M into its universal enveloping algebra. Then $\mu \circ \gamma$ is a linear map of V into $\mathscr{U}(M)$. By the basic characteristic property of $\mathscr{T}(V)$, there is one and only one homomorphism of associative algebras $(\mu \circ \gamma)^*: \mathscr{T}(V) \to \mathscr{U}(M)$ such that the restriction of $(\mu \circ \gamma)^*$ to V coincides with $\mu \circ \gamma$. Then the restriction of $(\mu \circ \gamma)^*$ to L is evidently a Lie algebra homomorphism of L into the Lie subalgebra $\mu(M)$ of $\mathscr{U}(M)$. It is clear from Theorem 1.1 that μ is actually a Lie algebra *isomorphism* of M onto $\mu(M)$. Following up $(\mu \circ \gamma)^*_L$ with the inverse of this isomorphism, we obtain a Lie algebra homomorphism of L into M that extends γ. Since there can evidently be at most one such extension of γ, this shows that L has indeed the required property.

Now we shall see that *the universal enveloping algebra of the free Lie algebra generated by V may be identified with* $\mathscr{T}(V)$. The proof of this consists in verifying that $\mathscr{T}(V)$ has the characteristic property of the universal enveloping algebra. Let L be the model of the free Lie algebra generated by V that we have defined above, and let α be a Lie algebra homomorphism of L into an associative algebra A. The restriction of α to V extends uniquely to a homomorphism of associative algebras $\alpha^*: \mathscr{T}(V) \to A$, and it is evident that $\alpha^*_L = \alpha$. Thus the above assertion is proved.

Let us write T for $\mathscr{T}(V)$ and, as before, let L be the Lie subalgebra of T that is generated by V. We shall need the following characterization of L as a subset of T.

PROPOSITION 2.1. *Let V, T, L be as above, and assume that the base field K is of characteristic 0. Let δ denote the unique homomorphism of associative algebras $T \to T \otimes T$ such that $\delta(v) = v \otimes 1 + 1 \otimes v$ for every element v of V. Then L coincides with the set of all elements t of T such that $\delta(t) = t \otimes 1 + 1 \otimes t$.*

Proof. It is easy to see that the elements with the property of Proposition 2.1 constitute a Lie subalgebra of T, whence every element of L has this property. Let (t_α) be a totally ordered K-basis of L. By Theorem 1.1, the ordered monomials $t_{\alpha_1}^{e_1} \cdots t_{\alpha_n}^{e_n}$, where the e_i's are non-negative integers and $\alpha_1 < \cdots < \alpha_n$, constitute a K-basis for $\mathscr{U}(L) = T$. Since $\delta(t_\alpha) = t_\alpha \otimes 1 + 1 \otimes t_\alpha$, we have

$$\delta(t_{\alpha_1}^{e_1} \cdots t_{\alpha_n}^{e_n}) = (t_{\alpha_1}^{e_1} \cdots t_{\alpha_n}^{e_n}) \otimes 1 + 1 \otimes (t_{\alpha_1}^{e_1} \cdots t_{\alpha_n}^{e_n}) + \Sigma$$

where Σ is the sum of the mixed terms

$$c(e_1, \cdots, e_n; f_1, \cdots, f_n) t_{\alpha_1}^{f_1} \cdots t_{\alpha_n}^{f_n} \otimes t_{\alpha_1}^{e_1-f_1} \cdots t_{\alpha_n}^{e_n-f_n},$$

$c(e_1, \cdots, e_n; f_1, \cdots, f_n)$ being the product of the binomial coefficients C_{e_i, f_i} $(i = 1, \cdots, n)$, and the summation going over all n-tuples $(f_1, \cdots, f_n)$ such that $0 \le f_i \le e_i$ and $0 < \sum_i f_i < \sum_i e_i$. Since K is of characteristic 0, the coefficients $c(e_1, \cdots, e_n, f_1, \cdots, f_n)$ are all different from 0. Hence it is clear from the linear independence of the ordered monomials in the t_α's that if t is a linear combination of such ordered monomials and $\delta(t) = t \otimes 1 + 1 \otimes t$ then t must actually be a linear combination of the t_α's, i.e., $t \in L$. This completes the proof of Proposition 2.1.

If A is any non-negatively graded algebra we denote by A^+ the two-sided ideal of A consisting of the elements whose components of degree 0 are equal to 0. We may regard A as a *topological algebra*, with the powers of A^+ serving as a fundamental system of neighborhoods of 0. As such, A has a *completion* A^*, which is a complete topological algebra containing A as a dense subalgebra. Here, completeness means simply the following. A sequence of elements a_n of A^* is a Cauchy sequence if, given m, there is an M such that $a_{n+1} - a_n$ belongs to $(A^+)^m A^*$ whenever $n \geq M$. The completeness of A^* means that every Cauchy sequence in A^* converges to an element of A^*. The completion A^* is constructed in the familiar way: the elements of A^* are equivalence classes of Cauchy sequences in A, and the equivalence classes of the constant sequences are identified with the corresponding elements of A.

In particular, we shall have to consider the completion T^* of T (with respect to the ideal generated by V) and the completion $(T \otimes T)^*$ of $T \otimes T$ (with respect to the ideal generated by $V \otimes 1 + 1 \otimes V$). The elements of T^* or $(T \otimes T)^*$ may evidently be identified with the formal non-commutative power series in basis elements of V or $V \otimes 1 + 1 \otimes V$, respectively. Clearly, we may regard $T^* \otimes T^*$ as a subalgebra of $(T^* \otimes T)^*$. The continuous homomorphism $\delta: T \to T \otimes T$ extends to a uniquely determined continuous homomorphism $\delta^*: T^* \to (T \otimes T)^*$. We denote the closure of L in T^* by L^*. It is easy to see that Proposition 2.1 implies that the same proposition holds with L^* and δ^* in the places of L and δ.

Let X denote the set of all elements x of $1 + VT^*$ such that $\delta^*(x) = x \otimes x$. Clearly, the product of any two elements of X is again an element of X. Moreover, every element x of X is a unit; in fact $x^{-1} = \sum_{n=0}^{\infty}(1 - x)^n$. Hence $x \otimes x$ is a unit of $(T \otimes T)^*$, and $(x \otimes x)^{-1} = x^{-1} \otimes x^{-1}$. Since δ^* is an algebra homomorphism sending the identity element of T^* onto the identity element of $(T \otimes T)^*$, it follows that $\delta^*(x^{-1}) = x^{-1} \otimes x^{-1}$. Thus $x^{-1} \in X$, and we have shown that X is a subgroup of the multiplicative group of units of T^*.

The exponential maps $\mathrm{Exp}: VT^* \to 1 + VT^*$ and

$$\mathrm{Exp}: (V \otimes 1 + 1 \otimes V)(T \otimes T)^* \to 1 \otimes 1 + (V \otimes 1 + 1 \otimes V)(T \otimes T)^*$$

are defined by $\mathrm{Exp}(u) = \sum_{n=0}^{\infty}(n!)^{-1}u^n$. Clearly, if $uv = vu$ we have $\mathrm{Exp}(u + v) = \mathrm{Exp}(u)\mathrm{Exp}(v)$. Hence, for all elements x and y of VT^*,

$$\mathrm{Exp}(x \otimes 1 + 1 \otimes y) = \mathrm{Exp}(x \otimes 1)\mathrm{Exp}(1 \otimes y)$$
$$= ((\mathrm{Exp}(x) \otimes 1)(1 \otimes \mathrm{Exp}(y)) = \mathrm{Exp}(x) \otimes \mathrm{Exp}(y)$$

In particular, if $x \in L^*$, we obtain

$$\delta^*(\mathrm{Exp}(x)) = \mathrm{Exp}(\delta^*(x)) = \mathrm{Exp}(x \otimes 1 + 1 \otimes x) = \mathrm{Exp}(x) \otimes \mathrm{Exp}(x),$$

so that $\mathrm{Exp}(L^*) \subset X$.

The exponential maps, as defined above, are invertible, the inverse being given by $\mathrm{Log}(1 - u) = -\sum_{n=1}^{\infty} n^{-1} u^n$, for all elements u of VT^* or $(V \otimes 1 + 1 \otimes V)(T \otimes T)^*$, respectively.

Now suppose that y is an element of VT^* such that $1 - y$ belongs to X. Then we have

$$\delta^*(\mathrm{Log}(1 - y)) = \mathrm{Log}(1 \otimes 1 - \delta^*(y)) = \mathrm{Log}(\delta^*(1 - y))$$
$$= \mathrm{Log}((1 - y) \otimes (1 - y)).$$

The last expression is equal to $\mathrm{Log}(1 - y) \otimes 1 + 1 \otimes \mathrm{Log}(1 - y)$, as is seen from the above on applying Exp. Thus we have shown that $\mathrm{Log}(X) \subset L^*$.

Together with the above, this shows that the map $\mathrm{Exp} \colon L^* \to X$ is a bijection, its inverse being $\mathrm{Log} \colon X \to L^*$. We use these bijections in order to transport the group structure of X to a group structure on L^*; the resulting group composition on L^* is denoted by

$$(x, y) \to x \cdot y = \mathrm{Log}(\mathrm{Exp}(x)\mathrm{Exp}(y)).$$

In order to proceed, we require the following.

PROPOSITION 2.2.   *In the notation of Proposition* 2.1, *let D_u denote the derivation $t \to ut - tu$ effected on T by the element u of T. Then there is a linear projection π of T onto L with the following properties, $\pi(1) = 0$ and, if $v_1, \cdots, v_q$ are elements of V and $q > 1$, then*

$$\pi(v_1 \cdots v_q) = q^{-1}(D_{v_1} \circ \cdots \circ D_{v_{q-1}})(v_q).$$

Proof.   Clearly, there is one and only one linear endomorphism π of T satisfying the above conditions and the condition $\pi(v) = v$ for every element v of V. Moreover, it is evident from the definitions that we have then $\pi(T) \subset L$. All that remains to be proved is that $\pi(x) = x$ for every element x of L.

Let ρ denote the homomorphism of T^+ into the endomorphism algebra of T that is determined by the condition $\rho(v) = D_v$ for every element v of V. One shows easily by induction on the degree (with respect to V) that $\rho(x) = D_x$ for every element x of L. Define the linear endomorphism π^* of T such that π^* coincides with $d\pi$ on the homogeneous component of degree d of T. Then it is clear that $\pi^*(ut) = \rho(u)(\pi^*(t))$ for all elements u and t of T^+.

Now let x and y be elements of L. Then we have

$$\pi^*([x, y]) = \pi^*(xy - yx) = \rho(x)(\pi^*(y)) - \rho(y)(\pi^*(x))$$
$$= D_x(\pi^*(y)) - D_y(\pi^*(x)) = [x, \pi^*(y)] + [\pi^*(x), y].$$

Thus the restriction of π^* to L is a derivation of L. Using this, one shows easily by induction on the degree that if x is a homogeneous element of degree d in L then $\pi^*(x) = dx$. By the definition of π^*, this means that $\pi(x) = x$, so that Proposition 2.2 is proved.

Now let us return to the above composition on L^*. Let x and y be elements of V, and let us write $x \cdot y = \mathrm{Log}(\mathrm{Exp}(x)\mathrm{Exp}(y))$ explicitly as a power series in x and y. We have

$$\mathrm{Log}(\mathrm{Exp}(x)\mathrm{Exp}(y))$$
$$= \mathrm{Log}(1 - (1 - \mathrm{Exp}(x)\mathrm{Exp}(y)))$$
$$= \textstyle\sum_{n>0}(-1)^{n+1}n^{-1}(\mathrm{Exp}(x)\mathrm{Exp}(y) - 1)^n$$
$$= \textstyle\sum_{n>0}(-1)^{n+1}n^{-1}(\sum_{p_i+q_i>0}(p_1!\cdots p_n!q_1!\cdots q_n!)^{-1}x^{p_1}y^{q_1}\cdots x^{p_n}y^{q_n}).$$

Since $x \cdot y$ belongs to L^*, it is clear from the topology used in forming T^* that the (finite) homogeneous partial sums of the above series must all lie in L. Hence it follows from Proposition 2.2 that we may replace the terms of the above series by their images under π without changing the sum of the series. Let us write $\eta(x, y)$ for the resulting formal series

$$\textstyle\sum_{n>0}(-1)^{n+1}n^{-1}(\sum_{p_i+q_i>0} c(p_1,\cdots,p_n,q_1,\cdots,q_n)\pi^*(x^{p_1}y^{q_1}\cdots x^{p_n}y^{q_n})),$$

where $c(p_1,\cdots,p_n,q_1,\cdots,q_n) = (p_1!\cdots p_n!q_1!\cdots q_n!\sum_i(p_i+q_i))^{-1}$. Then the *Campbell-Hausdorff Formula* is the identity $\mathrm{Exp}(x)\mathrm{Exp}(y) = \mathrm{Exp}(\eta(x,y))$ in the freely non-commuting variables x and y or, in rigorous language, the equality of these as elements of T^*, with $V = Kx + Ky$.

For every non-negative integer k, denote by $\eta_k(x, y)$ the sum of the terms of total degree $\leq k$ in $\eta(x, y)$. Then, if M is any Lie algebra over a field of characteristic 0, η_k defines a map $M \times M \to M$, obtained by substituting elements of M for x and y and interpreting the term resulting from $\pi^*(x^{p_1}y^{q_1}\cdots x^{p_n}y^{q_n})$ by this substitution as the corresponding multiple commutator in M, in the way prescribed by the definition of π^*. Let us adopt the following notation for this: if u and v are elements of M, write $D_{(p_1,\cdots,p_n,q_1,\cdots,q_n)}(u, v)$ for the element of M obtained as described just now from $\pi^*(x^{p_1}y^{q_1}\cdots x^{p_n}y^{q_n})$ upon substituting u for x and v for y. For example, we have $D_{(2,1)}(u, v) = [u, [u, v]]$. Finally, let $\eta_k(u, v)$ stand for the result of substituting $D_{(p_1,\cdots,p_n,q_1,\cdots,q_n)}(u, v)$ for each $\pi^*(x^{p_1}y^{q_1}\cdots x^{p_n}y^{q_n})$ in $\eta_k(x, y)$.

3

Now let M be a finite-dimensional Lie algebra over the field R of the real numbers. We can evidently choose a basis $(\mu_1, \cdots, \mu_m)$ of M such that

$[\mu_i, \mu_j] = \sum_k c_{ijk}\mu_k$, with $|c_{ijk}| \leqq m^{-5/2}$. Let $|\ |$ be the Euclidean norm on M with respect to this basis. Then one verifies readily that $|[\alpha, \beta]| \leqq |\alpha| |\beta|$ for all elements α and β of M. Hence we obtain

$$|D_{(p_1, \cdots, p_n, q_1, \cdots, q_n)}(\alpha, \beta)| \leqq |\alpha|^{p_1}|\beta|^{q_1} \cdots |\alpha|^{p_n}|\beta|^{q_n}.$$

This shows that every term of $\eta_k(\alpha, \beta)$ is majorized in norm by a unique corresponding term of the expansion of $\sum_{n>0} n^{-1}(e^{|\alpha|}e^{|\beta|} - 1)^n$ in powers of $|\alpha|$ and $|\beta|$. Hence, for all (α, β) such that $|e^{|\alpha|}e^{|\beta|} - 1| < 1$, the sequence $(\eta_k(\alpha, \beta))$ converges to an element $\eta(\alpha, \beta)$ of M, which is given by an absolutely convergent power series in the coordinates of α and β. In other words, *there is a neighborhood W of 0 in M such that the sequence of maps η_k converges uniformly on $W \times W$ to a power series map $\eta \colon W \times W \to M$.*

In particular, let us consider the case where M is the Lie algebra $\mathscr{L}(G)$ of an analytic group G. Then we may take the above neighborhood W small enough to ensure that $\exp_G(\eta(W \times W))$ and $\exp_G(W)\exp_G(W)$ lie in an open connected neighborhood U of 1 in G on which $\log$ is defined as an analytic map into M, and that the map $(\alpha, \beta) \to \log(\exp_G(\alpha)\exp_G(\beta))$ is a power series map of $W \times W$ into M. We know from Theorem 4.3 of Chapter VII that if g is a linear function on M then $g(\log(\exp_G(\alpha)\exp_G(\beta)))$ is the sum of the absolutely convergent power series

$$(\mathrm{Exp}(\alpha_U)\mathrm{Exp}(\beta_U))(g \circ \log)(1) = \sum(p!q!)^{-1}((\alpha_U)^p(\beta_U)^q)(g \circ \log)(1),$$

and $g(\eta(\alpha, \beta))$ is the sum of the absolutely convergent power series $\sum(n!)^{-1}(\eta(\alpha, \beta)_U)^n(g \circ \log)(1)$; we regard these series as power series in the coordinates of α and β without indicating this explicitly by our notation. Because of the absolute convergence, we may sum these series by first forming the finite homogeneous (with respect to the total degree in the coordinates of α and β) partial sums and then summing the series of these. From the formal identity $\mathrm{Exp}(x)\mathrm{Exp}(y) = \mathrm{Exp}(\eta(x, y))$, it is clear that the homogeneous partial sums of the two series above are the same. Hence the sums of the two series are the same, whence $\log(\exp_G(\alpha)\exp_G(\beta)) = \eta(\alpha, \beta)$. Thus we have the following main result.

THEOREM 3.1. *Let G be an analytic group. Then there is a neighborhood W of 0 in $\mathscr{L}(G)$ such that the formal series of the Campbell-Hausdorff formula defines a power series map $\eta \colon W \times W \to \mathscr{L}(G)$, and $\exp_G(\alpha)\exp_G(\beta) = \exp_G(\eta(\alpha, \beta))$ for all elements α and β in W. Moreover, we have $\eta(\alpha, \beta) = \alpha + \beta + \tau(\alpha, \beta)$, where $\tau(\alpha, \beta)$ lies in the smallest subspace of $\mathscr{L}(G)$ that contains $[\alpha, \beta]$ and is stable under D_α and D_β.*

We conclude this section with the following important application of Theorem 3.1.

THEOREM 3.2. *Let G and H be analytic groups, and let σ be a Lie algebra homomorphism of $\mathscr{L}(G)$ into $\mathscr{L}(H)$. Then there exists an open connected neighborhood U of 1 in G and an analytic map s of U into H such that $s(xy) = s(x)s(y)$ whenever x, y and xy lie in U and $s_x^\circ(\gamma_x) = \sigma(\gamma)_{s(x)}$ for every x in U and every γ in $\mathscr{L}(G)$.*

Proof. Choose an open connected neighborhood W of 0 in $\mathscr{L}(G)$ with the property of Theorem 3.1 and such that $\exp_G$ induces an analytic manifold isomorphism of W onto the open connected neighborhood $U = \exp_G(W)$ of 1 in G. Furthermore, take W small enough to ensure that the same requirements are met by some neighborhood of 0 in $\mathscr{L}(H)$ containing $\sigma(W)$. Now define s on U by putting $s(x) = \exp_H(\sigma(\log(x)))$. Using that $\eta(\sigma(\alpha), \sigma(\beta)) = \sigma(\eta(\alpha, \beta))$ for all elements α and β of W, one verifies directly that $s(xy) = s(x)s(y)$ whenever x, y and xy lie in U. Evidently, s is an analytic map. If s were not only a local analytic homomorphism but a global analytic homomorphism $G \to H$ then the property $s_x^\circ(\gamma_x) = \sigma(\gamma)_{s(x)}$ for all x would simply mean that $s^\circ(\gamma) = \sigma(\gamma)$, which is an immediate consequence of Theorem 3.3 of Chapter VII and the definition of s. It is easily seen that the proof of that theorem actually applies here and gives the required result. Alternatively, we may proceed as follows. We know, for instance, from the proof of Theorem 4.3 of Chapter VII, that γ_x is given by $\gamma_x(g_x) = \rho_0((g \circ p_{x,\gamma})_0)$, where $p_{x,\gamma}$ is the map of R into G defined by $p_{x,\gamma}(r) = x \exp(r\gamma)$. Using this, we obtain $s_x^\circ(\gamma_x)(f_{s(x)}) = \gamma_x((f \circ s)_x) = \rho_0((f \circ s \circ p_{x,\gamma})_0)$. Now, for small r's, $(s \circ p_{x,\gamma})(r) = s(x \exp_G(r\gamma)) = s(x)s(\exp_G(r\gamma)) = s(x)\exp_H(r\sigma(\gamma))$. Thus, on some neighborhood of 0 in R, $s \circ p_{x,\gamma}$ coincides with $p_{s(x),\sigma(\gamma)}$. Hence, using the same result for $\sigma(\gamma)_{s(x)}$ that we used above for γ_x, we obtain

$$s_x^\circ(\gamma_x)(f_{s(x)}) = \rho_0((f \circ s \circ p_{x,\gamma})_0)$$
$$= \rho_0((f \circ p_{s(x),\sigma(\gamma)})_0) = \sigma(\gamma)_{s(x)}(f_{s(x)}),$$

which is what had to be shown.

4

Let G be an analytic group, and let L be a Lie subalgebra of $\mathscr{L}(G)$. Let H denote the subgroup of G that is generated by the subset $\exp_G(L)$. In general, H is not closed in G, so that it is not necessarily a Lie group with the topology induced from that of G. We define a stronger topology on H by prescribing as a fundamental system of neighborhoods of 1 the system of sets $\exp_G(T)$, where T ranges over the neighborhoods of 0 in L. We must verify that the conditions $N_1, \cdots, N_4$ of Section 2 of Chapter I are satisfied. Conditions N_1 and N_2 (the intersection properties) are obviously satisfied. Condition N_3 is satisfied in virtue of Theorem 3.1. Condition N_4 demands that if V is a member of the system and x is an element of H then xVx^{-1} should contain a member of the system. Evidently, it suffices to verify this in the case where $x = \exp_G(\gamma)$ with γ in L. But then the desired result follows immediately from Theorem 2.1 of Chapter IX. Thus we have indeed a fundamental system of neighborhoods for the structure of a topological group on H.

It is clear from Theorem 3.1 that if T is a sufficiently small open box around 0 in L then $\exp_G$ maps T homeomorphically onto the subspace $\exp_G(T)$ of H, topologized as above. Hence it is clear that H can be equipped with the structure of an analytic manifold such that the restriction to $\exp_G(T)$ of the log map for G is a chart of H at 1. Then it follows from Theorem 3.1 that this makes H into an analytic group, and the injection $H \rightarrow G$ is clearly an analytic group homomorphism. Alternatively, if one does not wish to enter into any details here, one merely notes that H is locally compact and connected and that the injection $H \rightarrow G$ is continuous, and applies Theorem 1.1 of Chapter VIII.

The analytic group H so defined is called *the analytic subgroup of G corresponding to the subalgebra L of $\mathscr{L}(G)$*. The differential of the injection $H \rightarrow G$ is a Lie algebra isomorphism of $\mathscr{L}(H)$ onto a subalgebra of $\mathscr{L}(G)$. It is easy to see that the image of $\mathscr{L}(H)$ in $\mathscr{L}(G)$ contains L. Since the dimension of H as an analytic manifold is equal to the vector space dimension of L, it follows that the image of $\mathscr{L}(H)$ in $\mathscr{L}(G)$ is precisely L. The following result characterizes L in terms of the subset H of G.

THEOREM 4.1. *Let G be an analytic group, L a Lie subalgebra of $\mathscr{L}(G)$. Let H be the analytic subgroup of G corresponding to L. Then an element α of $\mathscr{L}(G)$ belongs to L if and only if $\exp_G(R\alpha) \subset H$, where R stands for the field of the real numbers.*

Proof. Clearly, $\exp_G(R\alpha) \subset H$ whenever α belongs to L. In order to prove the converse, let us choose a vector subspace S of $\mathscr{L}(G)$ such that $\mathscr{L}(G) = S + L$ and $S \cap L = (0)$. By Proposition 4.1 of Chapter VII, there are open boxes U and V around 0 in S and L, respectively, such that the map $(\sigma, \alpha) \rightarrow \exp_G(\sigma)\exp_G(\alpha)$ is an analytic manifold isomorphism of $U \times V$ onto an open connected neighborhood W of 1 in G. Clearly, $H \cap W$ is the union of the family of mutually disjoint sets $\exp_G(\sigma)\exp_G(V)$, where σ ranges over a certain subset U_H of U. Each of these sets is open for the topology of the analytic group H. From the fact that an analytic group is generated by a Euclidean neighborhood of the identity, one sees immediately that there is a countable basis for its open sets. Hence it is clear that U_H is a countable set. Now let σ_1 and σ_2 be any two distinct elements of U_H. Let T be an open sphere around σ_1 in U whose radius is smaller than the distance between σ_1 and σ_2, and different from the distance of any element of U_H from σ_1. Put $A = \exp_G(T)\exp_G(V)$, and let B be the complement of the closure of A in G. Then A and B are disjoint open sets of G, $\exp_G(\sigma_1)\exp_G(V) \subset A$, $\exp_G(\sigma_2)\exp_G(V) \subset B$ and $W \cap H \subset A \cup B$. Hence the sets $\exp_G(\sigma_1)\exp_G(V)$ and $\exp_G(\sigma_2)\exp_G(V)$ lie in different connected components of $W \cap H$, *with respect to the topology induced from that of G.* The sets $\exp_G(\sigma)\exp_G(V)$ are therefore the connected components of $W \cap H$ as a subspace of G. Hence it is clear that if $\exp_G(R\alpha) \subset H$ then $\exp_G(R\alpha) \cap W \subset \exp_G(V)$, whence α belongs to L. This completes the proof of Theorem 4.1.

It is an immediate consequence of Theorem 4.1 that *if γ is an analytic homomorphism of an analytic group K into G such that $\gamma(K)$ is contained in the analytic subgroup H of G then γ is analytic also as a map of K into H.* In particular, if K is an analytic subgroup of G such that $K \subset H$ then K is also an analytic subgroup of H. On the other hand, it is obvious that every analytic subgroup of H is also an analytic subgroup of G.

The basic facts connecting analytic subgroups with analytic group homomorphisms are recorded in the following theorem.

THEOREM 4.2. *Let f be an analytic group homomorphism of the analytic group G into the analytic group H. Then $f(G)$ is the analytic subgroup of H that corresponds to the subalgebra $f^\circ(\mathscr{L}(G))$ of $\mathscr{L}(H)$, and the connected component of 1 in the kernel of f is the analytic subgroup of G that corresponds to the kernel of f°.*

Proof. The first statement evidently follows from the fact that $f \circ \exp_G = \exp_H \circ f^\circ$. Now let K be the connected component of 1 in the kernel of f. We identify $\mathscr{L}(K)$ with its canonical image in $\mathscr{L}(G)$, and it is clear that K is then the analytic subgroup of G corresponding to $\mathscr{L}(K)$. If γ is an element of $\mathscr{L}(K)$ we have $\exp_H(tf^\circ(\gamma)) = f(\exp_G(t\gamma)) = 1$ for every real number t, which implies that $f^\circ(\gamma) = 0$. Thus $\mathscr{L}(K)$ is contained in the kernel of f°. Conversely, if γ is in the kernel of f° then $\exp_G(t\gamma)$ belongs to the kernel of f for every real number t, whence $\exp_G(t\gamma) \in K$, so that, by Theorem 4.1, $\gamma \in \mathscr{L}(K)$. This completes the proof of Theorem 4.2.

EXERCISES

1. Let G be an analytic group, V an open neighborhood of 1 in G, $E(\mathscr{F}_G(V))$ the algebra of all linear endomorphisms of the space $\mathscr{F}_G(V)$ of analytic functions on V. Show that the algebra homomorphism $\mathscr{U}(\mathscr{L}(G)) \to E(\mathscr{F}_G(V))$ that corresponds canonically to the Lie algebra homomorphism $\gamma \to \gamma_V$ of $\mathscr{L}(G)$ into $E(\mathscr{F}_G(V))$ is injective if V is chosen small enough.

2. Verify that $\eta_3(\alpha, \beta) = \alpha + \beta + \frac{1}{2}[\alpha, \beta] + \frac{1}{12}[\beta, [\beta, \alpha]] + \frac{1}{12}[\alpha, [\alpha, \beta]]$.

3. A Lie algebra L is said to be nilpotent if there is a positive integer n such that $D_{\alpha_1} \cdots D_{\alpha_n} = 0$ for every n-tuple $(\alpha_1, \cdots, \alpha_n)$ of elements of L. Let G be an analytic group such that $\mathscr{L}(G)$ is nilpotent. Show that the exponential map $\exp_G \colon \mathscr{L}(G) \to G$ is surjective. [Note that, because of the nilpotency, η defines a map $\mathscr{L}(G) \times \mathscr{L}(G) \to \mathscr{L}(G)$.]

4. Show that the y-homogeneous part of degree 1 of the series $\eta(-x, x + y)$ is $\sum_{m=0}^{\infty}(-1)^m(m!)^{-1}\pi(x^m y)$. [Note that this is also the y-homogeneous part of degree 1 of $\mathrm{Exp}(\eta(-x, x + y)) = \mathrm{Exp}(-x)\mathrm{Exp}(x + y)$, and that it lies in L^*.]

5. Let G be an analytic group. Let α and β be elements of $\mathscr{L}(G)$, and define the map $\sigma_{\alpha, \beta}$ of R into G by $\sigma_{\alpha, \beta}(r) = \exp_G(\alpha + r\beta)$. Using the result of Exercise 4 above, show that the differential of $\sigma_{\alpha, \beta}$ at 0 is given by

$$(\sigma_{\alpha, \beta})_0^\circ(\rho_0) = (\sum_{m=0}^{\infty}(-1)^m((m + 1)!)^{-1}D_\alpha{}^m(\beta))_{\exp(\alpha)}.$$

6. Let G be an analytic group, H a closed subgroup of G. Suppose that A is an analytic subgroup of G such that $\mathscr{L}(A) \cap \mathscr{L}(H) = (0)$. Show that $A \cap H$ is a discrete subgroup *of the analytic group* A. In the case where G is a two-dimensional toroid and H is a one-dimensional direct toroidal factor of G, find an analytic subgroup A as above such that $A \cap H$ is *not discrete in* H.

XI. ELEMENTARY THEORY OF LIE ALGEBRAS [3, 5]

1

We begin with a lemma concerning linear endomorphisms.

LEMMA 1.1. *Let $E(V)$ be the algebra of all linear endomorphisms of a finite-dimensional vector space V over a field of characteristic* 0. *Let $x_1, \cdots, x_k, y_1, \cdots, y_k$ be elements of $E(V)$ and let $e = \sum_i(x_i y_i - y_i x_i)$. Suppose that e commutes with each x_i. Then $e^p = 0$ for some positive integer p.*

Proof. For each positive integer q, we have (agreeing that e^0 should stand for the identity element of $E(V)$)

$$e^q = \sum_i(x_i(e^{q-1}y_i) - (e^{q-1}y_i)x_i),$$

so that e^q is a sum of commutators. Hence $T(e^q) = 0$, where generally $T(z)$ denotes the trace of the linear endomorphism z. As is well known, this implies that some power of e is 0, provided that the base field is of characteristic 0. However, a direct proof of this can be given easily as follows.

By an evident dimensionality consideration, we see that there must be a positive integer p such that $e^p(V) = e^{p+1}(V)$. Let W be the subspace of V consisting of all elements that are annihilated by some power of e. Now if v is any element of V, there is an element v' of V such that $e^p(v) = e^{p+1}(v')$. Writing $v = e(v') + (v - e(v'))$, we see that $V \subset e(V) + W$. By applying e to this repeatedly, we find that $V = e^p(V) + W$. Clearly, both $e^p(V)$ and W are stable under e. Let e_1 denote the restriction of e to $e^p(V)$, and let e_2 be the restriction of e to W. Then e_2 is nilpotent, by the definition of W. Since $e^p(V) = e^{p+1}(V)$, it is clear that e_1 is a linear *automorphism* of

$e^p(V)$. Hence we see that $e^p(V) \cap W = (0)$, and that $T(e^q) = T(e_1{}^q) + T(e_2{}^q)$. Since e_2 is nilpotent, we have $T(e_2{}^q) = 0$, so that our assumption $T(e^q) = 0$ implies that $T(e_1{}^q) = 0$. Since e_1 is an automorphism, its minimum polynomial has a non-zero constant term. Thus we have a relation $e_1{}^m + r_1 e_1{}^{m-1} + \cdots + r_m = 0$, with $r_m \neq 0$. Taking the trace of this, we obtain $d r_m = 0$, where d is the dimension of $e^p(V)$. Since the base field is of characteristic 0, this gives $d = 0$, which means that $e^p = 0$.

Let L be a Lie algebra. The *center* of L is the ideal consisting of all elements x of L such that $D_x = 0$. If A is a subset of L then (A) will denote the subspace of L that is spanned by A. In particular, if A and B are subsets of L then $([A, B])$ is the subspace of L that is spanned by the commutators $[x, y]$, with x in A and y in B. If $([L, L]) = (0)$ we say that L is *abelian*.

A Lie algebra homomorphism $\alpha \colon L \to E(V)$ defines the structure of an *L-module* on V. We shall usually abbreviate $\alpha(x)(v)$ by $x \cdot v$. We shall consider modules for Lie algebras and for associative algebras. The notions of simplicity and semisimplicity for such modules are exactly those we discussed in Section 2 of Chapter II for the case of groups of linear automorphisms. When we speak of a Lie algebra of linear endomorphisms, it is understood that the commutation is given by $[x, y] = xy - yx$. A linear endomorphism e of the vector space V is said to be *semisimple* if V is semisimple as a module for the associative algebra of endomorphisms generated by e.

THEOREM 1.2. *Let L be a Lie algebra of linear endomorphisms of a finite-dimensional vector space V over a field of characteristic 0. Suppose that V is semi-simple as an L-module. Let Z denote the center of L. Then the factor algebra L/Z has no non-zero abelian ideal, $([L, L]) \cap Z = (0)$, and every element of Z is a semisimple linear endomorphism.*

Proof. Let A denote the associative algebra of linear endomorphisms of V that is generated by L and the identity map on V. Then V is semisimple as an A-module, because the A-stable subspaces of V are precisely the L-stable subspaces. This implies that A has no non-zero nilpotent left ideal; for otherwise A would have a left ideal $B \neq (0)$ such that $(BB) = (0)$. Then $(B \cdot V)$ is an A-submodule of V, so that, by the semisimplicity, $V = (B \cdot V) + W$, where W is an A-submodule and $(B \cdot V) \cap W = (0)$. This gives $(B \cdot W) \subset (B \cdot V) \cap W = (0)$, and hence $(B \cdot V) = ((BB) \cdot V) + (B \cdot W) = (0)$, contradicting the assumption that $B \neq (0)$.

Let T denote the center of A. Then, by what we have just shown, T has no non-zero nilpotent element. It follows that the associative algebra generated by an element of T is a direct sum of fields, whence that element is a semisimple linear endomorphism of V. Since $Z \subset T$, every element of Z is therefore a semisimple linear endomorphism of V.

By Lemma 1.1, every element of $([A, A]) \cap T$ is nilpotent. Since T is a direct sum of fields, this implies that $([A, A]) \cap T = (0)$. A fortiori, $([L, L]) \cap Z = (0)$.

Now let J be an ideal of L such that $[J, J] \subset Z$. Then the last result gives $[J, J] = (0)$. Now consider the abelian ideal $([L, J])$ of L. By Lemma 1.1, every element of $([L, J])$ is nilpotent. Since these elements commute with each other, it follows that the associative algebra B generated by $([L, J])$ is nilpotent. Writing the elements of B as polynomials in elements of $[L, J]$, we see easily that $(LB) \subset (BL) + B$, whence we deduce that $(AB) \subset (BA) + B$. By induction on k, we find that $(AB)^k \subset (B^k A) + (B^k)$ for all positive integers k, where, for any subset P of A, P^k denotes the set of products $p_1 \cdots p_k$ with each p_i in P. Hence we conclude that (AB) is a nilpotent left ideal of A, so that we must have $(AB) = (0)$, which gives $B = (0)$. In particular, $[L, J] = (0)$, i.e., $J \subset Z$. Since every abelian ideal of L/Z is the canonical image of an ideal J of L such that $[J, J] \subset Z$, this shows that L/Z has no non-zero abelian ideal, so that Theorem 1.2 is proved.

Let L be a Lie algebra, and define a sequence of ideals L_i of L by $L_0 = L$, $L_{i+1} = ([L_i, L_i])$. The Lie algebra L is said to be *solvable* if $L_i = (0)$ for some i. The following theorem is known as *Lie's Theorem*.

THEOREM 1.3. *Let L be a solvable Lie algebra over a field of characteristic 0. Then every finite-dimensional semisimple L-module is annihilated by $[L, L]$.*

Proof. Let V be such an L-module. Then the image L^* of L in the algebra of linear endomorphisms of V is a solvable Lie algebra of linear endomorphisms of V. Let Z denote the center of L^*. Since L^* is solvable, so evidently is L^*/Z. By Theorem 1.2, L^*/Z has no non-zero abelian ideal. Hence we must have $L^*/Z = (0)$, for otherwise some $(L^*/Z)_i$ would be a non-zero abelian ideal of L^*/Z. Thus $L^* = Z$, so that $[L^*, L^*] = (0)$, which means that $[L, L]$ annihilates V.

Let L be a Lie algebra, V an L-module. We say that *a subset S of L is nilpotent on V* if there is a positive integer n such that, if ρ denotes the given Lie algebra homomorphism of L into $E(V)$, we have $\rho(L)^n = (0)$.

PROPOSITION 1.4. *Let L be a Lie algebra, V an L-module, S a subspace of L that is nilpotent on V. Let x be an element of L such that $[x, S] \subset S$ and x is nilpotent on V. Then $(x) + S$ is nilpotent on V.*

Proof. There is no loss of generality if we assume that L is given as a Lie algebra of linear endomorphisms of V. If we do this then the assumption is that there are positive integers p and q such that $S^p = (0)$ and $x^q = 0$. We claim that then $((x) + S)^{pq} = (0)$. Consider a product $u_1 \cdots u_{pq}$, where each u_i is either an element of S or equal to x. For s in S, we have $sx = xs + [s, x]$. Hence we see that $u_1 \cdots u_{pq} \in \sum_{r=0}^{pq} x^r S^t$, where t is the number of indices i such that $u_i \in S$. Hence $u_1 \cdots u_{pq} = 0$ unless $t < p$. But if $t < p$ there must be an index i such that $u_{i+1}, \cdots, u_{i+q}$ are all equal to x, because there are $pq - t > p(q - 1)$ elements x in the $t + 1 \leqq p$ intervals not containing elements of S. Hence we have again $u_1 \cdots u_{pq} = 0$, so that Proposition 1.4 is proved.

Now we can easily deduce what is known as *Engel's Theorem*.

THEOREM 1.5. *Let L be a Lie algebra, and let V be a finite-dimensional L-module. Suppose that every element of L is nilpotent on V. Then L is nilpotent on V.*

Proof. As in the case of Proposition 1.4, we assume, without loss of generality, that L is given as a Lie algebra of linear endomorphisms of V. Let x and y be elements of L, and consider $D_x{}^m(y)$ for positive integers m. This is a sum of products $x^p y x^q$, where $p + q = m$. Hence our assumption gives that $D_x{}^m = 0$ as soon as m is sufficiently large.

Now we prove the theorem by induction on the dimension of L. Let H be a proper (i.e., $\neq L$) Lie subalgebra of L of the largest possible dimension; if no such H exists then $L = (0)$, and there is nothing to prove. Regarding L as an H-module by the map $x \to D_x$ of H into $E(L)$, we have, by the above, that every element of H is nilpotent on L. Since H is of lower dimension than L, we may therefore assume that H is nilpotent on L. Then it is clear that there must be an element y in L such that $y \notin H$ but $[H, y] \subset H$. Since H and y are nilpotent on V, it follows from Proposition 1.4 that $(y) + H$ is nilpotent on V. Since $(y) + H$ is a Lie subalgebra of L and H was chosen maximal, we have $(y) + H = L$. Thus L is nilpotent on V, and Theorem 1.5 is proved.

Next, we come to the most important basic result for the structure theory of Lie algebras. It is known as *Cartan's solvability criterion*.

THEOREM 1.6. *Let L be a Lie algebra of linear endomorphisms of a finite-dimensional vector space V over a field of characteristic* 0. *Suppose that* $T(xy) = 0$ *for all elements x and y of L. Then L is solvable.*

Proof. Let F denote the base field, and let F^* be an algebraically closed field containing F. Put $L^* = L \otimes F^*$ and $V^* = V \otimes F^*$. Evidently, we may regard L^* as a Lie algebra of linear endomorphisms of V^*. The assumption on L implies that $T(uv) = 0$ for all elements u and v of L^*. If we prove that L^* is solvable, it follows trivially that L is solvable. Thus we may assume that the base field F is algebraically closed.

Assuming this, we shall prove the theorem by induction on the dimension of L. Since the theorem is trivial if $L = (0)$, this reduces our task to proving the following. Suppose that H is a proper Lie subalgebra of L having the largest possible dimension, and that H is solvable. Then we must prove that L is solvable, provided that Theorem 1.6 holds for Lie algebras of lower dimension than that of L.

Consider the H-module L/H in which the endomorphism corresponding to an element x of H is that induced by D_x. Let V be a non-zero H-submodule of L/H of least possible dimension. Then V is a simple H-module, and we know from Theorem 1.3 that $[H, H]$ annihilates V. Since the base field is algebraically closed, we may therefore apply Schur's Lemma to conclude that V is one-dimensional. Hence the inverse image of V in L has the form $(y) + H$ and is a subalgebra of L. Since H was chosen maximal, we have therefore $L = (y) + H$. There is a linear function μ on H such that $[x, y] - \mu(x)y \in H$ for every element x of H.

Now let W be any non-zero simple L-module, and let W_0 be a non-zero simple H-submodule of W. As we have seen above, W_0 is necessarily one-dimensional; $W_0 = (w_0)$, where w_0 is a non-zero element of W. Define a sequence of elements w_i of W by $w_{i+1} = y \cdot w_i$. Put $W_i = (w_0) + \cdots + (w_i)$. For x in H, we have

$$x \cdot w_{i+1} = x \cdot (y \cdot w_i) = y \cdot (x \cdot w_i) + [x, y] \cdot w_i$$
$$= y \cdot (x \cdot w_i + \mu(x)w_i) + ([x, y] - \mu(x)y) \cdot w_i.$$

Since $[x, y] - \mu(x)y$ lies in H, we see from this inductively that each W_i is H-stable. Define the linear function σ on H by $x \cdot w_0 = \sigma(x)w_0$. We claim that for every element x of H and every i we have $x \cdot w_i - (\sigma(x) + i\mu(x))w_i \in W_{i-1}$, where W_{-1} stands for (0). This evidently holds for $i = 0$. If it holds for some i we obtain

$x \cdot w_{i+1} - (\sigma(x) + (i + 1)\mu(x))w_{i+1}$
$\quad = y \cdot (x \cdot w_i + \mu(x)w_i - (\sigma(x) + (i + 1)\mu(x))w_i) + ([x, y] - \mu(x)y) \cdot w_i$
$\quad = y \cdot (x \cdot w_i - (\sigma(x) + i\mu(x))w_i) + ([x, y] - \mu(x)y) \cdot w_i$
$\quad \in y \cdot W_{i-1} + W_i \subset W_i.$

Thus our above assertion follows by induction on i.

Now let q be the largest index i such that the set $(w_0, \cdots, w_i)$ is linearly independent. Then W_q is an L-submodule of W. Since W is simple, we have therefore $W_q = W$. Hence, if x is an element of H and x_W denotes the linear endomorphism of W corresponding to x, we have $T(x_W) = (q + 1)\sigma(x) + \frac{1}{2}q(q + 1)\mu(x)$.

If $([L, L]) \neq L$ then $([L, L])$ is solvable by our inductive hypothesis, and hence L is solvable. If $([L, L]) = L$ then, in particular, every element x of H is a sum of commutators of elements of L, so that $T(x_W) = 0$. Hence the above gives $\sigma(x) = -\frac{1}{2}q\mu(x)$, so that, from the above,

$$x \cdot w_i - (i - \tfrac{1}{2}q)\mu(x)w_i \in W_{i-1}.$$

Hence we obtain

$$T(x_W{}^2) = \textstyle\sum_{i=0}^{q}(i - \tfrac{1}{2}q)^2\mu(x)^2.$$

Let $(0) = V_k \subset \cdots \subset V_0 = V$ be a composition series for the L-module V. Applying the above result to the simple L-modules V_j/V_{j+1}, we obtain

$$T(x_V{}^2) = \textstyle\sum_{j=0}^{k-1}\left(\sum_{i=0}^{q_j}(i - \tfrac{1}{2}q_j)^2\right)\mu(x)^2,$$

where $q_j = \dim(V_j/V_{j+1}) - 1$.

If we had $\mu(x) = 0$ for every x in H, we would have $([L, L]) \subset H$, contrary to our assumption that $([L, L]) = L$. Otherwise, since $T(x_V{}^2) = 0$ for every x, we must have $i = \frac{1}{2}q_j$ for all i such that $0 \leq i \leq q_j$, whence each q_j must be 0, which means that each V_j/V_{j+1} is one-dimensional. But then the assumption $([L, L]) = L$ gives that L annihilates each V_j/V_{j+1}, whence L is nilpotent on V. This evidently implies that L is solvable, so that Theorem 1.6 is proved.

2

From now on, it will be assumed implicitly that *the base field is of characteristic* 0. A Lie algebra is called *semisimple* if it has no non-zero abelian ideal. If ρ is a finite-dimensional representation of a Lie algebra L we define the *trace form* τ_ρ on $L \times L$ by $\tau_\rho(x, y) = T(\rho(x)\rho(y))$. One verifies immediately that, for all elements x, y, z of L, $\tau_\rho([x, y], z) = \tau_\rho(x, [y, z])$. We say that ρ is *faithful* if the kernel of ρ is (0).

THEOREM 2.1. *Let L be a finite-dimensional Lie algebra. If L is semisimple and if ρ is a faithful finite-dimensional representation of L then the trace form τ_ρ is non-degenerate. If the trace form of the adjoint representation of L is non-degenerate then L is semisimple.*

Proof. Let H be the set of all elements x of L such that $\tau_\rho(x, y) = 0$ for every y in L. By the formal property of τ_ρ noted above, H is an ideal of L. By Theorem 1.6, applied to $\rho(H)$, we have that H is solvable. If H were not (0) then some H_i would therefore be a non-zero abelian ideal of L. If L is semisimple we must therefore have $H = (0)$, which means that τ_ρ is non-degenerate.

Now suppose that the trace form of the adjoint representation $x \to D_x$ of L is non-degenerate. Let A be any abelian ideal of L. Let x be an element of A and y an element of L. Then $D_x D_y$ sends L into A and A into (0), so that $T(D_x D_y) = 0$. Hence our assumption gives $x = 0$, and so $A = (0)$.

PROPOSITION 2.2. *If L is a finite-dimensional semisimple Lie algebra then $L = ([L, L])$ and, for every ideal I of L, there is one and only one ideal I' of L such that $L = I + I'$ and $I \cap I' = (0)$.*

Proof. Since L is semisimple, its center is (0), so that the adjoint representation of L is faithful. By Theorem 2.1, the trace form of the adjoint representation of L is therefore non-degenerate. Now let I be any ideal of L, and let I' be the set of all elements x of L such that $T(D_x D_y) = 0$ for every element y of I. Then we see at once from the formal property of the trace form noted at the beginning of this section that I' is an ideal of L. By Theorem 1.6, $I \cap I'$ is solvable, and hence (0). By taking a basis for I, we see that I' is the set of zeros in L of a system of $\dim(I)$ linear functions on L. Hence $\dim(I') \geqq \dim(L) - \dim(I)$. Since $I \cap I' = (0)$, we must therefore have $L = I + I'$.

In particular, $L = ([L, L]) + ([L, L])'$. But then we see by applying the endomorphisms D_x that $([L, L])'$ must lie in the center of L, which is (0). Thus $L = ([L, L])$.

Now let I, I' be as above, and suppose that J is any ideal of L such that $L = I + J$ and $I \cap J = (0)$. Since $L = ([L, L])$, we have $J = ([J, J])$. On the other hand, $[L, J] = [I + I', J] = [I', J] \subset I'$. Hence $J \subset I'$, whence $J = I'$. This completes the proof of Proposition 2.2.

Let ρ be a finite-dimensional representation of a finite dimensional semisimple Lie algebra L. Let P denote the kernel of ρ. Let P' be the complement of P in L that is obtained in Proposition 2.2. Clearly, every ideal of P' is also an ideal of L. Hence P' is semisimple. Let ρ' denote the restriction of ρ to P'. Then ρ' is faithful. Theorem 2.1 applies to ρ', so that $\tau_{\rho'}$ is non-degenerate.

There is an evident bilinear map of $P' \times P'$ into $E(P')$ sending each (x, y) onto the endomorphism $f_{(x,y)}$ of P' that is defined by $f_{(x,y)}(z) = \tau_{\rho'}(z, x)y$. To this bilinear map there corresponds canonically a linear map $u \to u^*$ of $P' \otimes P'$ into $E(P')$ such that $(x \otimes y)^*(z) = \tau_{\rho'}(z, x)y$. From the fact that $\tau_{\rho'}$ is non-degenerate it follows easily that the map $u \to u^*$ is injective. Since $\dim(P' \otimes P') = \dim(E(P'))$, this map $u \to u^*$ is therefore a linear isomorphism of $P' \otimes P'$ onto $E(P')$. Hence there is one and only one element u_ρ in $P' \otimes P'$ such that $(u_\rho)^*$ is the identity map on P'. We shall actually regard u_ρ as an element of $L \otimes L$ by identifying $P' \otimes P'$ with its canonical image in $L \otimes L$. This element u_ρ of $L \otimes L$ is called the *Casimir element of ρ in $L \otimes L$*.

If U and V are arbitrary L-modules, where L is an arbitrary Lie algebra, one defines the structure of an L-module on $U \otimes V$ such that $x \cdot (u \otimes v) = (x \cdot u) \otimes v + u \otimes (x \cdot v)$. With this L-module structure, $U \otimes V$ is called the *tensor product of the L-modules U and V*. In particular, $L \otimes L$ is thus equipped with the structure of an L-module, derived from the adjoint representation of L.

Returning to the above, we claim that $x \cdot u_\rho = 0$ for every element x of L. Since $[P, P'] = (0)$, it is clear that $x \cdot u_\rho = 0$ for all elements x of P. Now let x be an element of P', and regard $x \cdot u_\rho$ as an element of $P' \otimes P'$. In order to show that it is zero, it suffices to show that its image $(x \cdot u_\rho)^*$ in $E(P')$ is 0. Write $u_\rho = \sum_i y_i \otimes z_i$, with y_i and z_i in P'. Then

$$x \cdot u_\rho = \sum_i ([x, y_i] \otimes z_i + y_i \otimes [x, z_i]).$$

Hence

$$
\begin{aligned}
(x \cdot u_\rho)^*(t) &= \sum_i (\tau_{\rho'}(t, [x, y_i]) z_i + \tau_{\rho'}(t, y_i)[x, z_i]) \\
&= \sum_i (\tau_{\rho'}([t, x], y_i) z_i + [x, \tau_{\rho'}(t, y_i) z_i]) = [t, x] + [x, t] = 0.
\end{aligned}
$$

Let μ denote the canonical map of L into its universal enveloping algebra $\mathscr{U}(L)$. Then μ induces a map $\mu_2 \colon L \otimes L \to \mathscr{U}(L)$ such that $\mu_2(x \otimes y) = \mu(x)\mu(y)$. We may regard $\mathscr{U}(L)$ as an L-module such that the endomorphism of $\mathscr{U}(L)$ corresponding to the element x of L is $D_{\mu(x)}$, i.e., $x \cdot a = \mu(x)a - a\mu(x)$. Then it is clear that μ_2 is an L-module homomorphism. Hence $\mu_2(u_\rho)$ lies in the center of $\mathscr{U}(L)$. We shall write c_ρ for $\mu_2(u_\rho)$ and call it the *Casimir element of ρ in $\mathscr{U}(L)$*. Finally, we note that the homomorphism ρ^μ of $\mathscr{U}(L)$ into the endomorphism algebra of the representation space of ρ makes this representation space into a $\mathscr{U}(L)$-module. If we identify L with its image in $\mathscr{U}(L)$ by means of μ, which is justified by Theorem 1.1 of Chapter X, we may regard ρ^μ as an extension of ρ. We shall usually write ρ for ρ^μ. The image $\rho^\mu(c_\rho)$ of c_ρ in the endomorphism algebra of the representation space of ρ is called the *Casimir operator* of ρ. Since c_ρ lies in the center of $\mathscr{U}(L)$, the Casimir operator commutes with every $\rho(x)$ for x in L.

We shall show that if ρ is not trivial then $T(\rho(c_\rho))$ is not 0. In particular, we shall then have that *the Casimir operator of a non-trivial representation is not* 0.

In order to see this, let us choose a basis $(y_1, \cdots, y_m)$ for P', and let us write $u_\rho = \sum_i x_i \otimes y_i$. Then

$$\rho(c_\rho) = \sum_i \rho(x_i)\rho(y_i), \quad \text{and} \quad T(\rho(c_\rho)) = \sum_i \tau_{\rho'}(x_i, y_i).$$

Since $(u_\rho)^*$ is the identity map, we have $\sum_i \tau_{\rho'}(y_j, x_i)y_i = (u_\rho)^*(y_j) = y_j$. Hence $\tau_{\rho'}(y_j, x_i)$ is equal to 1 or 0 according to whether $i = j$ or $i \neq j$. Since $\tau_{\rho'}$ is symmetric, this gives $T(\rho(c_\rho)) = \dim(P')$, which is different from 0 if ρ is non-trivial.

THEOREM 2.3. *Let L be a finite-dimensional semisimple Lie algebra. Then every finite-dimensional L-module is semisimple.*

Proof. Let V be a finite-dimensional L-module, and let $(0) = V_n \subset \cdots \subset V_0 = V$ be a composition series for it. Then each factor module V_i/V_{i+1} is either one-dimensional and annihilated by L or is simple and non-trivial. Let $0 \leq i_1 < \cdots < i_m \leq n - 1$ be the indices i for which V_i/V_{i+1} is simple and non-trivial. Let γ_q denote the Casimir operator of the representation of L on V_{i_q}/V_{i_q+1}. Then γ_q is an L-module *automorphism*. Let f_q be the minimum polynomial of γ_q, normalized so that the constant term is 1. Let c_q denote the Casimir element in $\mathscr{U}(L)$ of the representation of L on V_{i_q}/V_{i_q+1}, and put $d_q = f_q(c_q) - f_q(0) = f_q(c_q) - 1$. This is a non-zero element of the center of $\mathscr{U}(L)$ and actually lies in $L\mathscr{U}(L)$; we identify L with its image in $\mathscr{U}(L)$. Moreover, for the induced $\mathscr{U}(L)$-module structure of V_{i_q}/V_{i_q+1}, $1 + d_q$ annihilates V_{i_q}/V_{i_q+1}, which means that, for the induced $\mathscr{U}(L)$-module structure of V, $1 + d_q$ sends V_{i_q} into V_{i_q+1}. Hence, if $x_1, \cdots, x_{n-m}$ are arbitrary elements of L then

$$x_1 \cdots x_{n-m}(1 + d_1) \cdots (1 + d_m)$$

annihilates V. Since $L = ([L, L])$, every element of L can be written, in

$\mathscr{U}(L)$, as a sum of products of $n - m$ elements of L. Hence $L(1 + d_1) \cdots$ $(1 + d_m)$ annihilates V. Let V^L denote the submodule of V consisting of all elements that are annihilated by every element of L, and write V_L for the submodule of V spanned by the elements $x \cdot v$ with x in L and v in V. What we have just shown means that $(1 + d_1) \cdots (1 + d_m) \cdot V \subset V^L$. Since each d_i lies in $L\mathscr{U}(L)$, this shows that $V = V_L + V^L$.

Now Theorem 2.3 follows immediately from the analogue for Lie algebra modules of Lemma 2.1 of Chapter II. The present modules V^L and V_L take the place of the modules V^G and V_G of that lemma. The appropriate L-module structure on a space of linear maps of one module into another is given by $(x \cdot f)(v) = x \cdot f(v) - f(x \cdot v)$. With these definitions, the proof of the analogue of the lemma is identical with the proof given in Chapter II.

3

We are now in a position to prove the basic structure theorems for Lie algebras. The assumption that the base field be of characteristic 0 is still in force.

THEOREM 3.1. *Let L be a finite-dimensional semisimple Lie algebra, and let π be a surjective homomorphism of a finite-dimensional Lie algebra E onto L. Then there exists a Lie algebra homomorphism $\rho: L \to E$ such that $\pi \circ \rho$ is the identity map on L.*

Proof. We prove the theorem by induction on the dimension of the kernel, P say, of π. If this is 0 there is nothing to prove. Thus we may suppose that $\dim(P) > 0$, and that the theorem holds in the cases where the dimension of the kernel is smaller than that of P. If E is semisimple then we know from Proposition 2.2 that it is the direct sum of P and a complementary ideal P'. Clearly, π maps P' isomorphically onto L, so that the theorem holds in this case. Hence we may suppose that E has a non-zero abelian ideal. Let A be a non-zero abelian ideal of E having the smallest possible dimension. Now $(A + P)/P$ is an abelian ideal of E/P. But E/P is isomorphic with L and hence is semisimple. Hence $(A + P)/P = (0)$, i.e., $A \subset P$.

Suppose first that $A \neq P$. Then we consider the surjective Lie algebra homomorphism $\pi^A: E/A \to L$ that is induced by π. Its kernel is P/A, and by our inductive hypothesis there is a Lie algebra homomorphism $\delta: L \to E/A$ such that $\pi^A \circ \delta$ is the identity map on L. We have $\delta(L) = F/A$, where F is a Lie subalgebra of E containing A. Since $\dim(A) < \dim(P)$, we may again apply our inductive hypothesis to conclude that there is a Lie algebra homomorphism $\sigma\colon \delta(L) \to F$ such that $\alpha \circ \sigma$ is the identity map on $\delta(L)$, where α is the canonical homomorphism $F \twoheadrightarrow F/A = \delta(L)$. Clearly, $\sigma \circ \delta$ satisfies the requirements of Theorem 3.1.

It remains to dispose of the case $P = A$. Since P is now abelian, the adjoint representation of E induces an L-module structure on P such that $\pi(e) \cdot p = [e, p]$ for every element e of E and every element p of P. The L-submodules of P are precisely the ideals of E that are contained in P. Since A was chosen minimal, and since $P = A$, it is clear that P is a simple L-module. If the representation of L on P is trivial we have $[E, P] = (0)$, so that E may be regarded as an L-module in the same way in which we regard P as an L-module. Clearly, π is now an L-module homomorphism if we regard L as an L-module by the adjoint representation of L. By Theorem 2.3, we have $E = P + P'$, where P' is an L-submodule and $P' \cap P = (0)$. Now π induces an L-module isomorphism of P' onto L whose inverse evidently satisfies the requirements of Theorem 3.1.

Hence we may now suppose that P is a simple non-trivial L-module. Let $u = \sum_i x_i \otimes y_i$ be the Casimir element in $L \otimes L$ of the representation of L on P, and let γ be the corresponding Casimir operator on P. We know that γ is an L-module automorphism of P. We begin by choosing a linear map f of L into E such that $\pi \circ f$ is the identity map on L, and we attempt to find a linear map h of L into P such that $f - h$ is a Lie algebra homomorphism. Thus we consider the deviation of f from a Lie algebra homomorphism, i.e., we consider the bilinear map $g\colon L \times L \to P$ that is given by $g(x, y) = [f(x), f(y)] - f([x, y])$. It is clear from the definition of the L-module structure on P that $x \cdot p = [f(x), p]$ for every element x of L and every element p of P. Using this and the Jacobi identity for E, we find that g satisfies the identity

$$x \cdot g(y, z) - y \cdot g(x, z) + z \cdot g(x, y)$$
$$= g([x, y], z) - g([x, z], y) + g([y, z], x).$$

We use this in order to put $\gamma(g(x, y)) = \sum_i x_i \cdot (y_i \cdot g(x, y))$ into a form from which h can be found.

We obtain, first,

$$y_i \cdot g(x, y)$$
$$= x \cdot g(y_i, y) - y \cdot g(y_i, x) + g([y_i, x], y) - g([y_i, y], x) + g([x, y], y_i).$$

Now we apply the operator corresponding to x_i and transform the first two terms to obtain

$$x_i \cdot (y_i \cdot g(x, y))$$
$$= [x_i, x] \cdot g(y_i, y) - [x_i, y] \cdot g(y_i, x) + x \cdot (x_i \cdot g(y_i, y)) - y \cdot (x_i \cdot g(y_i, x))$$
$$+ x_i \cdot (g([y_i, x], y) - g([y_i, y], x) + g([x, y], y_i)).$$

Since $x \cdot u = 0$, we have (interchanging the arguments in the commutators) $\sum_i([x_i, x] \otimes y_i + x_i \otimes [y_i, x]) = 0$. This implies that if k is any bilinear map on $L \times L$ then $\sum_i(k([x_i, x], y_i) + k(x_i, [y_i, x])) = 0$. Using this for the map $k: L \times L \to P$ given by $k(u, v) = u \cdot g(v, y)$, we obtain

$$\sum_i([x_i, x] \cdot g(y_i, y) + x_i \cdot g([y_i, x], y)) = 0.$$

Similarly,

$$\sum_i([x_i, y] \cdot g(y_i, x) + x_i \cdot g([y_i, y], x)) = 0.$$

Hence the above yields

$$\gamma(g(x, y)) = \sum_i(x \cdot (x_i \cdot g(y_i, y)) - y \cdot (x_i \cdot g(y_i, x)) + x_i \cdot g([x, y], y_i)).$$

Now put $h(x) = \gamma^{-1}(\sum_i x_i \cdot g(y_i, x))$. Then the last result gives $g(x, y) = x \cdot h(y) - y \cdot h(x) - h([x, y])$. One verifies immediately from this that $f - h$ is a Lie algebra homomorphism of L into E, and we have $\pi \circ (f - h) = \pi \circ f$, which is the identity map on L. This completes the proof of Theorem 3.1.

Let A and B be solvable ideals of an arbitrary Lie algebra L. Then $(A + B)/A$ is isomorphic with $B/(A \cap B)$, and it is clear that $B/(A \cap B)$ is solvable. Hence $(A + B)/A$ is solvable. Since A is solvable, this implies that $A + B$ is solvable. Hence it is clear that every finite-dimensional Lie algebra L has a solvable ideal R such that R contains every solvable ideal of L. This unique maximum solvable ideal R of L is called the *radical* of L. The above argument about factor algebras shows also that L/R is semisimple. If A is any ideal of L then $(A + R)/R$ is an ideal of the semisimple Lie algebra L/R and hence is semisimple. It is isomorphic with $A/(A \cap R)$, so that $A \cap R$ must contain the radical of A and hence must coincide with the radical of A. *Thus the radical of an ideal A of the finite-dimensional Lie algebra L is the intersection of A with the radical of L.*

THEOREM 3.2. *Let L be a finite-dimensional Lie algebra, R the radical of L. Then $([L, L]) \cap R$ coincides with $([L, R])$. If V is any finite-dimensional L-module then $([L, R])$ is nilpotent on V.*

Proof. By Theorem 3.1, there is a Lie algebra homomorphism ρ of L/R

into L such that ρ followed by the canonical homomorphism $L \to L/R$ is the identity map on L/R. Hence, if we put $S = \rho(L/R)$ then S is a semi-simple subalgebra of L that is mapped isomorphically onto L/R by the canonical map, so that $L = S + R$ and $S \cap R = (0)$. Hence $([L, L]) = S + ([L, R])$, because (by Proposition 2.2) $([S, S]) = S$. It follows immediately that $([L, L]) \cap R = ([L, R])$.

We know from Theorem 1.3 that $([R, R])$ is nilpotent on V. Let T be any subspace of $([L, R])$ that contains $([R, R])$ and is nilpotent on V. If $T \neq ([L, R])$ there is an element z in L and an element x in R such that $[z, x]$ does not belong to T. The Lie subalgebra $(z) + R$ of L is evidently solvable. Hence it follows from Theorem 1.3 that $[(z) + R, (z) + R]$ is nilpotent on V. In particular, $[z, x]$ is nilpotent on V. By Proposition 1.4, $([z, x]) + T$ is therefore nilpotent on V, because $[[z, x], T] \subset [R, R] \subset T$. Hence if T is chosen maximal we must have $T = ([L, R])$, so that Theorem 3.2 is proved.

In particular, D_x is nilpotent for every element x of $([L, R])$. Hence $\mathrm{Exp}(D_x)$ is defined as a polynomial $\sum_{i=0}^{m-1} (i!)^{-1} D_x{}^i$, where m may be taken to be $\dim(L)$; if D_x is nilpotent then $D_x(L)$ must have smaller dimension than L, etc., up to the point where $D_x{}^m(L) = (0)$. One verifies directly that $\mathrm{Exp}(D_x)$ is a Lie algebra automorphism of L, with inverse $\mathrm{Exp}(-D_x) = \mathrm{Exp}(D_{-x})$, of course. Moreover, since $([L, R])$ is nilpotent on L, the formal series of the Campbell-Hausdorff formula specializes to a *finite* series in elements of $([L, R])$ and thus defines a map $\eta\colon ([L, R]) \times ([L, R]) \to ([L, R])$ such that $\mathrm{Exp}(D_x)\mathrm{Exp}(D_y) = \mathrm{Exp}(D_{\eta(x, y)})$. Hence the automorphisms $\mathrm{Exp}(D_x)$, as x ranges over $([L, R])$, constitute a group.

THEOREM 3.3. *Let L be a finite-dimensional Lie algebra, and let R be the radical of L. Let S be a semisimple subalgebra of L such that $L = S + R$, whose existence is guaranteed by Theorem 3.1. Let T be any semisimple subalgebra of L. Then there is an element x in $([L, R])$ such that $\mathrm{Exp}(D_x)$ maps T into S.*

Proof. For every element t of T write $t = \sigma(t) + \rho(t)$ with uniquely determined (because $S \cap R$ is necessarily (0)) elements $\sigma(t)$ in S and $\rho(t)$ in R. Then

$$[\sigma(t_1) + \rho(t_1), \sigma(t_2) + \rho(t_2)] = \sigma([t_1, t_2]) + \rho([t_1, t_2]),$$

whence
$$[\sigma(t_1), \sigma(t_2)] = \sigma([t_1, t_2])$$

and
$$[\sigma(t_1), \rho(t_2)] - [\sigma(t_2), \rho(t_1)] + [\rho(t_1), \rho(t_2)] = \rho([t_1, t_2]).$$

Since $T = ([T, T])$, it follows from the second relation that $\rho(T) \subset ([L, R])$. Let $f(t)$ denote the coset of $\rho(t)$ mod. $([R, R])$. Then f is a linear map of T into $([L, R])/([R, R])$. The adjoint representation of L induces the structure of a T-module on $([L, R])/([R, R])$ in the natural fashion. In terms of this T-module structure, the second relation above shows that $t_1 \cdot f(t_2) - t_2 \cdot f(t_1) = f([t_1, t_2])$ for all elements t_1 and t_2 of T. It follows that f may be used for defining a T-module structure on the direct sum $K + ([L, R])/([R, R])$, where K denotes the base field, regarded as a one-dimensional vector space over itself, such that $t \cdot (\alpha, u) = (0, \alpha f(t) + t \cdot u)$, for every element t of T, every element α of K and every element u of $([L, R])/([R, R])$. Since T is semisimple, this T-module is semisimple. Hence the submodule $([L, R])/([R, R])$ has a T-module complement. Choosing u in $([L, R])/([R, R])$ so that $(1, u)$ is in this module complement, we see that we must have $t \cdot (1, u) = 0$, whence $f(t) = -t \cdot u$.

Now let x_1 be a representative of $-u$ in $([L, R])$. Then we have $\rho(t) + [x_1, t] \in ([R, R])$, so that $t + [x_1, t] \in \sigma(t) + ([R, R])$. Hence we see that $\mathrm{Exp}(D_{x_1})(T) \subset S + ([R, R])$. Now we assume inductively that Theorem 3.3 holds for Lie algebras with lower dimensional radicals. Applying this inductive hypothesis to the Lie algebra $S + ([R, R])$ (assuming, as we may, that $R \neq (0)$), we may therefore suppose that there is an element x_2 in $([S + ([R, R]), ([R, R])]) \subset ([L, R])$ such that

$$\mathrm{Exp}(D_{x_2})(\mathrm{Exp}(D_{x_1})(T)) \subset S.$$

Then, if $x = \eta(x_2, x_1)$, we have $\mathrm{Exp}(D_x)(T) \subset S$,   q.e.d.

THEOREM 3.4. *Let L be a finite-dimensional Lie algebra, V a finite-dimensional L-module. There is an ideal P of L that is nilpotent on V and contains every ideal of L that is nilpotent on V. Moreover, every element of the radical of L that is nilpotent on V belongs to P.*

Proof. Let $(0) = V_0 \subset \cdots \subset V_n = V$ be a composition series for the L-module V. Let P_i be the kernel of the representation of L on V_i/V_{i-1}, and put $P = \bigcap_{i=1}^{n} P_i$. Then it is clear that P is nilpotent on V. Now let J be any ideal of L that is nilpotent on V, and let W be one of the factor modules V_i/V_{i-1}. Then $(J \cdot W)$ is an L-submodule of W, because J is an ideal of L. Hence we have either $(J \cdot W) = (0)$ or $(J \cdot W) = W$. But the second possibility is ruled out because J is nilpotent on W. Hence we must have $J \subset P$.

Let R denote the radical of L, and let x be an element of R that is nilpotent on V. By Proposition 1.4, $(x) + P$ is nilpotent on V. By Theorem 3.2, $([L, R])$ is nilpotent on V. Since $([L, R])$ is an ideal of L, we have therefore $([L, R]) \subset P$. Hence $(x) + P$ is an ideal of L, and is therefore contained in P. This completes the proof of Theorem 3.4.

Define a series of ideals L^i of L by putting $L^0 = L$ and $L^{i+1} = ([L, L^i])$ for each $i \geq 0$. The Lie algebra L is called *nilpotent* if $L^m = (0)$ for some m, or, equivalently, if L is nilpotent on L with respect to the adjoint representation. If we apply Theorem 3.4 to the adjoint representation, we see that there is a unique *maximum nilpotent ideal* of L, i.e. a nilpotent ideal of L that contains every nilpotent ideal of L. One must merely observe that an ideal of L is nilpotent if and only if it is nilpotent on L with respect to the adjoint representation of L. Note also that *the maximum nilpotent ideal of L consists precisely of all elements of the radical that are nilpotent on L.*

EXERCISES

1. Let e be a nilpotent linear endomorphism of a finite-dimensional vector space A. Show that there is a linear endomorphism f of A such that $fe - ef = e$. [By the elementary theory of a single linear endomorphism, A can be decomposed into a direct sum of "cyclic" subspaces, each having a basis of the form $(a, e(a), \cdots, e^k(a))$ with $e^{k+1}(a) = 0$. The desired f may be chosen so that, on each cyclic component, it takes a diagonal form with respect to the above basis.]

2. Let L be a semisimple finite-dimensional Lie algebra, and let x be an element of L such that D_x is nilpotent. Show that there is an element y in L such that $[y, x] = x$. [Consider the representation of L on the space $E(L)$ of all linear endomorphisms of L in which $z \cdot h = D_z h - h D_z$. Note that the subspace consisting of the D_z's is L-stable and that, because L is semisimple, it has an L-module complement in $E(L)$. Now use the result of Exercise 1 above with D_x for e.]

3. With L and x as in Exercise 2 above, prove that if ρ is any finite-dimensional representation of L then $\rho(x)$ is nilpotent. [If y is an element of L such that $[y, x] = x$ then $(y) + (x)$ is a solvable Lie subalgebra of L and $([(y) + (x), (y) + (x)]) = (x)$; now apply Theorem 1.3.]

4. Let L be a finite-dimensional Lie algebra, R the radical of L, N the maximum nilpotent ideal of L, V a finite-dimensional L-module such

131

that N is nilpotent on V. Show that if x is an element of L such that D_x is nilpotent then x is nilpotent on V. [Write $L = S + R$, where S is a semisimple subalgebra, and, accordingly, $x = s + r$. Show first that D_s is nilpotent on S, then apply the result of Exercise 3 to show that D_s is nilpotent on L. Now use Proposition 1.3 to show, first, that $(s) + N$ is nilpotent on L, next, that $(s + r) + (s) + N$ is nilpotent on L, which gives that D_r is nilpotent, so that $r \in N$. Finally, show that $(s) + N$ is nilpotent on V, whence x is nilpotent on V.]

5. Prove that every derivation of a finite-dimensional semisimple Lie algebra L is of the form D_x, with some x in L. [If δ is the given derivation, consider the L-module $K + L$, where K is the base field and $x \cdot (\alpha, y) = (0, \alpha\delta(x) + [x, y])$.]

6. Prove the converse of Theorem 2.3.

XII. SIMPLY CONNECTED ANALYTIC GROUPS [1]

1

We shall now assemble a large number of the preceding results in proving the following theorem.

THEOREM 1.1. *Let L be a finite-dimensional Lie algebra over the field of the real numbers. Then there exists an analytic group G such that $\mathscr{L}(G)$ is isomorphic with L.*

Given a finite-dimensional real Lie algebra L, let us denote by $\mathscr{A}(L)^*$ the connected component of the identity in the group $\mathscr{A}(L)$ of all Lie algebra automorphisms of L, regarded as a subgroup of the full linear group on L. Since $\mathscr{A}(L)$ is evidently a closed subgroup of the full linear group on L, we know from Theorem 1.1 of Chapter VIII that $\mathscr{A}(L)^*$ is an analytic group. If we identify the Lie algebra of the full linear group on L with the Lie algebra $E(L)$ of all linear endomorphisms of L (Theorem 2.1 of Chapter VII) then the canonical image of $\mathscr{L}(\mathscr{A}(L)^*)$ in the Lie algebra of the full linear group on L becomes identified with the Lie algebra $\mathscr{D}(L)$ of all derivations of L. In order to see this, one merely has to note that if α is an element of $E(L)$ then α belongs to the canonical image of $\mathscr{L}(\mathscr{A}(L)^*)$ if and only if, for all elements x and y of L and all real numbers r, one has $\mathrm{Exp}(r\alpha)([x,y]) = [\mathrm{Exp}(r\alpha)(x), \mathrm{Exp}(r\alpha)(y)]$. Since the canonical homomorphism of $\mathscr{L}(\mathscr{A}(L)^*)$ into $E(L)$ is injective (by Theorems 3.2 and 3.3 of Chapter VII), we conclude that $\mathscr{L}(\mathscr{A}(L)^*)$ is canonically isomorphic with $\mathscr{D}(L)$.

Since not every Lie algebra is isomorphic with some $\mathscr{D}(L)$, Theorem 1.1 lies considerably deeper than our considerations up to this point. However,

133

these considerations do suffice for proving Theorem 1.1 in the case where L is semisimple. Indeed, if L is semisimple then the map $x \to D_x$ is an isomorphism of L onto $\mathcal{D}(L)$; a proof for this is indicated in Exercise 5 of Chapter XI. Thus if L is semisimple then the Lie algebra of $\mathcal{A}(L)^*$ is isomorphic with L.

In order to use this result in proving the general case, we need to make a further adjustment. Let G be any analytic group, and let $f: H \to G$ be a group covering of G, in the sense of Section 3 of Chapter IV. Since f maps a neighborhood of the neutral element of H homeomorphically onto a neighborhood of the neutral element of G, it is clear that the analytic manifold structure of G defines an analytic manifold structure of H with which H becomes an analytic group, and f is now an analytic group homomorphism. By Theorems 3.2 and 3.3 of Chapter VII, the differential f° of f is injective, and since the dimension of H is equal to that of G, f° is therefore a Lie algebra isomorphism of $\mathcal{L}(H)$ onto $\mathcal{L}(G)$. Evidently, an analytic group is locally arcwise simply connected. Hence it is clear from Theorems 2.2 and 3.2 of Chapter IV that *a group covering $f: H \to G$ exists such that H is simply connected.*

Now suppose that H and G are analytic groups, that H is simply connected, and that σ is a Lie algebra homomorphism of $\mathcal{L}(H)$ into $\mathcal{L}(G)$. By Theorem 3.2 of Chapter X and Theorem 3.1 of Chapter IV, there is an analytic homomorphism σ^* of H into G whose differential is σ, and by Theorem 3.4 of Chapter VII, there is only one such σ^*. If σ is an isomorphism of $\mathcal{L}(H)$ onto $\mathcal{L}(G)$ and if G is also simply connected then we can reverse the roles of H and G, whence we see that σ^* is then an analytic group isomorphism of H onto G. In particular, if $H = G$ we may combine this result with Theorem 1.2 of Chapter IX to conclude that *if G is simply connected then the canonical map $\alpha \to \alpha^\circ$ of $\mathcal{A}(G)$ into $\mathcal{A}(\mathcal{L}(G))$ is a topological group isomorphism of $\mathcal{A}(G)$ onto $\mathcal{A}(\mathcal{L}(G))$.* (In the notation of Theorem 1.2 of Chapter IX, we have now $\mathcal{A}^\circ(G) = \mathcal{A}(\mathcal{L}(G))$.)

Let us now suppose that we are given simply connected analytic groups G and H and a Lie algebra homomorphism τ of $\mathcal{L}(H)$ into the derivation algebra $\mathcal{D}(\mathcal{L}(G))$ of $\mathcal{L}(G)$. We identify $\mathcal{D}(\mathcal{L}(G))$ with the Lie algebra of $\mathcal{A}(\mathcal{L}(G))^*$ and conclude from the above that τ is the differential of a unique analytic group homomorphism τ^* of H into $\mathcal{A}(\mathcal{L}(G))^*$. Since G is simply connected, the map $\alpha \to \alpha^\circ$ is a topological group isomorphism of the connected component $\mathcal{A}(G)^*$ of the identity in $\mathcal{A}(G)$ onto $\mathcal{A}(\mathcal{L}(G))^*$. Hence there is one and only one continuous homomorphism t of H into

$\mathscr{A}(G)^*$ such that $t(x)^\circ = \tau^*(x)$ for every element x of H. Now let us form the semidirect product $G \times_t H$. By Theorem 3.1 of Chapter IX, this is an analytic group, and its Lie algebra may be identified with the semidirect sum $\mathscr{L}(G) + \mathscr{L}(H)$ in which the commutation is given by

$$[\alpha_1 + \beta_1, \alpha_2 + \beta_2] = ([\alpha_1, \alpha_2] + \tau(\alpha_1)(\beta_2) - \tau(\alpha_2)(\beta_1)) + [\beta_1, \beta_2],$$

where α_1, α_2 are in $\mathscr{L}(G)$ and β_1, β_2 are in $\mathscr{L}(H)$.

Now we are in a position to prove Theorem 1.1. Let L be any finite-dimensional real Lie algebra. We can evidently find a sequence of sub-algebras $(0) = L_0 \subset \cdots \subset L_p = L$ such that each L_i is an ideal in L_{i+1}, and L_{i+1}/L_i is either one-dimensional or semisimple. If L_{i+1}/L_i is one-dimensional then L_{i+1} is evidently isomorphic with a suitably defined semi-direct sum $L_i + (L_{i+1}/L_i)$. If L_{i+1}/L_i is semisimple then the same is true by virtue of Theorem 3.1 of Chapter XI. A one-dimensional Lie algebra is isomorphic with the Lie algebra $\mathscr{L}(R)$ of the one-dimensional vector group R. By the above, a semisimple Lie algebra S is isomorphic with the Lie algebra of a simply connected covering group of $\mathscr{A}(S)^*$. Hence, in either case, L_{i+1}/L_i may be identified with the Lie algebra of a simply connected analytic group H_i.

Now suppose that we have already constructed a simply connected analytic group G_i whose Lie algebra is isomorphic with L_i. The semidirect product decomposition of L_{i+1} then defines a Lie algebra homomorphism τ_i of $\mathscr{L}(H_i)$ into $\mathscr{D}(\mathscr{L}(G_i))$. If t_i is the corresponding continuous homo-morphism of H_i into $\mathscr{A}(G_i)$ then, by the above, the semidirect product $G_i \times_{t_i} H_i$ is a simply connected analytic group G_{i+1} such that $\mathscr{L}(G_{i+1})$ is isomorphic with L_{i+1}. Thus we finally obtain a simply connected analytic group $G = G_p$ such that $\mathscr{L}(G)$ is isomorphic with L. This completes the proof of Theorem 1.1.

The proof of Theorem 1.1 yields a useful result concerning normal analytic subgroups of simply connected analytic groups, which is as follows.

THEOREM 1.2. *Let G be a simply connected analytic group, and let H be a normal analytic subgroup of G. Then H is closed in G and, if π denotes the canonical analytic map $G \to G/H$, there is an analytic map $\rho: G/H \to G$ such that $\pi \circ \rho$ is the identity map on G/H and the map $(x, u) \to x\rho(u)$ is an analytic manifold isomorphism of $H \times (G/H)$ onto G.*

Proof. We identify $\mathscr{L}(H)$ with the corresponding subalgebra of $\mathscr{L}(G)$. Since H is normal in G, Theorem 2.1 of Chapter IX shows that $\mathscr{L}(H)$ is an ideal of $\mathscr{L}(G)$. Hence we can find a sequence $(0) = L_0 \subset \cdots \subset L_p = \mathscr{L}(G)$ such as was used in the proof of Theorem 1.1 and such that one of the terms, say L_q, is $\mathscr{L}(H)$. Now let $G_0, \cdots, G_p$ be the sequence of simply connected analytic groups that was constructed in the proof of Theorem 1.1 by successively forming semidirect products. Since G_{i+1} is a semidirect product $G_i \times_{t_i} H_i$, it is evident that Theorem 2.1 holds for the pair (G_{i+1}, G_i). It follows trivially by composing the maps ρ_i for these pairs that Theorem 1.2 holds for the pair (G_p, G_q). Now G_p is a simply connected analytic group, and there is an isomorphism σ of $\mathscr{L}(G_p)$ onto $\mathscr{L}(G)$ such that, if $\mathscr{L}(G_q)$ is identified with the corresponding subalgebra of $\mathscr{L}(G_p)$, we have $\sigma(\mathscr{L}(G_q)) = \mathscr{L}(H)$. Since G and G_p are simply connected, there is an analytic group isomorphism s of G_p onto G such that $s^\circ = \sigma$. Clearly, s maps G_q onto H, whence it is clear that the conclusions of Theorem 1.2 carry over from (G_p, G_q) to (G, H).

Note that *Theorem 1.2 implies that both H and G/H are simply connected*, for if $S \xrightarrow{\alpha} H$ and $T \xrightarrow{\beta} G/H$ are coverings of H and G/H then $S \times T \xrightarrow{\alpha \times \beta} H \times (G/H)$ is a covering of $H \times (G/H)$ and must therefore be a homeomorphism, which implies that both α and β are homeomorphisms.

2

We shall say that an analytic group G is nilpotent, solvable or semisimple if $\mathscr{L}(G)$ is nilpotent, solvable or semisimple. We know from Exercise 3 of Chapter X that if G is nilpotent then $\exp_G$ is surjective. The following theorem strengthens this result in the case where G is simply connected, and yields the former result on considering a simply connected group covering of G.

THEOREM 2.1. *Let G be a simply connected nilpotent analytic group. Then $\exp_G$ is an analytic manifold isomorphism of $\mathscr{L}(G)$ onto G.*

Proof. Let T denote the connected component of 1 in the center of G. By Theorem 1.2, T is simply connected, whence it is clear that T is a vector group. Evidently, Theorem 2.1 holds for T; let $\log_T$ denote the analytic inverse of $\exp_T$. Now we make an induction on the dimension of G and suppose that Theorem 2.1 holds for lower dimensional groups. By what we have just seen, we may suppose also that $G \neq T$. Since $\mathscr{L}(G)$ is nilpotent, it evidently has a non-trivial center, whence also T is non-trivial. Since, by Theorem 1.2, G/T is simply connected and evidently nilpotent, our inductive hypothesis applies to G/T; let $\log_{G/T}$ denote the analytic inverse of $\exp_{G/T}$.

Let π denote the canonical map $G \to G/T$, and choose a linear map σ of $\mathscr{L}(G/T)$ into $\mathscr{L}(G)$ such that $\pi^\circ \circ \sigma$ is the identity map on $\mathscr{L}(G/T)$. Now let α denote the analytic map $\sigma \circ \log_{G/T} \circ \pi$ of G into $\mathscr{L}(G)$. One verifies immediately by applying π that $\exp_G(-\alpha(x))x \in T$ for every element x of G. Now define the analytic map β of G into $\mathscr{L}(G)$ by

$$\beta(x) = \alpha(x) + \log_T(\exp_G(-\alpha(x))x).$$

Now note that (quite generally, for any analytic group G) if γ and δ are elements of $\mathscr{L}(G)$ such that $[\gamma, \delta] = 0$ then $\exp_G(\gamma)\exp_G(\delta) = \exp_G(\gamma + \delta)$. In fact, by Theorem 2.1 of Chapter IX, $\exp_G(r\gamma)$ and $\exp_G(s\delta)$ then commute with each other for arbitrary real numbers r and s, whence it is clear that the map $r \to \exp_G(r\gamma)\exp_G(r\delta)$ is an analytic homomorphism of R into G. The differential of this analytic homomorphism is evidently the same as the differential of the analytic homomorphism $r \to \exp_G(r(\gamma + \delta))$, whence our above assertion follows. Using this, one verifies immediately that $\beta \circ \exp_G$ is the identity map on $\mathscr{L}(G)$ and $\exp_G \circ \beta$ is the identity map on G. This completes the proof of Theorem 2.1.

Already for simply connected solvable analytic groups, the exponential map may fail to be even surjective. The following result can often serve as a substitute for Theorem 2.1.

THEOREM 2.2. *Let G be a simply connected solvable analytic group, and let S be an analytic subgroup of G. Then there is a basis $(\gamma_1, \cdots, \gamma_n)$ of $\mathscr{L}(G)$ containing a basis $(\gamma_{i_1}, \cdots, \gamma_{i_m})$ of $\mathscr{L}(S)$ such that the map $\mu: \mathscr{L}(G) \to G$ defined by $\mu(\sum_i r_i\gamma_i) = \exp_G(r_1\gamma_1) \cdots \exp_G(r_n\gamma_n)$ is an analytic manifold isomorphism and sends $\mathscr{L}(S)$ onto S. In particular, S is therefore closed in G and simply connected.*

Proof. Since $\mathscr{L}(G)$ is solvable, we can find a sequence $(0) = L_0 \subset \cdots \subset L_n = \mathscr{L}(G)$ of subalgebras such that each L_i is an ideal in L_{i+1} and L_{i+1}/L_i is one-dimensional. Now we choose a basis $(\gamma_1, \cdots, \gamma_n)$ of $\mathscr{L}(G)$ as follows: if L_i contains an element of $\mathscr{L}(S)$ that does not belong to L_{i-1} we let γ_i be such an element; otherwise we let γ_i be any element of L_i that does not belong to L_{i-1}. Then it is easy to see that $(\gamma_1, \cdots, \gamma_n)$ is a basis of $\mathscr{L}(G)$ and contains a basis $(\gamma_{i_1}, \cdots, \gamma_{i_m})$ of $\mathscr{L}(S)$.

Arguing as in the proof of Theorem 1.2, we may identify G with the analytic group G_n obtained by successively forming semidirect products

$G_{i+1} \times_{t_i} H_i$, where now each H_i is a one-dimensional vector group. It is clear from this that μ is an analytic manifold isomorphism of $\mathscr{L}(G)$ onto G.

In order to show that $\mu(\mathscr{L}(S)) = S$, let us consider a group covering $\tau \colon T \to S$ with T simply connected. Then $\mathscr{L}(T)$ has a basis $(\delta_1, \cdots, \delta_m)$ such that $\tau°(\delta_k) = \gamma_{i_k}$, which evidently defines a sequence of subalgebras of $\mathscr{L}(T)$ with the property of the above sequence (L_i), the k-th member of the sequence being $(\delta_1) + \cdots + (\delta_k)$. Hence we know from what we have already shown that the map $\eta \colon \mathscr{L}(T) \to T$ defined by $\eta(\sum_k r_k \delta_k) = \exp_T(r_1 \delta_1) \cdots \exp_T(r_m \delta_m)$ is an analytic manifold isomorphism. Now we have $\tau(\exp_T(r_k \delta_k)) = \exp_S(\tau°(r_k \delta_k)) = \exp_S(r_k \gamma_{i_k}) = \exp_G(r_k \gamma_{i_k})$. Since $S = \tau(T)$, it follows that $S = \mu(\mathscr{L}(S))$, so that Theorem 2.2 is proved.

THEOREM 2.3. *Let G be a simply connected solvable analytic group. Then G has no non-trivial compact subgroup.*

Proof. Let T be a compact subgroup of G, and let G' be the normal analytic subgroup of G that corresponds to the ideal $([\mathscr{L}(G), \mathscr{L}(G)])$. By Theorem 1.2, G' is closed in G and both G' and G/G' are simply connected solvable analytic groups. If G' is trivial then $\mathscr{L}(G)$ is abelian, so that G is a vector group. Evidently (cf. Chapter III), T must be trivial in this case. If G' is non-trivial then G/G' is of lower dimension than G. Proceeding by induction on $\dim(G)$, we may therefore suppose that the compact subgroup $(TG')/G'$ of G/G' is trivial, i.e., that $T \subset G'$. Since $\mathscr{L}(G)$ is solvable, it does not coincide with $([\mathscr{L}(G), \mathscr{L}(G)])$, unless $\mathscr{L}(G) = (0)$. Thus G' is of lower dimension than G, if G is non-trivial. Hence the inductive hypothesis that Theorem 2.3 holds in lower dimension gives that T must be trivial.

3

The notions of solvability and nilpotency of analytic groups that we have used above are actually in accord with the usual group theoretical notions. The following theorem contains this result.

THEOREM 3.1. *Let G be an analytic group, and let K be a normal analytic subgroup of G. Denote by $[G, K]$ the subgroup of K that is generated by the commutators $xyx^{-1}y^{-1}$ with x in G and y in K. Then $[G, K]$ coincides with the analytic subgroup of G that corresponds to the ideal $([\mathscr{L}(G), \mathscr{L}(K)])$ of $\mathscr{L}(G)$.*

Proof. Let H denote the analytic subgroup of G that corresponds to $([\mathscr{L}(G), \mathscr{L}(K)])$. We shall show first that $[G, K] \subset H$. Let x_1, x_2 be elements of G, and let y be an element of K. Then

$$(x_1 x_2) y (x_1 x_2)^{-1} y^{-1} = x_1 (x_2 y x_2^{-1} y^{-1}) x_1^{-1} (x_1 y x_1^{-1} y^{-1}).$$

Since H is normal in G, this shows that if $xyx^{-1}y^{-1}$ lies in H for $x = x_1$ and for $x = x_2$ then it lies in H also for $x = x_1x_2$. Similarly, we see that if $xyx^{-1}y^{-1}$ lies in H for $y = y_1$ and for $y = y_2$ then it lies in H also for $y = y_1y_2$. Hence it suffices to show that there is a neighborhood U of 0 in $\mathscr{L}(G)$ such that $\exp(\gamma)\exp(\delta)\exp(-\gamma)\exp(-\delta)$ lies in H whenever γ belongs to U and δ belongs to $U \cap \mathscr{L}(K)$. If we take for U a neighborhood W such as in Theorem 3.1 of Chapter X, so that the Campbell-Hausdorff formula is applicable, the element written above is equal to $\exp(\eta(\text{Exp}(D_\gamma)(\delta), -\delta))$, and $\eta(\text{Exp}(D_\gamma)(\delta), -\delta)$ lies in $([\mathscr{L}(G), \mathscr{L}(K)])$, so that the element lies in H. Thus we have $[G, K] \subset H$.

Now choose elements $\alpha_1, \cdots, \alpha_p$ in $\mathscr{L}(G)$ and $\beta_1, \cdots, \beta_p$ in $\mathscr{L}(K)$ such that the elements $[\alpha_i, \beta_i]$ constitute a basis for $([\mathscr{L}(G), \mathscr{L}(K)])$. Replacing each α_i with $s\alpha_i$, where s is a sufficiently small non-zero real number, we ensure that the elements $\gamma_i = \text{Exp}(D_{\alpha_i})(\beta_i) - \beta_i$ still constitute a basis for $([\mathscr{L}(G), \mathscr{L}(K)])$.

Put

$$\mu_i(t) = \exp(\alpha_i)\exp(t\beta_i)\exp(-\alpha_i)\exp(-t\beta_i) = \exp(t\,\text{Exp}(D_{\alpha_i})(\beta_i))\exp(-t\beta_i)$$

and $\mu(t_1, \cdots, t_p) = \mu_1(t_1) \cdots \mu_p(t_p)$. There is a neighborhood V of 0 in R^p such that the Campbell-Hausdorff formula is applicable repeatedly to yield $\log \circ \mu$ as a power series map of V into $([\mathscr{L}(G), \mathscr{L}(K)])$. If we identify $([\mathscr{L}(G), \mathscr{L}(K)])$ with R^p via our basis $(\gamma_1, \cdots, \gamma_p)$, we see easily that the Jacobian of the power series map $\log \circ \mu$ takes the value 1 at 0. Hence it is clear from Theorem 3.1 of Chapter V that $\log(\mu(V))$ contains a neighborhood of 0 in $([\mathscr{L}(G), \mathscr{L}(K)])$, so that $\mu(V)$ contains a neighborhood of 1 in the analytic group H. Since $\mu(V) \subset [G, K]$, it follows that $H \subset [G, K]$, because every neighborhood of 1 in H generates H. This completes the proof of Theorem 3.1.

We close this chapter with the following generalization of Theorem 2.3 of Chapter III.

THEOREM 3.2. *Let G be a locally compact topological group containing a simply connected solvable analytic group S as a closed normal subgroup, and suppose that G/S is compact. Then S is a semidirect factor in G.*

Proof. We make an induction on the dimension of S, and thus assume that Theorem 3.2 holds in the lower dimensional cases, and, of course, that S is non-trivial. Put $L_0 = \mathscr{L}(S), L_{i+1} = ([L_i, L_i])$, and let p be the highest index i such that $L_i \neq (0)$.   Clearly, each L_i is G-stable with respect to the adjoint representation of G on $\mathscr{L}(S)$.   Hence the analytic subgroup, V say, of S that corresponds to L_p is normal in G.   By the choice of p, V is abelian. By Theorem 1.2, V is closed in S and both V and S/V are simply connected solvable analytic groups.   In particular, V is therefore a vector group. Now $(G/V)/(S/V)$ is isomorphic with G/S and hence is compact.   By our inductive hypothesis, we have therefore a continuous homomorphism γ of G/S into G/V such that $\pi \circ \gamma$ is the identity map on G/S, where π is the canonical homomorphism $G/V \rightarrow G/S$.   Now let P be the subgroup of G that contains V and is such that $P/V = \gamma(G/S)$.   Since $\gamma(G/S)$ is compact and since V is a vector group, we know from Theorem 2.3 of Chapter III that there is a continuous homomorphism δ of P/V into P such that $\mu \circ \delta$ is the identity map on P/V, where μ is the canonical homomorphism $P \rightarrow P/V$.   Evidently, $\delta \circ \gamma$ is a continuous homomorphism inverting the canonical map $G \rightarrow G/S$, so that Theorem 3.2 is proved.

EXERCISES

1. Let G be the multiplicative group of all matrices of the form

$$\begin{pmatrix} 1 & 0 & 0 & 0 \\ 0 & 1 & 0 & 0 \\ c & 0 & e^{2\pi i r} & 0 \\ 0 & r & 0 & 1 \end{pmatrix}$$

    where c ranges over all complex numbers and r over all real numbers. Note that G is a simply connected solvable analytic group, exhibit $\mathscr{L}(G)$ as a Lie algebra of matrices, and show that the matrices in G in which c is not 0 and r is a non-zero integer do not belong to $\exp(\mathscr{L}(G))$.

2. Let H be the nilpotent analytic group whose underlying manifold is R^4 and where the multiplication is given by

    $(x_1, y_1, z_1, t_1)(x_2, y_2, z_2, t_2)$
    $$= (x_1 + x_2 + z_1 t_2, y_1 + y_2 + \alpha z_1 t_2, z_1 + z_2, t_1 + t_2)$$

    where α is a fixed real number.   Let D be the discrete central subgroup of H consisting of the elements $(p, q, 0, 0)$, with arbitrary integers p and q.   Let $G = H/D$.   Show that if α is irrational then $[G, G]$ is not closed in G.

3. Show that if a solvable analytic group is not simply connected it has a non-trivial compact subgroup.

140

4. Show that the group $\mathscr{A}(G)$ of all topological group automorphisms of the analytic group G is a Lie group. [Let $\pi: H \to G$ be a group covering with H simply connected, and let F be the kernel of π. Show that $\mathscr{A}(G)$ is isomorphic with the stabilizer of F in $\mathscr{A}(H)$, so that it is isomorphic with a closed subgroup of the Lie group $\mathscr{A}(\mathscr{L}(H)) \approx \mathscr{A}(H)$.]

XIII. COMPACT ANALYTIC
GROUPS [9, 10]

1

We shall begin with a characterization of the Lie algebras of compact analytic groups. If L is a Lie algebra and F is a bilinear form on $L \times L$ then we shall say that F is *invariant* if $F([x, y], z) = F(x, [y, z])$ for all elements x, y and z of L.

THEOREM 1.1. *Let L be a finite-dimensional real Lie algebra. Then L is isomorphic with the Lie algebra of a compact analytic group if and only if there exists a positive definite invariant symmetric bilinear form on $L \times L$. If G is a compact semisimple analytic group then the trace form of the adjoint representation of L is negative definite.*

Proof. Suppose that L is the Lie algebra of a compact analytic group G, and choose any positive definite symmetric bilinear form H on $L \times L$. For α and β in L, define the continuous real-valued function $H_{\alpha, \beta}$ on G by

$$H_{\alpha, \beta}(x) = H(x^*(\alpha), x^*(\beta))$$

where x^* denotes the image of x under the adjoint representation of G on L. Now define $F(\alpha, \beta) = I(H_{\alpha, \beta})$, where I is a Haar integral for G. Clearly, F is a positive definite symmetric bilinear form on $L \times L$. The translate $x \cdot H_{\alpha, \beta}$, where $x \in G$, has the same integral as $H_{\alpha, \beta}$ and is equal to $H_{x*(\alpha), x*(\beta)}$. Hence $F(\alpha, \beta) = F(x^*(\alpha), x^*(\beta))$ for every element x of G. Let γ be an element of L, t a real number, and put $x = \exp(t\gamma)$. Since the differential of the adjoint representation of G is the adjoint representation of L, we have then $x^* = \mathrm{Exp}(tD_\gamma)$. If we substitute this in our above result on F, we see immediately that $F([\gamma, \alpha], \beta) + F(\alpha, [\gamma, \beta]) = 0$, whence it is clear that F is invariant in the sense defined at the beginning.

142

Now let $\alpha_1, \cdots, \alpha_n$ be an orthonormal basis of L with respect to F. Let us write $[\alpha, \alpha_i] = \sum_{j=1}^n r_{ji}(\alpha)\alpha_j$, where $\alpha \in L$ and the $r_{ji}(\alpha)$'s are real numbers. Then the invariance relation $F([\alpha, \alpha_i], \alpha_j) + F(\alpha_i, [\alpha, \alpha_j]) = 0$ gives $r_{ji}(\alpha) = -r_{ij}(\alpha)$. Now we have

$$D_\alpha^2(\alpha_i) = \sum_{j,k} r_{ji}(\alpha)r_{kj}(\alpha)\alpha_k$$

so that we obtain

$$T(D_\alpha^2) = \sum_{j,i} r_{ji}(\alpha)r_{ij}(\alpha) = -\sum_{j,i} r_{ji}(\alpha)^2.$$

Thus $T(D_\alpha^2) < 0$ whenever not all the $r_{ji}(\alpha)$'s are 0, i.e., whenever $D_\alpha \neq 0$. If G is semisimple, which means that L is semisimple, then the map $\alpha \to D_\alpha$ is injective, so that our result is that the trace form of the adjoint representation of L is negative definite.

Now let L be any finite-dimensional real Lie algebra such that there exists a positive definite invariant symmetric bilinear form F on $L \times L$. Then the F-orthogonal complement of any ideal of L is again an ideal of L, so that L is semisimple as an L-module under the adjoint representation. Let Z denote the center of L, and let T be its F-orthogonal complement. If I is an abelian ideal of T then, since I is a direct ideal summand of T, it is clear that $I \subset Z$, so that $I = (0)$. Thus T is a semisimple Lie algebra. Since Z is the Lie algebra of a toroid, we shall know that L is isomorphic with the Lie algebra of a compact analytic group as soon as we have shown that T is isomorphic with the Lie algebra of a compact analytic group. The restriction of F to $T \times T$ is a positive definite invariant symmetric bilinear form. Hence we may now assume that L is semisimple.

Assuming this, let G be the connected component of the identity in the group of all Lie algebra automorphisms of L. We know from Section 1 of Chapter XII that the Lie algebra of G may be identified with L. Hence it suffices to prove that G is compact. Now G is generated by the automorphisms of L of the form $\mathrm{Exp}(tD_\alpha)$ where $\alpha \in L$ and t is a real number. Let β and γ be elements of L, and consider the function f on R defined by $f(t) = F(\mathrm{Exp}(tD_\alpha)(\beta), \mathrm{Exp}(tD_\alpha)(\gamma))$. The invariance property of F gives $f'(t) = 0$ for every t in R. Hence f is a constant, which means that $\mathrm{Exp}(tD_\alpha)$ is an F-orthogonal linear automorphism of L. Thus G is contained in the group, K say, of all F-orthogonal linear automorphisms of L. Since G is closed in the full linear group on L, it is closed in K. But K is easily seen to be compact. Hence G is compact. This completes the proof of Theorem 1.1.

143

COROLLARY 1.2. *If L is isomorphic with the Lie algebra of a compact analytic group, so is every subalgebra of L.*

Proof. By Theorem 1.1, there is a positive definite invariant symmetric bilinear form F on $L \times L$. If S is any subalgebra of L then the restriction of F to $S \times S$ is such a form again, so that, by Theorem 1.1, S is isomorphic with the Lie algebra of a compact group.

THEOREM 1.3. *If L is isomorphic with the Lie algebra of a compact analytic group then L is the direct sum of its center and a semisimple ideal. If, moreover, L is semisimple then every analytic group whose Lie algebra is isomorphic with L is compact. Every compact analytic group is of the form $(T \times G)/D$, where T is a toroid, G is a compact semisimple analytic group and D is a finite central subgroup of $T \times G$ such that $D \cap T$ and $D \cap G$ are trivial.*

Proof. The proof of the first statement is contained in our above proof of Theorem 1.1. Now suppose that L is semisimple, and let G be a compact analytic group such that $\mathscr{L}(G)$ is isomorphic with L. Let $\eta: H \to G$ be a group covering of G, with H simply connected, and let F denote the kernel of η. Then F is a discrete central subgroup of H, and H/F is isomorphic with G, so that H/F is compact. Since $\mathscr{L}(G)$ is semisimple, we have $([\mathscr{L}(G), \mathscr{L}(G)]) = \mathscr{L}(G)$, so that, by Theorem 3.1 of Chapter XII, the commutator subgroup of G coincides with G. Hence the commutator subgroup of H/F coincides with H/F. Now it follows from Theorem 2.4 of Chapter III that F is finite, whence H is compact.

Now let K be any analytic group whose Lie algebra is isomorphic with L. Since the Lie algebra of H is isomorphic with L and since H is simply connected, there is an analytic group homomorphism of H into K whose differential is an isomorphism of $\mathscr{L}(H)$ onto $\mathscr{L}(K)$. It follows that this group homomorphism is surjective, whence it is clear that K is compact.

Let P be any compact analytic group. By the first part of Theorem 1.3, $\mathscr{L}(P)$ is the direct sum of its center Z and a semisimple ideal L. Let T be the analytic subgroup of P that corresponds to Z. Then T is evidently the connected component of 1 in the center of P, so that T is compact. On the other hand, there is a covering of T by a vector group whose Lie algebra is isomorphic with Z. Hence it is clear from Theorem 1.4 of Chapter III that T is a toroid. Let G be the analytic subgroup of P that corresponds to L. By Corollary 1.2, L is isomorphic with the Lie algebra of a compact group. Hence it follows from the second part of Theorem 1.3, which we have already established, that G is compact for its topology as an analytic group.

Now let f be the homomorphism of $T \times G$ into P given by $f(x,y) = xy$. Then f is evidently a surjective analytic homomorphism, and the differential of f is an isomorphism of $\mathscr{L}(T \times G)$ onto $\mathscr{L}(P)$. Hence it is clear that f is a group covering, and that the kernel D of f is a discrete central subgroup of $T \times G$. Since $T \times G$ is compact, D is therefore finite. Since the restrictions of f to T and to G are injective, $D \cap T$ and $D \cap G$ are both trivial. We may identify P with $(T \times G)/D$, so that Theorem 1.3 is proved.

2

We apply the results of Section 1 in the proof of the following classical structure theorem on topological groups.

THEOREM 2.1. *Let G be a connected locally compact topological group, and suppose there exists a continuous injective homomorphism of G into a compact group. Then G is the direct product of a vector group and a compact group.*

Proof. Let $f: G \to U$ be the given continuous injective homomorphism of G into a compact group U. Let N be a compact neighborhood of 1 in G such that $N = N^{-1}$. Since NNN is compact, the restriction of f to NNN is a homeomorphism of NNN onto $f(NNN)$. It follows that if V is any neighborhood of 1 in G there is a neighborhood V^* of 1 in U such that $f^{-1}(V^*) \cap (NNN) \subset V$. We take V so that $V \subset N$.

Consider the representations of U on the finite-dimensional submodules of the U-module of all representative functions on U. It is clear from Theorem 1.4 of Chapter II (the Peter-Weyl Theorem) that the intersection of the family of kernels of these representations is trivial. Using the compactness of the complement of the interior of V^*, we conclude that one of these kernels, K_{V*} say, must be contained in V^*. Now the compact group U/K_{V*} has a continuous faithful representation on a finite-dimensional vector space and may therefore be identified with a compact subgroup of the corresponding full linear group. Thus U/K_{V*} is a Lie group. Put $L_V = f^{-1}(K_{V*}) \cap N \subset V$. Let x be an element of $L_V{}^{-1}L_V$. Then $x \in NN$ and $f(x) \in K_{V*} \subset V^*$, whence $x \in L_V$. Thus L_V is a subgroup of G. Moreover, if $x \in L_V$ and $y \in N$ then $yxy^{-1} \in NNN$ and $f(yxy^{-1}) \in K_{V*}$, whence $yxy^{-1} \in L_V$. Since G is connected, it is generated by N, so that we may conclude that L_V is normal in G. Since L_V is a closed subset of the compact set N, it is compact.

Let γ denote the canonical homomorphism $G \to G/L_V$ and let μ denote the canonical homomorphism $U \to U/K_{V*}$. Then $\mu \circ f$ induces a continuous homomorphism $\eta\colon G/L_V \to U/K_{V*}$. Let x and y be elements of N such that $\mu(f(x)) = \mu(f(y))$. Then $f(x^{-1}y) \in K_{V*}$, and $x^{-1}y \in NN$, so that $x^{-1}y \in L_V$. Thus η is injective on the neighborhood $\gamma(N)$ of 1 in G/L_V. Hence we may apply Theorem 1.1 of Chapter VIII to conclude (since G/L_V is connected) that G/L_V is an analytic group and that η is an analytic homomorphism of G/L_V into the connected component of 1 in U/K_{V*}. The differential of η maps $\mathscr{L}(G/L_V)$ isomorphically onto a subalgebra of $\mathscr{L}(U/K_{V*})$. Since U/K_{V*} is compact, it follows now from Corollary 1.2 that $\mathscr{L}(G/L_V)$ is isomorphic with the Lie algebra of a compact group. By Theorem 1.3, $\mathscr{L}(G/L_V)$ is therefore the direct sum of its center and the semisimple ideal $([\mathscr{L}(G/L_V), \mathscr{L}(G/L_V)])$, and the analytic subgroup of G/L_V corresponding to this semisimple ideal is compact and therefore closed in G/L_V. By Theorem 3.1 of Chapter XII, this analytic subgroup is the commutator subgroup $[G/L_V, G/L_V]$ of G/L_V. On the other hand, the analytic subgroup corresponding to the center of $\mathscr{L}(G/L_V)$ is the connected component $Z(G/L_V)$ of 1 in the center of G/L_V, which is evidently closed in G/L_V. The product $[G/L_V, G/L_V]Z(G/L_V)$, taken within G/L_V, evidently contains a neighborhood of 1 in G/L_V and hence coincides with G/L_V.

Now consider two groups L_V as above, say L_1 and L_2, such that $L_1 \subset L_2$. Let $\gamma_{2,1}$ denote the canonical homomorphism of G/L_1 onto G/L_2. Clearly, $\gamma_{2,1}([G/L_1, G/L_1]) = [G/L_2, G/L_2]$ and $\gamma_{2,1}(Z(G/L_1)) \subset Z(G/L_2)$. Moreover, one sees immediately from the above decompositions of $\mathscr{L}(G/L_1)$ and $\mathscr{L}(G/L_2)$ that the differential of $\gamma_{2,1}$, which is surjective (by Theorem 4.2 of Chapter X), maps the center of $\mathscr{L}(G/L_1)$ onto all of the center of $\mathscr{L}(G/L_2)$. Hence we conclude from Theorem 4.2 of Chapter X that

$$\gamma_{2,1}(Z(G/L_1)) = Z(G/L_2).$$

Next we observe that, given any two subgroups L_V as above, say L_{V_1} and L_{V_2}, we can find an L_{V_3} that is contained in $L_{V_1} \cap L_{V_2}$. In fact, we may take $V_3 = V_1 \cap V_2$, $V_3{}^* = V_1{}^* \cap V_2{}^*$ and $K_{V_3*} = K_{V_1*} \cap K_{V_2*}$. Moreover, given any neighborhood W of 1 in G, there evidently exists an L_V that is contained in W.

For each subgroup L as above, let A_L be the complete inverse image of $Z(G/L)$ in G, and let A be the intersection of the family of all these groups A_L. Then A is evidently a closed subgroup of G. If $a \in A_L$ and $x \in G$ then $xax^{-1}a^{-1} \in L$. Since the intersection of the family of L's is (1), it follows that A lies in the center of G. We wish to show that $A_L = AL$ for every L. Let $a \in A_L$. Given $L_1, \cdots, L_k$, choose $L_0 \subset L \cap L_1 \cap \cdots \cap L_k$.

Then A_{L_0} is contained in each A_{L_i} and since the canonical map $Z(G/L_0) \to Z(G/L)$ is surjective we have $A_L = A_{L_0}L$, so that $(aL) \cap A_{L_0}$ is non-empty. Hence the family of sets $(aL) \cap A_{L_\alpha}$, where a and L are fixed and L_α ranges over all the L's, has the finite intersection property. Since these are closed subsets of the compact set aL, it follows that there must be a point common to all of them, i.e., $(aL) \cap A \neq \varnothing$. Since a was an arbitrary element of A_L, this shows that $A_L \subset AL$, so that $A_L = AL$.

On the other hand, the complete inverse image of $[G/L, G/L]$ in G is evidently $[G, G]L$. Thus $([G, G]L)/L$ is the compact group $[G/L, G/L]$. Since L is compact, it follows from Theorem 2.6 of Chapter I that $[G, G]L$ is compact. Let B denote the intersection of the family of these groups $[G, G]L$, as L ranges over all subgroups of the above type. Then B is a compact normal subgroup of G and contains $[G, G]$. Hence AB is a closed normal subgroup of G (Lemma 2.2 of Chapter I). Moreover, $G = LA_L[G, G] = AL[G, G] \subset ALB$, so that $G = ALB$. Since L may be chosen to lie in any given neighborhood of 1 in G, it follows that AB is dense in G. Since it is closed in G, we have therefore $G = AB$.

Now $(AL)/L = Z(G/L)$ and, since L is compact, we know from Theorem 2.3 of Chapter I that the injection $A \to AL$ induces a topological group isomorphism of $A/(A \cap L)$ onto $(AL)/L$. Hence $A/(A \cap L)$ is an abelian analytic group and is therefore a direct product $T_L \times S_L$, where T_L is a toroid and S_L is a vector group. Let P be the complete inverse image of T_L in A. Then, since $A \cap L$ and T_L are compact, so is P. Moreover, A/P is isomorphic with the vector group S_L, whence it is clear that P contains every compact subgroup of A. Thus P is the unique maximum compact subgroup of A.

Consider the family $\mathscr{F}$ of all closed subgroups V of A such that $A = PV$. Let $\mathscr{H}$ be any subfamily of $\mathscr{F}$ that is totally ordered by inclusion, and let X be the intersection of $\mathscr{H}$. We shall show that $X \in \mathscr{F}$, i.e., that $A = PX$. Let a be any element of A. Then, for each member V of $\mathscr{H}$, there is an element p_V in P and an element v in V such that $a = p_V v$. Then $p_V \in P \cap (aV)$. Since $\mathscr{H}$ is totally ordered, the family of closed subsets $P \cap (aV)$ of the compact set P has the finite intersection property, whence these sets have a point in common, i.e., $P \cap (aX) \neq \varnothing$. Hence $A = PX$. Now we may apply Zorn's lemma to conclude that there is a minimal member V of $\mathscr{F}$.

Now $(VL)/L$ is a closed subgroup of $(AL)/L$, which is isomorphic with $T_L \times S_L$. By Theorem 1.4 of Chapter III, $(VL)/L$ is therefore an elementary group. By Theorem 2.3 of Chapter I, $V/(V \cap L)$ is isomorphic with

$(VL)/L$. Thus $V/(V \cap L)$ is a direct product $Q \times S \times D$, where Q is compact, S is a vector group and D is a finitely generated free abelian discrete group. The complete inverse image Q' of Q in V is compact and therefore contained in P. Hence, if W is the complete inverse image of $S \times D$ in V, we have $PW = A$. Since V is minimal, we have therefore $W = V$, so that $V/(V \cap L) = S \times D$. Hence it is clear that $V \cap L$ is a maximal compact subgroup of V, whence $V \cap L = V \cap P$. Since this holds for all L's, it follows that $V \cap P = (1)$, so that $V = S \times D$.

We have $G = AB = VPB$, and PB is clearly a compact subgroup of G. Since V has no non-trivial compact subgroup, $(PB) \cap V = (1)$. Now it follows from Theorem 2.5 of Chapter I that the multiplication induces a topological group isomorphism of the direct product $V \times (PB)$ onto G. Since G is connected, V must therefore be connected, so that $V = S$, a vector group. This completes the proof of Theorem 2.1.

3

We wish to prove that if G is a compact analytic group then $\exp_G$ is surjective. For this purpose, we require the following result.

PROPOSITION 3.1. *Let G be a compact analytic group, and let F be a positive definite invariant symmetric bilinear form on $\mathscr{L}(G)$ (whose existence is guaranteed by Theorem 1.1). Regard $\mathscr{L}(G)$ as a normed vector space, the norm being defined by $|\alpha| = F(\alpha, \alpha)^{1/2}$ for every α in $\mathscr{L}(G)$. For a positive real number r, let B_r denote the open ball of radius r around 0 in $\mathscr{L}(G)$, and put $V_r = \exp_G(B_r)$. Then there are real numbers a and c such that $0 < a < c$ and the following holds: V_c is an open connected neighborhood of 1 in G and $\exp_G$ induces an analytic manifold isomorphism of B_c onto V_c, whose inverse is denoted by $\log$, $V_a V_a \subset V_c$ and $|\log(xy)| \leq |\log(x)| + |\log(y)|$ for all elements x and y in V_a, the inequality being strict whenever $\log(x)$ and $\log(y)$ are linearly independent.*

Proof. First choose c so that $\exp_G$ induces an analytic manifold isomorphism of B_c onto the open connected neighborhood V_c of 1 in G. Then choose b such that $0 < b < c$, $V_b V_b \subset V_c$ and B_b has the properties with respect to the Campbell-Hausdorff series η that are described (for W) in Theorem 3.1 of Chapter X, so that $\exp(\alpha)\exp(\beta) = \exp(\eta(\alpha, \beta))$ for all elements α and β of B_b. Write $\eta(\alpha, \beta) = \alpha + \beta + \tau(\alpha, \beta)$. Consider the terms resulting from the expansion of $F(\eta(\alpha, \beta), \tau(\alpha, \beta))$ as a series $\sum_{i,j} F(u_i, v_j)$, where the u_i's are the terms of the series η and the v_j's are the terms of the series τ. With the exception of the terms of the expansions of

$F(\alpha, \tau(\alpha, \beta))$ and $F(\beta, \tau(\alpha, \beta))$, these are evidently of the form $rF(\rho, \sigma)$, where r is a rational number not depending on (α, β) and ρ and σ are composite commutators formed from α and β. The exceptional terms are of the form $rF(\alpha, \sigma)$ or $rF(\beta, \sigma)$, where σ is as before. Because of the invariance of F, these can be rewritten in the previous form $rF(\rho, \sigma_1)$ (with ρ and σ_1 composite commutators), except in the case where σ is of the lowest possible forms $[\alpha, \beta]$ or $[\beta, \alpha]$. But in these cases, it follows from the invariance of F that $F(\alpha, \sigma)$ and $F(\beta, \sigma)$ are both 0. Thus $F(\eta(\alpha, \beta), \tau(\alpha, \beta))$ can be written as an absolutely convergent series of terms, each of which is of the form $rF(\rho, \sigma)$ as described above.

Now we know from Section 3 of Chapter **X** that there is a fixed positive constant K such that, for all elements γ and δ of $\mathscr{L}(G)$, $|[\gamma, \delta]| \leq K|\gamma||\delta|$. Hence, if ρ and σ are composite commutators formed from α and β whose total degrees in α and β are $r \geq 2$ and $s \geq 2$, respectively, we have, with $t = \max(|\alpha|, |\beta|)$,

$$|F(\rho, \sigma)| \leq |\rho||\sigma| \leq (K^{r-2}|[\alpha, \beta]|t^{r-2})(K^{s-2}|[\alpha, \beta]|t^{s-2})$$
$$= K^{r+s-4}t^{r+s-4}|[\alpha, \beta]|^2.$$

Hence it follows from what we have said above concerning

$$F(\eta(\alpha, \beta), \tau(\alpha, \beta))$$

that if b is chosen small enough there is a positive constant L such that

$$F(\eta(\alpha, \beta), \eta(\alpha, \beta)) \leq F(\alpha + \beta, \alpha + \beta) + LF([\alpha, \beta], [\alpha, \beta]),$$

for all elements α and β of B_b.

Now let us choose an orthonormal basis $(\mu_1, \cdots, \mu_n)$ for $\mathscr{L}(G)$ and write $\alpha = \sum_i a_i\mu_i$, $\beta = \sum_i b_i\mu_i$. Put $M = \max_{i,j}(|a_ib_j - a_jb_i|)$. Then we have

$$(|\alpha||\beta| - F(\alpha, \beta))(|\alpha||\beta| + F(\alpha, \beta))$$
$$= F(\alpha, \alpha)F(\beta, \beta) - F(\alpha, \beta)^2 = (\sum_i a_i{}^2)(\sum_i b_i{}^2) - (\sum_i a_ib_i)^2$$
$$= \sum_{i<j}(a_ib_j - a_jb_i)^2 \geq M^2,$$

so that, a fortiori, $(|\alpha||\beta| - F(\alpha, \beta))2|\alpha||\beta| \geq M^2$. Hence, if α and β belong to B_a, where $0 < a \leq b$, then

$$2(|\alpha||\beta| - F(\alpha, \beta)) \geq (M/a)^2.$$

On the other hand, we may write

$$[\alpha, \beta] = \sum_k(\sum_{i<j} c_{ijk}(a_ib_j - a_jb_i))\mu_k,$$

where the coefficients c_{ijk} do not depend on α and β. Put

$$p = \max_{i,j,k}(|c_{ijk}|).$$

Then we obtain

$$F([\alpha, \beta], [\alpha, \beta]) \leq \sum_k(\sum_{i<j} pM)^2 = n^3(n-1)^2 4^{-1}p^2 M^2.$$

Hence we see from the above that, if we choose $a < 2(n(n-1)p)^{-1}(nL)^{-1/2}$, we shall have

$$2(|\alpha|\,|\beta| - F(\alpha, \beta)) \geq LF([\alpha, \beta], [\alpha, \beta]),$$

and the inequality will be strict unless $M = 0$, i.e., unless α and β are linearly dependent.   Here we suppose, as we evidently may, that $n > 1$.

Our above inequality for $F(\eta(\alpha, \beta), \eta(\alpha, \beta))$ then yields

$$F(\eta(\alpha, \beta), \eta(\alpha, \beta)) \leq F(\alpha + \beta, \alpha + \beta) + 2(|\alpha|\,|\beta| - F(\alpha, \beta)),$$

i.e., $F(\eta(\alpha, \beta), \eta(\alpha, \beta)) \leq (|\alpha| + |\beta|)^2$, and this inequality is strict unless α and β are linearly dependent.   This is clearly equivalent to the conclusion of Proposition 3.1, whose proof is therefore complete.

THEOREM 3.2.   *If G is a compact analytic group then $\exp_G$ is surjective.*

Proof.   We use the notation and the results of Proposition 3.1.   If x and y are elements of G such that $x^{-1}y$ lies in V_c we put $d(x, y) = \log(x^{-1}y)$. With the real number a as in Proposition 3.1, choose a real number b such that $0 < b < a$ and such that, if V_b^* denotes the closure of V_b, we have $V_b^* V_b^* \subset V_a$.   If x, y, z are elements of V_b^* then $x^{-1}y$ and $y^{-1}z$ belong to V_a, so that Proposition 3.1 yields $d(x, z) \leq d(x, y) + d(y, z)$, the inequality being strict unless $\log(x^{-1}y)$ and $\log(y^{-1}z)$ are linearly dependent.

Since G is connected, it is generated by V_b^*.   Thus, if x is any element of G we may write $x = x_1 \cdots x_m$, where each x_i lies in V_b^*.   Put $z_0 = 1$ and $z_i = x_1 \cdots x_i$ if $i > 0$.   Then $z_m = x$ and $z_i^{-1}z_{i+1} \in V_b^*$ for $i = 0, \cdots, m-1$.   For the minimum m, consider all sequences of $m + 1$ elements of G, $(t_0, \cdots, t_m)$, such that $t_0 = 1$, $t_m = x$, and $t_i^{-1}t_{i+1} \in V_b^*$ for $i = 0, \cdots, m-1$.   With each such sequence, associate its *length* $\sum_i d(t_i, t_{i+1})$.   Let s denote the infimum of the lengths of such sequences.   Let

$$u_k = (t_0^{(k)}, \cdots, t_m^{(k)}), \qquad k = 0, 1, \cdots,$$

be a sequence of such sequences such that the length s_k of u_k converges to s as k becomes large.   Since G is compact with a countable basis of open sets for its topology, we can ensure, by taking a subsequence if necessary, that $t_i^{(k)}$ converges to a point t_i in G as k becomes large, for each i.   Then we have

$t_0 = 1$, $t_m = x$, $t_i^{-1}t_{i+1} \in V_b{}^*$, and the length of this sequence $(t_0, \cdots, t_m)$ is s. Moreover, since m is minimal, the t_i's are all distinct.

Now write $t_i^{-1}t_{i+1} = \exp(\tau_i)$, with $|\tau_i| \leqq b$. We claim that τ_i and τ_{i+1} are linearly dependent. In fact, if this is not the case we have, by Proposition 3.1,

$$d(t_i, t_{i+2}) < d(t_i, t_{i+1}) + d(t_{i+1}, t_{i+2}).$$

Also,

$$t_i^{-1}t_{i+2} = (t_i^{-1}t_{i+1})(t_{i+1}^{-1}t_{i+2}) \in V_b{}^*V_b{}^* \subset V_a.$$

Put $t_{i+1}{}^* = t_i \exp(\tfrac{1}{2}\log(t_i^{-1}t_{i+2}))$. Then we have

$$d(t_i, t_{i+1}{}^*) = \tfrac{1}{2}d(t_i, t_{i+2}) < \max(d(t_i, t_{i+1}), d(t_{i+1}, t_{i+2})) \leqq b,$$

so that $t_i^{-1}t_{i+1}{}^* \in V_b{}^*$. Similarly, $(t_{i+1}{}^*)^{-1}t_{i+2} \in V_b{}^*$. Thus the sequence $(t_0, \cdots, t_i, t_{i+1}{}^*, t_{i+2}, \cdots, t_m)$ satisfies the requirements specified above. On the other hand, its length is evidently less than s. This contradicts the definition of s, so that τ_i and τ_{i+1} are linearly dependent. Since $t_i \neq t_{i+1}$, we have $\tau_i \neq 0$, and it follows recursively that, for each $k < m - 1$, $\tau_0 + \cdots + \tau_k$ is a real multiple of τ_{k+1}, so that

$$\exp(\tau_0 + \cdots + \tau_k)\exp(\tau_{k+1}) = \exp(\tau_0 + \cdots + \tau_{k+1}).$$

Hence we see that $x = \exp(\tau_0 + \cdots + \tau_{m-1})$, and Theorem 3.2 is proved.

4

We shall derive the basic results concerning toroidal subgroups of compact analytic groups.

Theorem 4.1. *Let T be a maximal toroid in the compact analytic group G. Then every element of G lies in some conjugate xTx^{-1} of T.*

Proof. Let y be an element of G. By Theorem 3.2, we have $y = \exp(\beta)$ with some β in $\mathscr{L}(G)$. By Proposition 1.6 of Chapter III, there is an element t in T such that the group generated by t is dense in T. Let us call such an element a *quasigenerator* of T. Write $t = \exp(\tau)$ with τ in $\mathscr{L}(T)$ (which we regard as a subalgebra of $\mathscr{L}(G)$). Let $x \to x^*$ denote the adjoint representation of G, and let F be an invariant inner product for $\mathscr{L}(G)$, as per Theorem 1.1. We know from Section 1 that every x^* is an F-orthogonal linear automorphism of $\mathscr{L}(G)$. Since G is compact, the minimum of the function $z \to F(\tau, z^*(\beta))$ is attained at some point x of G. Replacing β with $x^*(\beta)$, and thus y with xyx^{-1}, we ensure that the function $z \to F(\tau, z^*(\beta))$ has a minimum at $z = 1$. Hence, for every element α of

$\mathscr{L}(G)$, the function $f_\alpha \colon R \to R$ defined by $f_\alpha(r) = F(\tau, \exp(r\alpha)^*(\beta))$ has a minimum at 0. Hence $f_\alpha{}'(0) = 0$, i.e., $F(\tau, [\alpha, \beta]) = 0$. By the invariance and the non-degeneracy of F, this yields $[\beta, \tau] = 0$. Hence, for all real numbers r, the elements $\exp(r\beta)$ commute with the quasigenerator $\exp(\tau)$ of T and hence with every element of T. The closure of the group generated by T and the elements $\exp(r\beta)$ is evidently a toroid containing T, so that it follows from the maximality of T that $\exp(\beta) \in T$. For the original element y of G, this means that $xyx^{-1} \in T$, so that Theorem 4.1 is proved.

COROLLARY 4.2. *A maximal toroid in a compact analytic group G is a maximal abelian subgroup of G, and any two maximal toroids of G are conjugate by an inner automorphism of G.*

Proof. The second statement follows immediately by applying Theorem 4.1 with T one of the given maximal toroids and the element of G a quasigenerator of the other maximal toroid.

Now let T be a maximal toroid in G, and let A be an abelian subgroup of G that contains T. Let a be an element of A, and let B be the closure of the group generated by a and T. Then the connected component of 1 in B is a toroid containing T and hence must coincide with T. Thus B/T is discrete, and therefore finite, because it is compact. Moreover, B/T is generated by the image aT of a in B/T. There is an exponent m such that $(aT)^m = T$, i.e., $a^m \in T$. Since T is divisible, there is an element u in T such that $u^m = a^{-m}t$, where t is a quasigenerator of T. Now $(au)^m = t$, so that the closure of the group generated by au contains T and a, and thus coincides with B. By Theorem 3.2, we have $au = \exp(\beta)$ with some β in $\mathscr{L}(G)$. The closure of the group $(\exp(r\beta))_{r \in R}$ is evidently a toroid in G containing T, so that it must coincide with T. Hence $B = T$, and so $A = T$, q.e.d.

THEOREM 4.3. *Let T be a maximal toroid in the compact analytic group G. Then the coset space G/T is simply connected.*

Proof. By Corollary 4.2, T contains the center, P say, of G, and T/P is a maximal toroid in G/P. The coset space G/T may evidently be identified with the coset space $(G/P)/(T/P)$. It is clear from Theorem 1.3 that G/P is semisimple. Thus it suffices to prove Theorem 4.3 in the case where G is semisimple.

In that case, let $\pi \colon H \to G$ be a group covering with H simply connected. By Theorem 1.3 (since $\mathscr{L}(H)$ is isomorphic with $\mathscr{L}(G)$), H is a compact semisimple analytic group. Let U be the analytic subgroup of H such that

$\pi(U) = T$. Then U is clearly a maximal toroid in H and therefore contains the kernel of π, which is in the center of H. Hence $U = \pi^{-1}(T)$, whence we may identify G/T with H/U. Now the canonical map $\mu: H \to H/U$ is open, continuous and surjective, and $\mu^{-1}(x)$ is connected for every point x of H/U. Since H is simply connected, this implies, as is indicated in Exercise 1 of Chapter IV, that H/U is simply connected. This completes the proof of Theorem 4.3.

EXERCISES

1. Let G be an analytic group, and suppose that the closure, in the full linear group on $\mathscr{L}(G)$, of the image of G under the adjoint representation is compact. Prove that G is the direct product of a vector group and a compact group. [Show first that there is a positive definite invariant symmetric bilinear form on $\mathscr{L}(G) \times \mathscr{L}(G)$, and then apply the results of Section 1.]

2. For an analytic group G, show that the following three conditions are equivalent:
    (i)   the factor group of G by its center is compact;
    (ii) G is the direct product of a vector group and a compact group;
    (iii) every neighborhood U of 1 in G contains a neighborhood V of 1 in G such that $xVx^{-1} = V$ for every element x of G.
    [Use the result of Exercise 1 to show that (i) implies (ii), and an argument used in the proof of Lemma 1.1 of Chapter IX to show that (ii) implies (iii). In order to show that (iii) implies (i), consider $\log(V)$, where V is a small compact and conjugation invariant neighborhood of 1 in G, and show that the hypothesis of Exercise 1 is satisfied.]

3. Let G be a compact analytic group. Let $\pi_1(G)$ denote the group of the homotopy classes of closed arcs in G that start and end at 1. Show that every element of $\pi_1(G)$ is represented by a one parameter subgroup $r \to \exp_G(r\alpha)$, with α in $\mathscr{L}(G)$. [Take a group covering $H \to G$ with H simply connected, note that (by Exercises 2 and 3 of Chapter IV) the elements of $\pi_1(G)$ are in a certain 1-1 correspondence with the elements of the kernel of the covering, and use Theorem 3.2 to show that $\exp_H$ is surjective, etc.]

4. Let T be a maximal toroid in the compact analytic group G. Show that if N is the normalizer of T in G then N/T is a finite group.

XIV. CARTAN SUBALGEBRAS [3, 5, 9]

1

A *Cartan subalgebra* of a Lie algebra L is a nilpotent subalgebra H that coincides with its own *normalizer* in L, i.e., that has the property that $[x, H] \subset H$ only if $x \in H$.

PROPOSITION 1.1.   *If H is a Cartan subalgebra of the Lie algebra L then H is a maximal nilpotent subalgebra of L.*

Proof. Let N be a nilpotent subalgebra of L containing H. Consider the representation of H on N/H that is induced from the adjoint representation of N. Since this is nilpotent, it is clear that if N were not equal to H there would be an element x of N such that x does not belong to H but $[y, x] \in H$ for every element y of H. This would contradict the definition of a Cartan subalgebra, so that we must have $N = H$.

PROPOSITION 1.2.   *Let L be a Lie algebra, x an element of L. Denote by L^x the subspace of L consisting of all elements y for which there is an exponent n such that $D_x{}^n(y) = 0$. Then L^x is a subalgebra of L and coincides with its normalizer in L.*

Proof.   The formula $D_x{}^n([u, v]) = \sum_{k=0}^n C_{n, k} [D_x{}^k(u), D_x{}^{n-k}(v)]$, where $C_{n, k}$ is the binomial coefficient, shows immediately that $[L^x, L^x] \subset L^x$, so that L^x is a subalgebra of L.

Now suppose that y is an element of L such that $[y, L^x] \subset L^x$. Since $x \in L^x$, we have then $[x, y] \in L^x$, whence also $y \in L^x$. This completes the proof.

PROPOSITION 1.3.   *Let L be a finite-dimensional Lie algebra, x an element of L. Then there is a subspace L_x of L such that $L = L_x + L^x$, $L_x \cap L^x = (0)$ and $[L^x, L_x] \subset L_x$.*

Proof. The proof of Lemma 1.1 of Chapter XI has already given a decomposition $L = L_x + L^x$, with $D_x(L_x) \subset L_x$ and $L_x \cap L^x = (0)$; the space L_x is $D_x{}^p(L)$, where p is large enough to have $D_x{}^p(L) = D_x{}^{p+1}(L)$. It remains to be shown that $[L^x, L_x] \subset L_x$.

We shall prove by induction on m that if $D_x{}^m(y) = 0$ then $D_y(L_x) \subset L_x$. For $m = 0$, the assumption means that $y = 0$, so that the assertion holds for $m = 0$. For $m = 1$, we have $[x, y] = 0$ and hence $D_x D_y = D_y D_x$; since $L_x = D_x{}^p(L)$, it is clear that therefore $D_y(L_x) \subset L_x$. Now suppose that $m > 1$, and that we have already shown that $D_x{}^{m-1}(z) = 0$ implies $D_z(L_x) \subset L_x$. Let y be an element of L such that $D_x{}^m(y) = 0$, and let u be an element of L_x. Let $f(t)$ be the minimum polynomial of the restriction of D_x to L_x. Then the constant term $f(0)$ of f is different from 0, and $f(D_x)(u) = 0$, whence $(f(D_x)D_y)(u) = (f(D_x)D_y - D_y f(D_x))(u)$. One verifies immediately that, for every positive integer q,

$$D_x{}^q D_y - D_y D_x{}^q = \sum_{r=0}^{q-1} D_x{}^r D_{D_x(y)} D_x{}^{q-r-1}.$$

Hence $f(D_x)D_y - D_y f(D_x)$ is a linear combination of terms $D_x{}^a D_{D_x(y)} D_x{}^b$, so that our inductive hypothesis gives $f(D_x)(D_y(u)) \in L_x$. Now let n be a positive integer such that $D_x{}^n$ annihilates L^x. Since $f(0) \neq 0$, there are polynomials $g(t)$ and $h(t)$ such that $g(t)t^n + h(t)f(t) = 1$. Now if we write $D_y(u) = v + w$ with v in L_x and w in L^x, we obtain

$$D_y(u) = (g(D_x)D_x{}^n + h(D_x)f(D_x))(D_y(u))$$
$$= g(D_x)(D_x{}^n(v)) + h(D_x)(f(D_x)(D_y(u))) \in L_x.$$

This completes the proof of Proposition 1.3.

THEOREM 1.4. *Let L be a finite-dimensional Lie algebra over an infinite field, and let x be an element of L such that L^x has the least possible dimension. Then L^x is a Cartan subalgebra of L.*

Proof. By Proposition 1.2, it suffices to show that L^x is a *nilpotent* Lie algebra. Let y be an element of L^x, and let $f_y(t)$ denote the characteristic polynomial of D_y. By Propositions 1.2 and 1.3, both L^x and L_x are stable under D_y. Hence $f_y(t) = g_y(t)h_y(t)$, where $g_y(t)$ is the characteristic polynomial of the restriction of D_y to L^x and $h_y(t)$ is the characteristic polynomial of the restriction of D_y to L_x. Let $(y_1, \cdots, y_m)$ be a basis of L^x. Let t^n be the highest power of t that divides all the $g_y(t)$'s for y in L^x. There exists a polynomial $u(t_1, \cdots, t_m)$ such that the coefficient of t^n in $g_{c_1 y_1 + \cdots + c_m y_m}(t)$ is $u(c_1, \cdots, c_m)$, for all elements c_i of the base field. By the definition of n, $u(t_1, \cdots, t_m)$ is not the 0-polynomial. There also exists a polynomial $v(t_1, \cdots, t_m)$ such that $h_{c_1 y_1 + \cdots + c_m y_m}(0) = v(c_1, \cdots, c_m)$ for all elements c_i of the base field. Since no non-zero element of L_x is annihilated by D_x, we must have $h_x(0) \neq 0$. Hence $v(t_1, \cdots, t_m)$ is not the 0-polynomial. Since the base field is infinite, it contains elements c_i such that $u(c_1, \cdots, c_m)v(c_1, \cdots, c_m) \neq 0$, for the product of the polynomials u and v is not the 0-polynomial. Now if $y = c_1 y_1 + \cdots + c_m y_m$ then the coefficient of t^n in $f_y(t)$, which is $u(c_1, \cdots, c_m)v(c_1, \cdots, c_m)$, is different from 0, so that $f_y(t)$ is not divisible by t^{n+1}.

Since the dimension of L^x is minimal, we have $\dim(L^y) \geqq m$. On the other hand, $t^{\dim(L^y)}$ divides the characteristic polynomial $f_y(t)$, by the elementary theory of linear endomorphisms, applied to D_y. Since $f_y(t)$ is not divisible by t^{n+1}, we have therefore $\dim(L^y) \leqq n$, whence $m \leqq n$.

Now let y be an arbitrary element of L^x. By what we have just proved, $g_y(t)$ is divisible by t^m. On the other hand, the degree of $g_y(t)$ is $\dim(L^x) = m$. Hence $g_y(t) = t^m$. Hence D_y is nilpotent on L^x for every y in L^x. By Theorem 1.5 of Chapter XI (Engel's Theorem), this means that L^x is a nilpotent Lie algebra, so that Theorem 1.4 is proved.

2

Let L be a Lie algebra, and let L° denote the space dual to L. Let V be an L-module, and let γ be an element of L°. Let V_γ denote the subspace of V consisting of all elements that are annihilated by some power of $\rho(x) - \gamma(x)$ for every element x of L, where ρ denotes the representation of L on V. If $V_\gamma \neq (0)$, we say that γ is a *weight* of the representation ρ, and we call V_γ the corresponding *weight space*.

THEOREM 2.1. *Let L be a finite-dimensional nilpotent Lie algebra over an algebraically closed field of characteristic 0, and let ρ be a representation of L on a finite-dimensional vector space V. Then, for each γ in L°, V_γ is an L-submodule of V. If γ is a weight then there is a non-zero element v in V_γ such that $x \cdot v = \gamma(x)v$ for every x in L. Finally, V is the direct sum of the weight spaces V_γ.*

Proof. It is easily verified by induction on m that $(\rho(x) - \gamma(x))^m \rho(y)$ is a sum of endomorphisms of the form $\rho(D_x{}^p(y))(\rho(x) - \gamma(x))^q$, where $p + q = m$. Noting that L is nilpotent, we see from this that V_γ is an L-submodule of V.

By Lie's Theorem (Theorem 1.3 of Chapter XI), $[L, L]$ annihilates every simple L-module, so that the endomorphisms corresponding to the elements of L commute with each other. Since the base field is algebraically closed, we may therefore apply Schur's Lemma to conclude that every simple L-submodule of V_γ is one-dimensional, whence it is clear that there must be a non-zero element v in the weight space V_γ such that $x \cdot v \in (v)$ for every x in L. Since v is annihilated by some power of $\rho(x) - \gamma(x)$, it follows that we must actually have $x \cdot v = \gamma(x)v$.

Now let $\gamma_1, \cdots, \gamma_k$ be a set of distinct weights. Since the base field is infinite, there is an element x in L such that the values $\gamma_1(x), \cdots, \gamma_k(x)$ are all distinct. Then it is clear from the elementary theory of a single linear endomorphism, applied to the restriction of $\rho(x)$ to $V_{\gamma_1} + \cdots + V_{\gamma_k}$, that this last sum is direct. In particular, this implies that there are only a finite number of weights, so that we may suppose that $\gamma_1, \cdots, \gamma_k$ are all the weights.

Now let a be any element of the base field, and let V_a denote the set of all elements of V that are annihilated by some power of $\rho(x) - a$, where x is as above. From the first paragraph of this proof (using a γ such that $\gamma(x) = a$), we know that V_a is an L-submodule of V. The second paragraph of this proof then shows that if $V_a \neq (0)$ there is a non-zero element v in V_a and a weight γ_i such that $y \cdot v = \gamma_i(y)v$ for every element y of L. Since v is annihilated by some power of $\rho(x) - a$, it follows that we must have $a = \gamma_i(x)$. The elementary theory of a single linear endomorphism shows that V is the sum of the V_a's, whence $V = \sum_{i=1}^k V_{\gamma_i(x)}$. Hence it suffices to show that $V_{\gamma_i(x)} \subset V_{\gamma_i}$.

Let y be any element of L, and let $V_{i,a}$ denote the subspace of $V_{\gamma_i(x)}$ consisting of the elements that are annihilated by some power of $\rho(y) - a$. As above, if $V_{i,a} \neq (0)$ there is a non-zero element v in $V_{i,a}$ and a weight γ_j such that $z \cdot v = \gamma_j(z)v$ for every element z of L. Since v is annihilated by some power of $\rho(x) - \gamma_i(x)$, we must have $\gamma_j(x) = \gamma_i(x)$, whence $\gamma_j = \gamma_i$. Since v is annihilated by a power of $\rho(y) - a$, we must have $a = \gamma_j(y) = \gamma_i(y)$. But $V_{\gamma_i(x)}$ is the sum of the $V_{i,a}$'s. Hence $V_{\gamma_i(x)} = V_{i,\gamma_i(y)}$ for every y in L, which means that $V_{\gamma_i(x)} \subset V_{\gamma_i}$. This completes the proof of Theorem 2.1.

Now let L be any finite-dimensional Lie algebra over an algebraically closed field of characteristic 0, and let H be a Cartan subalgebra of L. A weight of the representation of H on L that is induced from the adjoint representation of L is called a *root* of L with respect to H. For any element γ of H°, L_γ is defined with respect to this representation of H on L, so that $L_\gamma \neq (0)$ means that γ is a root.

THEOREM 2.2.   *Let L be a finite-dimensional Lie algebra over an algebraically closed field of characteristic 0, and let H be a Cartan subalgebra of L.   Let L_y, for γ in $H°$, be defined with respect to the adjoint representation of H on L.   Then $[L_\gamma, L_\delta] \subset L_{\gamma+\delta}$ for all elements γ and δ of $H°$, and $L_0 = H$.*

Proof.   The first statement follows immediately from the formula

$$(D_z - (\gamma + \delta)(z))^n([x, y]) = \sum_k C_{n,k} [(D_z - \gamma(z))^k(x), (D_z - \delta(z))^{n-k}(y)],$$

which is easily established by induction on n for all elements z of H and all elements x and y of L.

Since H is nilpotent on H, we have $H \subset L_0$.   Since every element of H is nilpotent on L_0, it follows from Engel's Theorem that H is nilpotent on L_0. Hence, if we had $L_0 \neq H$ we could find an element v in $L_0 - H$ such that $[H, v] \subset H$, which is impossible, because the Cartan subalgebra H coincides with its normalizer in L.   Thus $L_0 = H$, and Theorem 2.2 is proved.

THEOREM 2.3.   *Let L and H be as in Theorem 2.2, and let B denote the trace form of the adjoint representation of L.   Let $d_y = \dim(L_y)$, where $\gamma \in H°$.   Then, for all elements x and y of H, $B(x, y) = \sum_\gamma d_\gamma \gamma(x)\gamma(y)$, where the summation is over the finite set of roots of L with respect to H.*

Proof.   By Theorem 2.1, L is the direct sum of the H-submodules L_y. Hence $B(x, x) = T(D_x^2) = \sum_\gamma T(D_{x,\gamma}^2)$, where $D_{x,\gamma}$ denotes the restriction of D_x to L_y.   Now $D_{x,\gamma}^2 - \gamma(x)^2$ is nilpotent, because $D_{x,\gamma} - \gamma(x)$ is nilpotent and

$$D_{x,\gamma}^2 - \gamma(x)^2 = (D_{x,\gamma} - \gamma(x))(D_{x,\gamma} + \gamma(x))$$
$$= (D_{x,\gamma} + \gamma(x))(D_{x,\gamma} - \gamma(x)).$$

Hence $T(D_{x,\gamma}^2 - \gamma(x)^2) = 0$, whence $T(D_{x,\gamma}^2) = d_\gamma \gamma(x)^2$.   Thus we have, for every x in L, $B(x, x) = \sum_\gamma d_\gamma \gamma(x)^2$.   Theorem 2.3 evidently follows from this.

THEOREM 2.4.   *In the notation of Theorem 2.3, if $x \in L_\gamma, y \in L_\delta$ and $\gamma + \delta \neq 0$ then $B(x, y) = 0$.*

Proof.   By Theorem 2.2, $D_x D_y$ maps each non-zero L_μ into $L_{\gamma+\delta+\mu}$. Since $\gamma + \delta \neq 0$, L_μ and $L_{\gamma+\delta+\mu}$ are different direct summands of L. Hence $T(D_x D_y) = 0$, q.e.d.

3

For all of this section, the following notation will be in force: *L is a finite-dimensional semisimple Lie algebra over an algebraically closed field of* characteristic 0, and H is a Cartan subalgebra of L. The trace form of the adjoint representation of L will be denoted by B. Let α and β be roots of L with respect to H, and suppose that $\beta \neq 0$. Let α^β denote the non-negative integer defined by the condition that $\alpha + m\beta$ be a root for every integer m such that $0 \leq m \leq \alpha^\beta$, while $\alpha + (1 + \alpha^\beta)\beta$ is not a root. Similarly, α_β is defined by the condition that $\alpha - m\beta$ be a root for all integers m such that $0 \leq m \leq \alpha_\beta$, while $\alpha - (1 + \alpha_\beta)\beta$ is not a root.

We know from Theorem 2.1 of Chapter XI that B is non-degenerate. Let α be a root, and let x be a non-zero element of L_α. Then there is an element y in L such that $B(x, y) \neq 0$. By Theorem 2.1, y is the sum of elements y_β in the root spaces L_β. By Theorem 2.4, we have then $B(x, y) = B(x, y_{-\alpha})$. This yields the following conclusions: *for every non-zero element x in L_α, there is an element y in $L_{-\alpha}$ such that $B(x, y) \neq 0$; in particular, if α is a root, so is $-\alpha$, and the restriction of B to $H \times H$ is non-degenerate,* because $H = L_0$ (Theorem 2.2). The last statement evidently implies that, *for every element μ of H°, there is one and only one element h_μ in H such that $B(h, h_\mu) = \mu(h)$ for every element h of H.*

PROPOSITION 3.1. *Let α and β be roots, and suppose that $\alpha \neq 0$. Then, in the notation introduced above, we have*

(1) *if x_α is a non-zero element of L_α such that $[h, x_\alpha] = \alpha(h)x_\alpha$ for every h in H, then $[x_\alpha, y] = B(x_\alpha, y)h_\alpha$ for every y in $L_{-\alpha}$;*

(2) $\alpha(h_\alpha)$ *is a positive rational number; in fact,* $\alpha(h_\alpha)\sum_\gamma(\gamma_\alpha - \gamma^\alpha)^2 = 4$ *(the summation being over all roots γ);*

(3) $2\beta(h_\alpha) = (\beta_\alpha - \beta^\alpha)\alpha(h_\alpha)$;

(4) *the only scalar multiples of α that are roots are 0, α, $-\alpha$;*

(5) $\dim(L_\alpha) = 1$;

(6) *if k is an integer such that $\beta + k\alpha$ is a root then $-\beta_\alpha \leq k \leq \beta^\alpha$.*

Proof. Let x_α and y be as in (1). By Theorem 2.2, we have $[x_\alpha, y] \in L_0 = H$. Now let h be any element of H and use the invariance property $B([x, y], z) = B(x, [y, z])$ to obtain

$$B(h, [x_\alpha, y]) = B([h, x_\alpha], y) = \alpha(h)B(x_\alpha, y)$$
$$= B(h, B(x_\alpha, y)h_\alpha).$$

Since B is non-degenerate on $H \times H$, this gives (1).

Let U denote the sum of the root spaces $L_{\beta + m\alpha}$, where $-\beta_\alpha \leq m \leq \beta^\alpha$. It is clear from Theorem 2.2 that U is stable under the endomorphisms D_z with z in $L_\alpha + L_{-\alpha}$. Let x_α be as in (1). We know that there is an

159

element y in $L_{-\alpha}$ such that $B(x_\alpha, y) \neq 0$. Hence it is clear from (1) that we may choose y in $L_{-\alpha}$ such that $[x_\alpha, y] = h_\alpha$. Then we have $D_{h_\alpha} = [D_{x_\alpha}, D_y]$, whence it is clear that the trace of the restriction of D_{h_α} to U is 0. By the definition of $L_{\beta + m\alpha}$, $D_{h_\alpha} - (\beta + m\alpha)(h_\alpha)$ is nilpotent on $L_{\beta + m\alpha}$ and hence has trace 0. Hence we have $\sum_m (\beta + m\alpha)(h_\alpha) \dim(L_{\beta + m\alpha}) = 0$, the summation being over $-\beta_\alpha \leq m \leq \beta^\alpha$. Now suppose that $\alpha(h_\alpha) = 0$. Then the last relation shows that $\beta(h_\alpha) = 0$. Since this holds for every root β, it follows from Theorem 2.3 that $B(h, h_\alpha) = 0$ for every h in H, i.e., that $\alpha(h) = 0$ for every h in H, contradicting our assumption that $\alpha \neq 0$. Thus we have $\alpha(h_\alpha) \neq 0$.

Let $V = H + (x_\alpha) + \sum_{m < 0} L_{m\alpha}$. Clearly, V is stable under D_{x_α} and under D_y. Hence it follows as above for U that the restriction of D_{h_α} to V has trace 0, i.e., that

$$\alpha(h_\alpha)(1 + \sum_{m < 0} m) \dim(L_{m\alpha}) = 0.$$

Since $\alpha(h_\alpha) \neq 0$, this implies that $L_{m\alpha} = (0)$ for $m < -1$, and $\dim(L_{-\alpha}) = 1$. This gives (5), because we may replace α by $-\alpha$ in the above. Moreover, this shows that the only *integral* multiples of α that are roots are 0, α, $-\alpha$. Hence $0_\alpha = 1$, $0^\alpha = 1$, $\alpha^\alpha = 0$, $\alpha_\alpha = 2$. In particular, this shows that (3) holds whenever the root β is an integral multiple of α.

Now suppose that β is not an integral multiple of α. Then, by (5), $\dim(L_{\beta + m\alpha}) = 1$ whenever $-\beta_\alpha \leq m \leq \beta^\alpha$. Substituting this in our first trace relation (for U), we obtain $\sum_{-\beta_\alpha \leq m \leq \beta^\alpha} (\beta(h_\alpha) + m\alpha(h_\alpha)) = 0$, which gives (3).

Now Theorem 2.3 yields

$$\alpha(h_\alpha) = B(h_\alpha, h_\alpha) = \sum_\beta \dim(L_\beta)\beta(h_\alpha)^2 = \sum_\beta \beta(h_\alpha)^2,$$

whence we obtain (2) by replacing the $\beta(h_\alpha)$'s with the rational multiples of $\alpha(h_\alpha)$ given by (3).

In order to prove (4), suppose that β is a root of the form $c\alpha$, where c is an element of the base field. Then it follows from (3) that $c = \frac{1}{2}p$, where p is an integer. If $c \neq 0$, we may interchange α and β and find that $c^{-1} = \frac{1}{2}q$, where q is an integer. Now $pq = 4$. Since we have already disposed of the integral multiples of α, we may assume that p is odd. But then the only possibilities are $p = 1$ and $p = -1$, which give $\alpha = 2\beta$ and $\alpha = -2\beta$, respectively. But each of these possibilities is ruled out, because the only integral multiples of β that are roots are 0, β, $-\beta$. Thus (4) is proved.

It remains only to prove (6). Suppose there are integers k larger than β^α, and hence larger than $\beta^\alpha + 1$, such that $\beta + k\alpha$ is a root. Let $k_1, \cdots, k_p$ be all of these. Put $W = \sum_{i=1}^p L_{\beta + k_i\alpha}$. One sees immediately that W is stable under D_{x_α} and under D_y. Hence we may again apply the same trace argument as twice before to obtain

$$\sum_{i=1}^p (\beta(h_\alpha) + k_i\alpha(h_\alpha)) = 0,$$

whence $\qquad\qquad p\beta(h_\alpha) = -(k_1 + \cdots + k_p)\alpha(h_\alpha).$

Together with (3), this gives

$$p(\beta^\alpha - \beta_\alpha) = 2(k_1 + \cdots + k_p) > 2p(\beta^\alpha + 1),$$

which is a contradiction. Similarly, we see that there are no integers k larger than β_α such that $\beta - k\alpha$ is a root. This completes the proof of Proposition 3.1.

THEOREM 3.2. *H is abelian, and the roots of L with respect to H span $H°$.*

Proof. Let α be a non-zero root. Since L_α is one-dimensional, it is clear from Theorem 2.1 that $[h, x] = \alpha(h)x$ for every element h of H and every element x of L_α. Let N be the subspace of H consisting of all elements that are annihilated by every root. By what we have just shown, $[L_\alpha, N] = (0)$, and $[H, H] \subset N$. Since L is the sum of H and the L_α's, N is therefore an ideal of L. Since N is contained in H, it is nilpotent. Hence we must have $N = (0)$, because the semisimple Lie algebra L has no non-zero nilpotent ideal. Evidently, this proves Theorem 3.2.

By Proposition 3.1, the non-zero roots come in pairs $(\alpha, -\alpha)$. For each such pair, choose a non-zero element x_α in L_α. We know that there is an element y in $L_{-\alpha}$ such that $B(y, x_\alpha) \neq 0$. Hence we may choose $x_{-\alpha}$ in $L_{-\alpha}$ such that $B(x_{-\alpha}, x_\alpha) = -1$. By Proposition 3.1, (1), we have then $[x_{-\alpha}, x_\alpha] = h_\alpha$. Note that, since $h_{-\alpha} = -h_\alpha$, this relation holds also with $-\alpha$ in the place of α. Let S denote the set of all non-zero roots. We define an antisymmetric map c of $S \times S$ into the base field as follows: let α and β be elements of S; if $\alpha + \beta$ does not belong to S we put $c(\alpha, \beta) = 0$; if $\alpha + \beta$ belongs to S then $c(\alpha, \beta)$ is the unique element of the base field such that $[x_\alpha, x_\beta] = c(\alpha, \beta)x_{\alpha + \beta}$ (see Theorem 2.2 and Proposition 3.1, (5)). We shall need to use a certain number of properties of this map c, in addition to the antisymmetry $c(\alpha, \beta) = -c(\beta, \alpha)$. These are collected in the following proposition.

PROPOSITION 3.3. *In the notation introduced above, we have*

(1) *if α, β and $\alpha + \beta$ belong to S then*
$$c(-\alpha, \alpha + \beta) = c(\alpha + \beta, -\beta) = c(-\beta, -\alpha),$$

(2) *if $\alpha, \beta, \gamma, \delta$ belong to S and $\alpha + \beta + \gamma + \delta = 0$ and δ is not one of $-\alpha, -\beta$ or $-\gamma$ then*
$$c(\alpha, \beta)c(\gamma, \delta) + c(\beta, \gamma)c(\alpha, \delta) + c(\gamma, \alpha)c(\beta, \delta) = 0,$$

(3) *if α is not equal to β or $-\beta$ then*
$$c(\alpha, \beta)c(-\alpha, -\beta) = c(\alpha, -\beta)c(-\alpha, \beta) - B(h_\alpha, h_\beta),$$

(4) *if $\alpha + \beta \neq 0$ then*
$$2c(\alpha, \beta)c(-\alpha, -\beta) = \beta^\alpha(1 + \beta_\alpha)\alpha(h_\alpha).$$

Proof. Property (1) follows immediately from the following evident relations:

$$B([x_{-\alpha}, x_{\alpha+\beta}], x_{-\beta}) = B(x_{-\alpha}, [x_{\alpha+\beta}, x_{-\beta}]) = B(x_{\alpha+\beta}, [x_{-\beta}, x_{-\alpha}]),$$

because $B(x_\beta, x_{-\beta})$, $B(x_{-\alpha}, x_\alpha)$ and $B(x_{\alpha+\beta}, x_{-\alpha-\beta})$ are all equal to -1.

The assumptions in (2) remain satisfied when α, β, γ are permuted. Hence (2) will follow from the Jacobi identity once we have shown that

$$-c(\alpha, \beta)c(\gamma, \delta) = B([[x_\alpha, x_\beta], x_\gamma], x_\delta).$$

The right-hand side is equal to $B([x_\alpha, x_\beta], [x_\gamma, x_\delta])$. Now suppose first that $\alpha + \beta$ belongs to S. Then we have, since $\gamma + \delta = -(\alpha + \beta) \in S$,

$$B([x_\alpha, x_\beta], [x_\gamma, x_\delta]) = c(\alpha, \beta)c(\gamma, \delta)B(x_{\alpha+\beta}, x_{\gamma+\delta}) = -c(\alpha, \beta)c(\gamma, \delta).$$

If $\alpha + \beta$ does not belong to S then $c(\alpha, \beta) = 0$, so that it suffices to show that $[x_\alpha, x_\beta] = 0$. By Theorem 2.2, $[x_\alpha, x_\beta] = L_{\alpha+\beta}$. But $\alpha + \beta = -(\gamma + \delta) \neq 0$, so that $L_{\alpha+\beta} = (0)$. Thus (2) is proved.

Let α and β be as in (3). Then the quadruple $(\alpha, \beta, -\alpha, -\beta)$ satisfies the assumptions of (2), so that we know from our proof of (2) that

$$c(\alpha, \beta)c(-\alpha, -\beta) = -B([x_\alpha, x_\beta], [x_{-\alpha}, x_{-\beta}]).$$

Replacing β by $-\beta$ we obtain

$$c(\alpha, -\beta)c(-\alpha, \beta) = -B([x_\alpha, x_{-\beta}], [x_{-\alpha}, x_\beta]).$$

Hence we obtain

$$c(\alpha, \beta)c(-\alpha, -\beta) - c(\alpha, -\beta)c(-\alpha, \beta)$$
$$= -B([x_\alpha, x_\beta], [x_{-\alpha}, x_{-\beta}]) + B([x_\alpha, x_{-\beta}], [x_{-\alpha}, x_\beta])$$
$$= -B([[x_{-\alpha}, x_{-\beta}], x_\alpha], x_\beta) + B([[x_\alpha, x_{-\beta}], x_{-\alpha}], x_\beta).$$

By the Jacobi identity, the right-hand side is equal to

$$-B([[x_{-\alpha}, x_\alpha], x_{-\beta}], x_\beta) = -B([x_{-\alpha}, x_\alpha], [x_{-\beta}, x_\beta]) = -B(h_\alpha, h_\beta),$$

so that (3) is proved.

For $\alpha + \beta \neq 0$, put

$$d(\alpha, \beta) = c(\alpha, \beta)c(-\alpha, -\beta) - \tfrac{1}{2}\beta^\alpha(1 + \beta_\alpha)\alpha(h_\alpha).$$

We shall prove by induction on β^α that $d(\alpha, \beta) = 0$, i.e., that (4) holds. If $\beta^\alpha = 0$ then $\beta + \alpha$ does not belong to S, so that $c(\alpha, \beta) = 0$, whence also $d(\alpha, \beta) = 0$. Now suppose that $\beta^\alpha > 0$ and that (4) has been established in the lower cases. Then $\beta + \alpha$ belongs to S and $(\beta + \alpha) + \alpha \neq 0$, because -2α is not a root. Since $(\beta + \alpha)^\alpha = \beta^\alpha - 1$, we have from our inductive hypothesis that $d(\alpha, \beta + \alpha) = 0$. On the other hand, we may apply (3) to the pair $(\alpha, \beta + \alpha)$ to obtain

$$c(\alpha, \beta + \alpha)c(-\alpha, -\beta - \alpha) = c(\alpha, -\beta - \alpha)c(-\alpha, \beta + \alpha) - B(h_\alpha, h_{\beta + \alpha}).$$

From (1) and the antisymmetry of c, we have

$$c(-\alpha, \beta + \alpha) = c(-\beta, -\alpha) = -c(-\alpha, -\beta)$$

and

$$c(\alpha, -\beta - \alpha) = c(\beta, \alpha) = -c(\alpha, \beta).$$

Hence we obtain

$$\begin{aligned} 0 = d(\alpha, \beta + \alpha) \\ = c(\alpha, \beta + \alpha)c(-\alpha, -\beta - \alpha) - \tfrac{1}{2}(\beta + \alpha)^\alpha(1 + (\beta + \alpha)_\alpha)\alpha(h_\alpha) \\ = c(\alpha, \beta)c(-\alpha, -\beta) - k(\alpha, \beta), \end{aligned}$$

where

$$\begin{aligned} k(\alpha, \beta) &= B(h_\alpha, h_{\beta + \alpha}) + \tfrac{1}{2}(\beta + \alpha)^\alpha(1 + (\beta + \alpha)_\alpha)\alpha(h_\alpha) \\ &= \beta(h_\alpha) + \alpha(h_\alpha) + \tfrac{1}{2}(\beta^\alpha - 1)(2 + \beta_\alpha)\alpha(h_\alpha). \end{aligned}$$

If, using Proposition 3.1, (3), we replace $\beta(h_\alpha)$ with $\tfrac{1}{2}(\beta_\alpha - \beta^\alpha)\alpha(h_\alpha)$ we find that $k(\alpha, \beta) = \tfrac{1}{2}\beta^\alpha(1 + \beta_\alpha)\alpha(h_\alpha)$, so that (4) is established. This completes the proof of Proposition 3.3.

We are now in a position to prove that a semisimple Lie algebra is determined up to an isomorphism by its root system. The precise result is the following.

THEOREM 3.4. *Let L and L' be semisimple Lie algebras of finite dimension over an algebraically closed field of characteristic 0, and let H, H' be Cartan subalgebras of L, L', respectively. Suppose there is given a bijection $\alpha \to \alpha'$ of the set of roots of L onto the set of roots of L' such that $\alpha' + \beta'$ is 0, a non-zero root or no root if and* *only if the corresponding statement holds for $\alpha + \beta$, and that $(\alpha + \beta)' = \alpha' + \beta'$ whenever $\alpha + \beta$ is a root. Then there is a Lie algebra isomorphism η of L onto L' such that $\eta(H) = H'$ and $\alpha' \circ \eta_H = \alpha$ for every root α of L.*

Proof. The assumptions imply that $\beta^\alpha = (\beta')^{\alpha'}$ and $\beta_\alpha = (\beta')_{\alpha'}$. Hence it is clear from Proposition 3.1, (2) and (3), that $\beta(h_\alpha) = \beta'(h_{\alpha'})$ for all roots α and β. Now let $(\alpha_1, \cdots, \alpha_r)$ be a maximal linearly independent set of roots of L. Since this is then a basis of H° and since $(h_{\alpha_1}, \cdots, h_{\alpha_r})$ is then a basis of H, the determinant formed from the values $\alpha_i(h_{\alpha_j})$ is different from 0. Since $\alpha_i'(h_{\alpha_j'}) = \alpha_i(h_{\alpha_j})$, this shows that the set $(\alpha_1', \cdots, \alpha_r')$ is also linearly independent. Making this argument with L and L' interchanged, we see that $(\alpha_1', \cdots, \alpha_r')$ is a maximal linearly independent set of roots of L', so that the $h_{\alpha_i'}$'s make up a basis of H'. Hence there is a linear isomorphism η_H of H onto H' such that $\eta_H(h_{\alpha_i}) = h_{\alpha_i'}$ for each i. Clearly, $\alpha_i' \circ \eta_H = \alpha_i$.

If α is any root of L, we may write $\alpha = \sum_{i=1}^r c_i \alpha_i$ and $\alpha' = \sum_{i=1}^r c_i' \alpha_i'$, with coefficients c_i, c_i' in the base field. Now we have

$$\sum_i c_i \alpha_i(h_{\alpha_j}) = \alpha(h_{\alpha_j}) = \alpha'(h_{\alpha_j'}) = \sum_i c_i' \alpha_i'(h_{\alpha_j'}) = \sum_i c_i' \alpha_i(h_{\alpha_j}).$$

Since the determinant formed from the values $\alpha_i(h_{\alpha_j})$ is different from 0, this gives $c_i = c_i'$ for each i, whence

$$\alpha' \circ \eta_H = \sum_i c_i'(\alpha_i' \circ \eta_H) = \sum_i c_i \alpha_i = \alpha.$$

Thus Theorem 3.4 will be proved once we have extended η_H to a Lie algebra isomorphism of L onto L'. For each non-zero root α of L, choose an element x_α in L_α as before, so that $B(x_{-\alpha}, x_\alpha) = -1$ and $[x_{-\alpha}, x_\alpha] = h_\alpha$, and choose elements $x_{\alpha'}$ in $L'_{\alpha'}$ similarly. The required isomorphism η will be determined by the images $\eta(x_\alpha)$. We shall obtain these as suitable scalar multiples $c_\alpha x_{\alpha'}$. From the requirement $\eta([x_\alpha, x_\beta]) = [\eta(x_\alpha), \eta(x_\beta)]$ we see that the c_α's must satisfy the following conditions:

(1) $c_\alpha c_{-\alpha} = 1$;

(2) if $\alpha + \beta$ is a non-zero root then $c(\alpha, \beta)c_{\alpha+\beta} = c(\alpha', \beta')c_\alpha c_\beta$, where $c(\alpha, \beta)$ and $c(\alpha', \beta')$ are as in Proposition 3.3.

These conditions are also sufficient. In fact, we have then $\eta([x_\alpha, x_\beta]) = [\eta(x_\alpha), \eta(x_\beta)]$, $\eta([x, y]) = 0 = [\eta(x), \eta(y)]$ whenever x and y are in H, and finally $\eta([h_\beta, x_\alpha]) = [\eta(h_\beta), \eta(x_\alpha)]$ follows from $\alpha(h_\beta) = \alpha'(h_{\beta'})$. Thus η is a Lie algebra homomorphism, and since it sends a basis of L onto a basis of L' it is therefore a Lie algebra isomorphism.

We order the set of all rational linear combinations of the α_i's lexicographically; if u_i and v_i are rational numbers, $\sum_i u_i \alpha_i > \sum_i v_i \beta_i$ means that the first non-zero difference $u_i - v_i$ is positive. Our proof that $\alpha' \circ \eta_H = \alpha$ has shown that the roots α of L are rational linear combinations of the α_i's. We shall define the required coefficients c_α for $\alpha > 0$ inductively with respect to this ordering and enforce (1) by putting $c_{-\alpha} = (c_\alpha)^{-1}$. Let ρ be a root > 0, and suppose that c_α has already been defined for every non-zero root α such that $-\rho < \alpha < \rho$, and that conditions (1) and (2) are satisfied for all α and β such that α, β and $\alpha + \beta$ are non-zero roots greater than $-\rho$ and less than ρ. We must define c_ρ such that, if $c_{-\rho} = (c_\rho)^{-1}$, condition (2) will hold for all α and β such that α, β and $\alpha + \beta$ are non-zero roots greater than or equal to $-\rho$ and less than or equal to ρ. If there is no such pair (α, β) with $\alpha + \beta = \rho$ we may evidently satisfy our requirements simply by putting $c_\rho = 1 = c_{-\rho}$.

Now suppose that there is a pair (α, β) as above with $\alpha + \beta = \rho$. Then $\beta^\alpha \neq 0$ so that, by Proposition 3.3, (4), we have $c(\alpha, \beta) \neq 0$. Also $(\beta')^{\alpha'} = \beta^\alpha \neq 0$, whence $c(\alpha', \beta') \neq 0$. We define $c_\rho = c(\alpha, \beta)^{-1} c(\alpha', \beta') c_\alpha c_\beta$, so as to satisfy condition (2) for this pair (α, β), and we put $c_{-\rho} = (c_\rho)^{-1}$. By Proposition 3.3, (4), we have $c(\alpha, \beta) c(-\alpha, -\beta) = c(\alpha', \beta') c(-\alpha', -\beta')$, whence it is clear that condition (2) holds also for the pair $(-\alpha, -\beta)$.

It remains to show that condition (2) holds for every other pair (γ, δ) with $-\rho \leqq \gamma \leqq \rho$, $-\rho \leqq \delta \leqq \rho$ and $\gamma + \delta = \rho$. Then δ is not equal to α, β or $-\gamma$, so that Proposition 3.3, (2), applies to the quadruple $(-\alpha, -\beta, \gamma, \delta)$ and gives

$$c(-\alpha, -\beta)c(\gamma, \delta) + c(-\beta, \gamma)c(-\alpha, \delta) + c(\gamma, -\alpha)c(-\beta, \delta) = 0. \quad (*)$$

Since $\alpha + \beta = \rho = \gamma + \delta$, it is clear from the order relations satisfied by α, β, γ, δ that these roots are all > 0, and that the difference of any two of these is greater than $-\rho$ and less than ρ. Now $\gamma - \beta \neq 0$ and $\delta - \alpha = -(\gamma - \beta)$. Hence if $\gamma - \beta$ is a root, so is $\delta - \alpha$ and by our inductive hypothesis we have

$$c(-\beta, \gamma)c_{\gamma-\beta} = c(-\beta', \gamma')c_{-\beta}c_\gamma \quad \text{and} \quad c(-\alpha, \delta)c_{\delta-\alpha} = c(-\alpha', \delta')c_{-\alpha}c_\delta.$$

If $\gamma - \beta$ is not a root these relations still hold, with the convention that $c_\mu = 1$ if μ is not a root. Similarly,

$$c(\gamma, -\alpha)c_{\gamma-\alpha} = c(\gamma', -\alpha')c_{-\alpha}c_\gamma \quad \text{and} \quad c(-\beta, \delta)c_{\delta-\beta} = c(-\beta', \delta')c_{-\beta}c_\delta.$$

Since $c_{\gamma-\beta}c_{\delta-\alpha} = 1 = c_{\gamma-\alpha}c_{\delta-\beta}$, the last four relations yield

$$c(-\beta, \gamma)c(-\alpha, \delta) = c(-\beta', \gamma')c(-\alpha', \delta')c_{-\alpha}c_{-\beta}c_{\gamma}c_{\delta}$$

and $\qquad c(\gamma, -\alpha)c(-\beta, \delta) = c(\gamma', -\alpha')c(-\beta', \delta')c_{-\alpha}c_{-\beta}c_{\gamma}c_{\delta}.$

If we substitute the right-hand sides in $(*)$ and multiply by $c_{\alpha}c_{\beta}c_{-\gamma}c_{-\delta}$ we obtain

$$c(-\alpha, -\beta)c(\gamma, \delta)c_{\alpha}c_{\beta}c_{-\gamma}c_{-\delta}$$
$$+ c(-\beta', \gamma')c(-\alpha', \delta') + c(\gamma', -\alpha')c(-\beta', \delta') = (0).$$

On the other hand, the relation $(*)$ holds also with α', β', γ', δ' in the places of α, β, γ, δ. Hence we must have

$$c(-\alpha, -\beta)c(\gamma, \delta)c_{\alpha}c_{\beta}c_{-\gamma}c_{-\delta} = c(-\alpha', -\beta')c(\gamma', \delta').$$

Now if we note that condition (2) holds for the pair $(-\alpha, -\beta)$, we see that this last relation yields condition (2) for the pair (γ, δ). Thus Theorem 3.4 is proved.

COROLLARY 3.5. *The basis elements x_α can be so chosen that, in addition to* $B(x_{-\alpha}, x_\alpha) = -1$ *and* $[x_{-\alpha}, x_\alpha] = h_\alpha$, *one has* $c(\alpha, \beta) = c(-\alpha, -\beta)$.

Proof. The map $\alpha \to -\alpha$ of the set of roots of L onto itself evidently satisfies the conditions of Theorem 3.4. Let η be the automorphism of L obtained in Theorem 3.4, so that $\eta(x_\alpha) = c_\alpha x_{-\alpha}$. For each pair $(\alpha, -\alpha)$ of non-zero roots, choose d_α in the base field such that $d_\alpha{}^2 = c_{-\alpha}$, and put $d_{-\alpha} = (d_\alpha)^{-1}$. Now let $y_\alpha = d_\alpha x_\alpha$. Then we still have $B(y_{-\alpha}, y_\alpha) = -1$ and $[y_{-\alpha}, y_\alpha] = h_\alpha$. If α, β and $\alpha + \beta$ are non-zero roots we have

$$[y_\alpha, y_\beta] = d_\alpha d_\beta [x_\alpha, x_\beta] = c'(\alpha, \beta)y_{\alpha+\beta},$$

where $c'(\alpha, \beta) = d_\alpha d_\beta d_{-\alpha-\beta}c(\alpha, \beta)$. We know that

$$c(\alpha, \beta) = c_\alpha c_\beta c_{-\alpha-\beta}c(-\alpha, -\beta).$$

Substitution yields $c'(\alpha, \beta) = c'(-\alpha, -\beta)$.

4

Let L be a Lie algebra over the field C of the complex numbers. We may evidently regard L also as a Lie algebra over the field R of the real numbers. Then a real Lie subalgebra M of L is called a *real form* of L if the canonical map $M \otimes_R C \to L$ is an isomorphism of complex Lie algebras.

Denote the usual complex conjugation of C by $c \to c^*$. A *conjugation* of a complex Lie algebra L is a map σ of L into itself satisfying the following conditions:

(1) σ is a *semilinear map*, i.e., $\sigma(ax + by) = a*\sigma(x) + b*\sigma(y)$ for all elements
    x and y of L and all complex numbers a and b;

(2) $\sigma([x, y]) = [\sigma(x), \sigma(y)]$ for all x and y in L;

(3) σ^2 is the identity map on L.

It is easy to see that if M is a real form of L then there is one and only one
conjugation σ of L such that M is the σ-fixed part L_σ of L. Conversely, if σ
is any conjugation of L then L_σ is evidently a real form of L.

A finite-dimensional real Lie algebra L will be said to be of *compact type*
if the trace form of its adjoint representation is negative definite. By the
results of Section 1 of Chapter XIII, the Lie algebra of a compact semisimple
analytic group is of compact type and, conversely, if L is a Lie algebra of
compact type then L is semisimple and every analytic group whose Lie
algebra is isomorphic with L is compact.

THEOREM 4.1.   *Every finite-dimensional semisimple complex Lie algebra has a
real form of compact type.*

Proof. Let L be the given finite-dimensional semisimple complex Lie
algebra, and let H be a Cartan subalgebra of L. We shall use the notation
and the results of Section 3. Let H_0 denote the R-subspace of H that is
spanned by the h_α's, where α ranges over the non-zero roots of L with respect
to H. We know from Corollary 3.5 that, for each such α, we have $L_\alpha =
Cx_\alpha$, where the x_α's are non-zero elements of L satisfying the conditions
$B(x_{-\alpha}, x_\alpha) = -1$, $[x_{-\alpha}, x_\alpha] = h_\alpha$ and, if α, β and $\alpha + \beta$ are non-zero
roots, $[x_\alpha, x_\beta] = c(\alpha, \beta)x_{\alpha+\beta}$, with $c(\alpha, \beta) = c(-\alpha, -\beta) \neq 0$. Moreover,
we know from Propositions 3.1 and 3.3 that $c(\alpha, \beta)c(-\alpha, -\beta)$ is a
positive rational number. Hence the last relation above shows that
$c(\alpha, \beta) \in R$.

Proposition 3.1 shows also that every non-zero root takes only real values
on H_0. Since the h_α's span H over C, we have $H = H_0 + iH_0$, and since
the non-zero roots separate the points of H it follows from our last remark
that $H_0 \cap (iH_0) = (0)$. We know that the x_α's are C-linearly independent
mod. H. Hence it is clear that there is one and only one semilinear map σ
of L into L such that $\sigma(z) = -z$ for every element z of H_0 and $\sigma(x_\alpha) = x_{-\alpha}$
for every non-zero root α. Clearly, σ^2 is the identity map on L.

We shall show that $\sigma([x, y]) = [\sigma(x), \sigma(y)]$ for all elements x and y of L,
which will prove σ to be a conjugation of L. Clearly, it suffices to verify
this for the pairs (z, x_α), $(x_{-\alpha}, x_\alpha)$ and (x_α, x_β), with z in H_0 and $\alpha + \beta \neq 0$.

We have $[\sigma(z), \sigma(x_\alpha)] = [-z, x_{-\alpha}] = \alpha(z)x_{-\alpha}$, and since $\alpha(z)$ is real the last element is equal to $\sigma(\alpha(z)x_\alpha) = \sigma([z, x_\alpha])$. Next,

$$[\sigma(x_{-\alpha}), \sigma(x_\alpha)] = [x_\alpha, x_{-\alpha}] = -h_\alpha = \sigma(h_\alpha) = \sigma([x_{-\alpha}, x_\alpha]).$$

Finally, if $\alpha + \beta \neq 0$, we have $[x_\alpha, x_\beta] = c(\alpha, \beta)x_{\alpha+\beta}$ in all cases, provided that we interpret $x_{\alpha+\beta}$ and $c(\alpha, \beta)$ as 0's when $\alpha + \beta$ is not a root. Hence we have

$$\sigma([x_\alpha, x_\beta]) = c(\alpha, \beta)x_{-\alpha-\beta} = c(-\alpha, -\beta)x_{-\alpha-\beta} = [\sigma(x_\alpha), \sigma(x_\beta)].$$

Thus σ is indeed a conjugation of L.

Now let x be any element of L, and write $x = h + \sum_\alpha t_\alpha x_\alpha$, with h in H and the t_α's in C. Then the corresponding decomposition of $\sigma(x)$ is $\sigma(x) = \sigma(h) + \sum_\alpha (t_\alpha)^* x_{-\alpha}$. We use Theorems 2.3 and 2.4 to obtain

$$\begin{aligned} B(x, \sigma(x)) &= B(h, \sigma(h)) + \sum_\alpha B(t_\alpha x_\alpha, (t_\alpha)^* x_{-\alpha}) \\ &= \sum_\alpha (\alpha(h)\alpha(\sigma(h)) - t_\alpha(t_\alpha)^*). \end{aligned}$$

If we write $h = z_1 + iz_2$, with z_1 and z_2 in H_0 we see that $\alpha(\sigma(h)) = -(\alpha(h))^*$. Hence we have $B(x, \sigma(x))$ real and strictly negative, unless $x = 0$. In particular, if $x \in L_\sigma$ then $B(x, x) < 0$, unless $x = 0$. Thus L_σ is of compact type, because the restriction of B to $L_\sigma \times L_\sigma$ is the trace form of the adjoint representation of L_σ. This completes the proof of Theorem 4.1.

PROPOSITION 4.2. *Let L be a finite-dimensional semisimple complex Lie algebra, and let σ be any conjugation of L. There is a Cartan subalgebra H of L such that $\sigma(H) = H$. For every such H, if α is a root of L with respect to H, so is $(\alpha \circ \sigma)^*$, where $(\alpha \circ \sigma)^*(h) = \alpha(\sigma(h))^*$, and $\sigma(L_\alpha) = L_{(\alpha \circ \sigma)^*}$.*

Proof. Let $r = \min_{x \in L}(\dim(L^x))$. For every element x of L, let $f_x(t)$ denote the characteristic polynomial of D_x. Then t^r divides $f_x(t)$, so that we have, with $n = \dim(L)$,

$$f_x(t) = t^n + a_1(x)t^{n-1} + \cdots + a_{n-r}(x)t^r.$$

The a_i's are evidently polynomial functions on L, i.e., are given by polynomials in linear functions on L, and a_{n-r} is not the zero function, by the definition of r. Since L has a C-basis in L_σ, we can therefore find an element x in L_σ such that $a_{n-r}(x) \neq 0$. Then $\dim(L^x)$ has the minimum value r, so that, by Theorem 1.4, L^x is a Cartan subalgebra of L. Let z be an element of L^x. Then we have $[x, \sigma(z)] = [\sigma(x), \sigma(z)] = \sigma([x, z]) = 0$, so that $\sigma(z) \in L^x$. Since σ is an R-linear automorphism of L, we have therefore $\sigma(L^x) = L^x$.

Now let H be any Cartan subalgebra of L such that $\sigma(H) = H$, and let α be a root of L with respect to H. Let z be an element of H, and let x be an element of L_α. Then

$$[z, \sigma(x)] = \sigma([\sigma(z), x]) = \sigma(\alpha(\sigma(z))x) = \alpha(\sigma(z))^*\sigma(x).$$

This shows that $(\alpha \circ \sigma)^*$ is a root of L with respect to H and that $\sigma(L_\alpha) \subset L_{(\alpha \circ \sigma)^*}$. Since σ is an R-linear automorphism and L_α and $L_{(\alpha \circ \sigma)^*}$ are of the same R-dimension 2, we have therefore $\sigma(L_\alpha) = L_{(\alpha \circ \sigma)^*}$, so that Proposition 4.2 is proved.

THEOREM 4.3. *Let L be a finite-dimensional semisimple complex Lie algebra, and let σ be any conjugation of L. Then there is a conjugation τ of L such that τ commutes with σ and L_τ is of compact type.*

Proof. By Proposition 4.2, there is a Cartan subalgebra H of L such that $\sigma(H) = H$. Corresponding to the non-zero roots α of L with respect to H, choose elements x_α in L_α as in the proof of Theorem 4.1. By Proposition 4.2, we have then $\sigma(x_\alpha) = c_\alpha x_{(\alpha \circ \sigma)^*}$, where $0 \neq c_\alpha \in C$. There is evidently one and only one semilinear map τ of L into L such that $\tau(z) = -z$ for every element z of H_0 (defined as in the proof of Theorem 4.1) and $\tau(x_\alpha) = |c_\alpha|x_{-\alpha}$ for every non-zero root α. We follow the pattern of the proof of Theorem 4.1 in showing that τ is actually a conjugation of L:

$$[\tau(z), \tau(x_\alpha)] = [-z, |c_\alpha|x_{-\alpha}] = |c_\alpha|\alpha(z)x_{-\alpha} = \tau(\alpha(z)x_\alpha) = \tau([z, x_\alpha]).$$

Since $[\sigma(x_{-\alpha}), \sigma(x_\alpha)] = \sigma([x_{-\alpha}, x_\alpha])$, we have $c_{-\alpha}c_\alpha h_{(\alpha \circ \sigma)^*} = \sigma(h_\alpha)$. Now we shall show that $h_{(\alpha \circ \sigma)^*} = \sigma(h_\alpha)$. In order to do this, note that, for every element x of L, we have $\sigma \circ D_x \circ \sigma = D_{\sigma(x)}$ and, for every linear endomorphism η of L, $T(\sigma \circ \eta \circ \sigma) = T(\eta)^*$. Let h be an arbitrary element of H. Then we obtain

$$\begin{aligned}
B(h_{(\alpha \circ \sigma)^*}, h) &= (\alpha \circ \sigma)^*(h) = \alpha(\sigma(h))^* = B(h_\alpha, \sigma(h))^* \\
&= T(D_{h_\alpha}D_{\sigma(h)})^* = T(\sigma D_{h_\alpha}D_{\sigma(h)}\sigma) = T(\sigma D_{h_\alpha}\sigma D_h \sigma\sigma) \\
&= T(D_{\sigma(h_\alpha)}D_h) = B(\sigma(h_\alpha), h).
\end{aligned}$$

Hence we have indeed $h_{(\alpha \circ \sigma)^*} = \sigma(h_\alpha)$, so that the above shows that $c_{-\alpha}c_\alpha = 1$. Hence we obtain

$$\begin{aligned}
[\tau(x_{-\alpha}), \tau(x_\alpha)] &= [|c_{-\alpha}|x_\alpha, |c_\alpha|x_{-\alpha}] = [x_\alpha, x_{-\alpha}] \\
&= -h_\alpha = \tau(h_\alpha) = \tau([x_{-\alpha}, x_\alpha]).
\end{aligned}$$

Now suppose that α and β are non-zero roots and $\alpha + \beta \neq 0$. From $\sigma([x_\alpha, x_\beta]) = [\sigma(x_\alpha), \sigma(x_\beta)]$, we have

$$c(\alpha, \beta)c_{\alpha+\beta} = c((\alpha \circ \sigma)^*, (\beta \circ \sigma)^*)c_\alpha c_\beta,$$

where we interpret $c_{\alpha+\beta}$ as 1 if $\alpha + \beta$ is not a root. Since the map $\alpha \rightarrow (\alpha \circ \sigma)^*$ satisfies the conditions of Theorem 3.4, it is clear from Propositions 3.1 and 3.3 that we have

$$c(\alpha, \beta)c(-\alpha, -\beta) = c((\alpha \circ \sigma)^*, (\beta \circ \sigma)^*)c(-(\alpha \circ \sigma)^*, -(\beta \circ \sigma)^*),$$

i.e., $c(\alpha, \beta)^2 = c((\alpha \circ \sigma)^*, (\beta \circ \sigma)^*)^2$. Hence our last result gives $|c_{\alpha+\beta}| = |c_\alpha||c_\beta|$, in case $\alpha + \beta$ is a root. Using this, we obtain, in all cases,

$$[\tau(x_\alpha), \tau(x_\beta)] = |c_\alpha||c_\beta|[x_{-\alpha}, x_{-\beta}] = |c_\alpha||c_\beta|c(-\alpha, -\beta)x_{-\alpha-\beta}$$
$$= |c_{\alpha+\beta}|c(\alpha, \beta)x_{-\alpha-\beta} = \tau([x_\alpha, x_\beta]).$$

Now it follows, because τ is a semilinear map, that $\tau([x, y]) = [\tau(x), \tau(y)]$ for all elements x and y of L. Moreover, since $|c_{-\alpha}||c_\alpha| = 1$, it is clear that τ^2 is the identity map on L. Thus τ is a conjugation of L.

Clearly, $\tau \circ \sigma$ coincides with $\sigma \circ \tau$ on H. Next,

$$\sigma(\tau(x_\alpha)) = \sigma(|c_\alpha|x_{-\alpha}) = |c_\alpha|c_{-\alpha}x_{-(\alpha \circ \sigma)^*},$$

while

$$\tau(\sigma(x_\alpha)) = \tau(c_\alpha x_{(\alpha \circ \sigma)^*}) = (c_\alpha)^*|c_{(\alpha \circ \sigma)^*}|x_{-(\alpha \circ \sigma)^*}.$$

Since σ^2 is the identity map on L, we have $(c_\alpha)^*c_{(\alpha \circ \sigma)^*} = 1$. Hence

$$(c_\alpha)^*|c_{(\alpha \circ \sigma)^*}| = (c_\alpha)^*|c_\alpha|^{-1} = |c_\alpha|(c_\alpha)^{-1} = |c_\alpha|c_{-\alpha},$$

so that $\sigma(\tau(x_\alpha)) = \tau(\sigma(x_\alpha))$. Thus τ commutes with σ. Finally, one shows exactly as in the proof of Theorem 4.1 that L_τ is of compact type, which completes the proof of Theorem 4.3.

EXERCISES

1. Let L be a Lie algebra over a field F, and let H be a subalgebra of L. If P is any extension field of F show that $H \otimes_F P$ is a Cartan subalgebra of $L \otimes_F P$ if and only if H is a Cartan subalgebra of L.

2. Let L be a finite-dimensional Lie algebra over a field F of characteristic 0, let K be an ideal of L and let H be a Cartan subalgebra of L. Show that $(H + K)/K$ is a Cartan subalgebra of L/K. [By Exercise 1, it may be assumed that F is algebraically closed. Let L_α denote the root spaces of L for the non-zero roots α with respect to H, and show first that $H + K = H + \sum_\alpha (K \cap L_\alpha)$. Since $(H + K)/K$ is evidently nilpotent, it suffices to show that if y is an element of L such that $[y, H] \subset H + K$ then $y \in H + K$. The above decomposition of $H + K$ shows that, in doing this, one may assume that $y \in L_\alpha$ (see

Theorem 2.2). Starting from $(D_x - \alpha(x))^m(y) = 0$ for all x in H, show that $(D_x - \alpha(x))(y) \in H + K$, and hence that $y \in H + K$.]

3. Prove that, up to isomorphisms, there is only one three-dimensional semisimple Lie algebra over an algebraically closed field of characteristic 0, and that every finite-dimensional Lie algebra over such a field is a sum of three-dimensional semisimple subalgebras which, of course, are not necessarily ideals.

4. Let L be a finite-dimensional Lie algebra over a field of characteristic 0, K a solvable ideal of L, S a subalgebra of L such that L is the semidirect sum $S + K$ and is semisimple as an S-module under the adjoint representation. Show that there is a nilpotent subalgebra P of L such that $[S, P] = (0)$ and $K = P + ([L, K])$ (not necessarily semidirect). [P can be found as a Cartan subalgebra of the *centralizer* of S in L, consisting of all elements x in L such that $[x, S] = (0)$.]

5. Build up a four-dimensional complex Lie algebra as follows: begin with a two-dimensional abelian Lie algebra $Cu + Cv$; now adjoin a one-dimensional space Cy to obtain a Lie algebra $Cy + Cu + Cv$ containing $Cu + Cv$ as an ideal, where $[y, u] = v$ and $[y, v] = 0$; now define the four-dimensional Lie algebra $L = Cx + Cy + Cu + Cv$ containing $Cy + Cu + Cv$ as an ideal such that $[x, v] = iv$, $[x, u] = u$ and $[x, y] = (i - 1)y$. Show that L has no conjugation, and thus no real form. [Exploit the fact that a conjugation would map $[L, L] = Cy + Cu + Cv$ into itself and would also map the center Cv of $[L, L]$ into itself, to obtain a contradiction from the assumption that a conjugation exists.]

XV. COMPACT SUBGROUPS
OF LIE GROUPS [4, 7, 9]

1

We shall require a fixed point theorem for compact groups of linear automorphisms which we shall prove first in order not to disrupt the continuity later on. Let V be a finite-dimensional complex vector space, and let F be a positive definite Hermitian form on $V \times V$. If x is any linear endomorphism of V we denote by x^* the Hermitian conjugate of x, which is determined by the condition that $F(x(u), v) = F(u, x^*(v))$ for all elements u and v of V. We say that x is Hermitian if $x = x^*$. If x is a Hermitian linear endomorphism of V then x is said to be positive definite if $F(x(v), v)$ is positive for all non-zero elements v of V. This will be the case if and only if all the characteristic values of x are positive.

Let G denote the group of all linear automorphisms of V, and let Σ denote the set of all positive definite Hermitian linear automorphisms of V. For x in G and h in Σ, put $x \cdot h = xhx^*$. One verifies directly that $x \cdot h$ still belongs to Σ. A map $\eta : [0, 1] \to \Sigma$ is called a *geodesic arc* in Σ if there is an element x in G and a Hermitian linear endomorphism H of V such that $\eta(r) = x \cdot \mathrm{Exp}(rH)$ for every r in $[0, 1]$.

LEMMA 1.1. *For every pair (h_0, h_1) of points of Σ, there is one and only one geodesic arc η in Σ such that $\eta(0) = h_0$ and $\eta(1) = h_1$.*

Proof. Let S denote the real vector space consisting of all Hermitian linear endomorphisms of V. It is easily seen that Σ is an open subset of S, and that Exp is an analytic map of S into Σ. Moreover, this map has an analytic inverse, Log, given by

$$\mathrm{Log}(h) = \log(T(h))I - \sum_{n=1}^{\infty} n^{-1}(I - T(h)^{-1}h)^n,$$

172

where T stands for trace and I for the identity map on V. In fact, since h is positive definite Hermitian, its characteristic roots are positive real numbers. With respect to a C-basis of V for which the corresponding matrix form of h is diagonal, the matrix form of $(I - T(h)^{-1}h)^n$ is diagonal, and the entries on the diagonal are of the form a_i^n, where $0 \leqq a_i < 1$. Hence it is clear that the above series for $\mathrm{Log}(h)$ is absolutely convergent and defines a power series map $h \rightarrow \mathrm{Log}(h)$ of Σ into S. It follows from the usual power series relations that $\mathrm{Exp} \circ \mathrm{Log}$ is the identity map on Σ and $\mathrm{Log} \circ \mathrm{Exp}$ is the identity map on S.

For h in Σ, we define $h^{1/2}$ and $h^{-1/2}$ in Σ as $\mathrm{Exp}(\frac{1}{2} \mathrm{Log}(h))$ and $\mathrm{Exp}(-\frac{1}{2} \mathrm{Log}(h))$, respectively. Now define the geodesic arc η in Σ by

$$\eta(r) = h_0^{1/2} \cdot \mathrm{Exp}(r \, \mathrm{Log}(h_0^{-1/2} h_1 h_0^{-1/2})).$$

Then $\eta(0) = h_0$ and $\eta(1) = h_1$.

It remains to prove the uniqueness part of Lemma 1.1. Suppose that, for $r = 0$ and for $r = 1$, we have $x_1 \cdot \mathrm{Exp}(rH_1) = x_2 \cdot \mathrm{Exp}(rH_2)$. This means that $x_1 x_1^* = x_2 x_2^*$ and $x_1 \mathrm{Exp}(H_1) x_1^* = x_2 \mathrm{Exp}(H_2) x_2^*$. Hence $x_2^{-1} x_1 = x_2^* x_1^{*-1} = z$, say, and $z \, \mathrm{Exp}(H_1) z^{-1} = \mathrm{Exp}(H_2)$, i.e., $\mathrm{Exp}(zH_1 z^{-1}) = \mathrm{Exp}(H_2)$. Now $z^* = x_1^*(x_2^{-1})^* = x_1^*(x_2^*)^{-1} = z^{-1}$, whence we see that $zH_1 z^{-1}$ is Hermitian. Hence our last result gives $zH_1 z^{-1} = H_2$, because Exp is injective on S. Now we have

$$\begin{aligned} x_2 \cdot \mathrm{Exp}(rH_2) &= x_2 \, \mathrm{Exp}(zrH_1 z^{-1}) x_2^* = x_2 z \, \mathrm{Exp}(rH_1) z^{-1} x_2^* \\ &= x_1 \, \mathrm{Exp}(rH_1) x_1^* = x_1 \cdot \mathrm{Exp}(rH_1). \end{aligned}$$

This completes the proof of Lemma 1.1.

A subset E of Σ is called *totally geodesic* if, for every pair (h_0, h_1) of points of E, the geodesic arc η such that $\eta(0) = h_0$ and $\eta(1) = h_1$ lies in E. We are now ready to state the fixed point theorem.

THEOREM 1.2. *Let E be a non-empty closed totally geodesic subset of Σ, and let K be a compact subgroup of G such that E is stable under K with respect to the action $h \rightarrow x \cdot h$. Then K has a fixed point in E.*

Proof. Define the function Q on $\Sigma \times \Sigma$ by

$$Q(h_1, h_2) = T(h_1 h_2^{-1}) + T(h_2 h_1^{-1}).$$

One verifies immediately that $Q(x \cdot h_1, x \cdot h_2) = Q(h_1, h_2)$ for all elements x of G and all elements h_1 and h_2 of Σ. Moreover,

$$Q(h_1, h_2) = T(h_2^{-1/2} h_1 h_2^{-1/2}) + T(h_1^{-1/2} h_2 h_1^{-1/2}),$$

173

which shows that $Q(h_1, h_2)$ is a positive real number, because the arguments for T on the right are positive definite Hermitian automorphisms of V.

Now let η be a geodesic arc in Σ. We claim that the function $r \to Q(h, \eta(r))$, where h is an element of Σ, is strictly convex if η is not constant. Since $Q(x \cdot h_1, x \cdot h_2) = Q(h_1, h_2)$, we may assume in proving this that η is of the form $\eta(r) = \mathrm{Exp}(rH)$, where H is an element of S. Let $(v_1, \cdots, v_n)$ be an orthonormal basis of V with respect to which H is diagonal, so that, if e_i is the coordinate projection of V onto (v_i), we have $H = \sum_{i=1}^n r_i e_i$, with real numbers r_i. Then $\eta(r) = \sum_{i=1}^n e^{r r_i} e_i$ and

$$Q(h, \eta(r)) = \sum_{i=1}^n (a_i e^{r r_i} + b_i e^{-r r_i}),$$

where $a_i = T(h^{-1/2} e_i h^{-1/2})$ and $b_i = T(h^{1/2} e_i h^{1/2})$. Now we have

$$T(h^{1/2} e_i h^{1/2}) = \sum_{j=1}^n F(h^{1/2} e_i h^{1/2}(v_j), v_j),$$

and

$$\begin{aligned} F(h^{1/2} e_i h^{1/2}(v_j), v_j) &= F(e_i h^{1/2}(v_j), h^{1/2}(v_j)) \\ &= F(e_i h^{1/2}(v_j), e_i h^{1/2}(v_j)) \geqq 0. \end{aligned}$$

Since $h^{1/2}$ is a linear automorphism of V, it is clear from this that $b_i > 0$, and similarly that $a_i > 0$. Hence we see from the above expression for $Q(h, \eta(r))$ that the function $r \to Q(h, \eta(r))$ is strictly convex unless each $r_i = 0$, i.e., unless η is constant.

In order to proceed, we require the following lemma.

LEMMA 1.3. *Let P be a compact subset of Σ, and let M be a positive real number. Let $P(M)$ denote the subset of Σ consisting of the elements h in Σ such that $\inf_{p \in P}(Q(p, h)) \leqq M$. Then $P(M)$ is compact.*

Proof. Since Q is continuous, $P(M)$ is closed. Hence it will suffice to show that $P(M)$ is contained in a compact subset of Σ. Let P' be the set of all elements of the form $u p u^{-1}$, where p belongs to P and u belongs to the group U of all unitary automorphisms of V. Then P' is evidently a compact subset of Σ, $P \subset P'$ and hence $P(M) \subset P'(M)$. Hence it suffices to show that $P'(M)$ is compact. Accordingly, we shall now assume that $P = P'$, i.e., that $u P u^{-1} = P$ for every element u of U.

Now we have, with p in P and h in Σ,

$$Q(p, h) = Q(u \cdot p, u \cdot h) = Q(u p u^{-1}, u h u^{-1}),$$

so that, for every u in U, $\inf_{p \in P}(Q(p, h)) \leqq M$ if and only if

$$\inf_{p \in P}(Q(p, u h u^{-1})) \leqq M.$$

Given h in Σ, we may choose an element u in U such that $u h u^{-1}$ is diagonal with respect to a fixed orthonormal basis $(v_1, \cdots, v_n)$ of V. Let $P_d(M)$

denote the set of the diagonal elements of $P(M)$. Then what we have just said shows that $P(M)$ is the set of all elements of the form $u^{-1}hu$, with u in U and h in $P_d(M)$. Hence it suffices to show that $P_d(M)$ is compact. If the e_i's are the coordinate projections we have used before, the elements h of $P_d(M)$ have the form $\sum_{i=1}^{n} h_i e_i$, where the h_i's are positive real numbers. As we have seen above, the traces $T(pe_i)$ and $T(e_i p^{-1})$ are positive for every element p of P. Since P is compact, these have therefore positive infima a_i and b_i, respectively. Now if $h = \sum_{i=1}^{n} h_i e_i$ then

$$\begin{aligned}
\inf_{p \in P}(Q(p, h)) &\geq \inf_{p \in P}(T(ph^{-1})) + \inf_{p \in P}(T(hp^{-1})) \\
&\geq \sum_{i=1}^{n}(\inf_{p \in P}(h_i^{-1}T(pe_i)) + \inf_{p \in P}(h_i T(e_i p^{-1}))) \\
&= \sum_{i=1}^{n}(h_i^{-1}a_i + h_i b_i).
\end{aligned}$$

Hence the condition $\inf_{p \in P}(Q(p, h)) \leq M$ implies that there are positive real numbers r and s such that $s \leq h_i \leq r$ for each i. This evidently implies that $P_d(M)$ is compact, so that Lemma 1.3 is proved.

Now we can complete the proof of Theorem 1.2. Let h and h_0 be points of Σ. Define the function f_{h,h_0} on the given compact subgroup K of G by $f_{h,h_0}(x) = Q(h, x \cdot h_0)$. Now let I_K denote the normalized Haar integral on K and define the function F_{h_0} on Σ by $F_{h_0}(h) = I_K(f_{h,h_0})$. Since K is compact, $K \cdot h_0$ is a compact subset of Σ. By Lemma 1.3, $(K \cdot h_0)(M)$ is compact, which means that the set of the elements h of Σ such that $\inf_{k \in K}(f_{h,h_0}(k)) \leq M$ is compact. Now take h_0 to lie in the given closed totally geodesic subset E of Σ. Then the set of all elements h of E such that $F_{h_0}(h) \leq M$ is evidently a closed subset of the above set and is therefore compact. Hence there is an h_1 in E for which $F_{h_0}(h_1)$ is minimal. We shall show that $x \cdot h_1 = h_1$ for every element x of K.

Let x be an element of K, and let η be the geodesic arc in Σ such that $\eta(0) = h_1$ and $\eta(1) = x \cdot h_1$. We know that, for every k in K, the function $r \to Q(k \cdot h_0, \eta(r)) = f_{\eta(r)h, 0}(k)$ is strictly convex if η is not constant. This is easily seen to imply that $F_{h_0} \circ \eta$ is strictly convex if η is not constant. On the other hand, a straightforward computation, using the invariance of I_K, shows that $F_{h_0}(x \cdot h_1) = F_{h_0}(h_1)$ for every x in K, i.e., $(F_{h_0} \circ \eta)(0) = (F_{h_0} \circ \eta)(1)$. Since E is totally geodesic, $\eta(r) \in E$ for every r in $[0, 1]$. Therefore, by the minimal property of h_1, $(F_{h_0} \circ \eta)(r) \geq (F_{h_0} \circ \eta)(0)$ for every r in $[0, 1]$. This rules out strict convexity of $F_{h_0} \circ \eta$, so that η must be constant. Hence $h_1 = x \cdot h_1$, and Theorem 1.2 is proved.

2

Let L be a finite-dimensional semisimple Lie algebra over the field C of the complex numbers, and suppose that L has a conjugation σ. By Theorem 4.3 of Chapter XIV, there is a conjugation τ of L such that $\sigma \circ \tau = \tau \circ \sigma$ and L_τ is of compact type. Let B denote the trace form of the adjoint representation of L. For x and y in L, put $F(x, y) = -B(x, \tau(y))$. Since the restriction of B to $L_\tau \times L_\tau$ is negative definite, we have $F(x, x) > 0$ for all non-zero elements x of L_τ. Using that B takes only real values on $L_\tau \times L_\tau$ and that $L = L_\tau + iL_\tau$, one verifies directly that $B(\tau(x), \tau(y))$ is the complex conjugate $B(x, y)^*$ of $B(x, y)$ for all elements x and y of L. Hence we obtain $F(x, y) = -B(x, \tau(y)) = -B(\tau(y), x) = -B(y, \tau(x))^* = F(y, x)^*$, so that F is a Hermitian form on $L \times L$. If x and y are elements of L_τ we have $F(x + iy, x + iy) = -B(x + iy, x - iy) = -B(x, x) - B(y, y)$, and since B is negative definite on $L_\tau \times L_\tau$ this shows that F is positive definite on $L \times L$.

Now let A be the group of all Lie algebra automorphisms of L that send L_σ onto itself. We may evidently regard L also as a Lie algebra over the field R of the real numbers, and it is clear that L is semisimple also as a Lie algebra over R. Clearly, A is a closed subgroup of the group of all R-Lie algebra automorphisms of L. Hence A is a Lie group, and its Lie algebra $\mathscr{L}(A)$ is a subalgebra of the Lie algebra of all derivations of the R-Lie algebra L. Since L is semisimple, we know (from Exercise 5 of Chapter XI) that every derivation of L is a D_x, with x in L. If D_x belongs to $\mathscr{L}(A)$ we must have $D_x(L_\sigma) \subset L_\sigma$ and, conversely, if $D_x(L_\sigma) \subset L_\sigma$ then $\mathrm{Exp}(D_x)$ belongs to A. We have $D_x(L_\sigma) \subset L_\sigma$ if and only if x belongs to L_σ, as is seen immediately from the fact that the center of L_σ is (0) and that $L = L_\sigma + iL_\sigma$. Hence $\mathscr{L}(A)$ consists precisely of the derivations D_x with x in L_σ, and the map $x \to D_x$ is an isomorphism of L_σ onto $\mathscr{L}(A)$.

Next we wish to show that A is stable under the Hermitian conjugation $\alpha \to \alpha^*$, where α^* denotes the Hermitian conjugate of α with respect to F. First we show that if α belongs to A then $\alpha^*(L_\sigma) = L_\sigma$. Let x be an element of L_σ, and write $\alpha^*(x) = x_1 + ix_2$, where x_1 and x_2 belong to L_σ. Then, for every element y of L_σ, we have

$$F(x_1 + ix_2, y) = F(x, \alpha(y)) = -B(x, \tau(\alpha(y))),$$

i.e.,
$$-B(x_1, \tau(y)) - iB(x_2, \tau(y)) = -B(x, \tau(\alpha(y))).$$

Since τ commutes with σ, it sends L_σ into itself, so that $\tau(\alpha(y)) \in L_\sigma$. Since B takes only real values on $L_\sigma \times L_\sigma$, the last result therefore implies that $B(x_2, \tau(y)) = 0$ for all elements y of L_σ. Since B is non-degenerate on

$L_\sigma \times L_\sigma$, it follows that $x_2 = 0$. Thus $\alpha^*(L_\sigma) \subset L_\sigma$. Since α^* is a linear automorphism of L, we have therefore $\alpha^*(L_\sigma) = L_\sigma$.

It remains to show that $\alpha^*([x, y]) = [\alpha^*(x), \alpha^*(y)]$ for all elements x and y of L. We do this by showing that

$$F(\alpha^*([x, y]) - [\alpha^*(x), \alpha^*(y)], z) = 0$$

for all elements z of L. Note that

$$F([u, v], w) = -B([u, v], \tau(w)) = B(v, [u, \tau(w)])$$
$$= B(v, \tau([\tau(u), w])) = -F(v, [\tau(u), w]).$$

Hence

$$F([\alpha^*(x), \alpha^*(y)], z) = -F(\alpha^*(y), [\tau(\alpha^*(x)), z])$$
$$= -F(y, [(\alpha \circ \tau \circ \alpha^*)(x), \alpha(z)])$$
$$= F([(\tau \circ \alpha \circ \tau \circ \alpha^*)(x), y], \alpha(z)).$$

Now we show that if β is any Lie algebra automorphism of L then $\tau \circ \beta \circ \tau \circ \beta^*$ is the identity map on L. We have $\beta \circ D_u = D_{\beta(u)} \circ \beta$, whence the definition of B gives $B(\beta(u), v) = B(u, \beta^{-1}(v))$ for all elements u and v of L. Hence we obtain, for all elements x and y of L,

$$B((\tau \circ \beta \circ \tau \circ \beta^*)(x), y) = B((\beta \circ \tau \circ \beta^*)(x), \tau(y))^*$$
$$= B((\tau \circ \beta^*)(x), (\beta^{-1} \circ \tau)(y))^*$$
$$= B(\beta^*(x), (\tau \circ \beta^{-1} \circ \tau)(y))$$
$$= -F(\beta^*(x), (\beta^{-1} \circ \tau)(y))$$
$$= -F(x, \tau(y)) = B(x, y),$$

whence it evidently follows that $\tau \circ \beta \circ \tau \circ \beta^*$ is the identity map on L.

In particular, the above now reduces to

$$F([\alpha^*(x), \alpha^*(y)], z) = F([x, y], \alpha(z)) = F(\alpha^*([x, y]), z),$$

which completes the proof that α^* lies in A whenever α lies in A.

Let U denote the group of all F-unitary C-linear automorphisms of the C-space L. Since $\tau \circ \beta \circ \tau \circ \beta^*$ is the identity map on L for every Lie algebra automorphism β of L, it is clear that a Lie algebra automorphism of L belongs to U if and only if it commutes with τ. In particular, $A \cap U$ is the group of all elements of A that commute with τ. Hence the Lie algebra $\mathcal{L}(A \cap U)$ of $A \cap U$ consists of the derivations D_x with x in L_σ that commute with τ. This means that, for every y in L, $[\tau(x), \tau(y)] = [x, \tau(y)]$, which gives $x = \tau(x)$. Thus $\mathcal{L}(A \cap U)$ is the Lie algebra of the derivations D_x with x in $L_\sigma \cap L_\tau$.

Let G be the group of all C-linear automorphisms of the C-space L, and let Σ be the set of all positive definite Hermitian C-linear automorphisms of L (with respect to F). Evidently, $\gamma\gamma^* \in \Sigma$ for every element γ of G. Put $\delta = \mathrm{Exp}(\frac{1}{2} \mathrm{Log}(\gamma\gamma^*))$. Then we have $(\delta^{-1}\gamma)^*(\delta^{-1}\gamma) = \gamma^*(\delta^{-1})^*\delta^{-1}\gamma = \gamma^*\delta^{-2}\gamma$, which is the identity automorphism of L. Thus $\delta^{-1}\gamma \in U$. We have $\gamma = \delta(\delta^{-1}\gamma)$, $\delta \in \Sigma$, $\delta^{-1}\gamma \in U$. Hence the multiplication map $\Sigma \times U \to G$ is surjective and, since $(\Sigma^{-1}\Sigma) \cap U = (1)$, it is bijective. It is evidently an analytic map. Since the map $\gamma \to \mathrm{Exp}(\frac{1}{2} \mathrm{Log}(\gamma\gamma^*))$ is analytic, the inverse of the map $\Sigma \times U \to G$ is also analytic, so that the multiplication map $\Sigma \times U \to G$ is an analytic manifold isomorphism. Let S denote the R-space of all Hermitian linear endomorphisms of L. We know that $\mathrm{Exp}\colon S \to \Sigma$ is an analytic manifold isomorphism. Moreover, S is a subspace of $\mathscr{L}(G)$ and Exp is the exponential map for the analytic group G. In view of this, we shall call Σ an *exponential manifold factor* of G. We have seen that the analytic manifold G is the Cartesian product of the exponential manifold factor Σ and the manifold of the compact subgroup U of G. Note also that Σ is stable under the conjugations with the elements of U. It is the main purpose of this chapter to generalize this structural result to the case of arbitrary Lie groups with finite component groups. What follows now aims at the case of the adjoint image of a semisimple Lie group.

Let E be the space of all C-linear endomorphisms of the C-space L, but regard E as an R-space. We shall say that a subgroup H of G is a *real algebraic subgroup* of G if there is a set P of polynomial functions on E such that H consists of all those invertible elements of E which are zeros of P. Evidently, G itself is such a group, and A is a real algebraic subgroup of G.

Let T be any subgroup of G that is contained in a real algebraic subgroup H of G such that H is stable under the Hermitian conjugation, and suppose that, if the subscript 1 denotes "connected component of 1", $T_1 = H_1$. Given an element t of T, write $t = su$, with s in Σ and u in U. Then we have $tt^* = s^2$, whence $s^{2m} \in H$ for all integers m. Also, $s^2 \in \Sigma$, so that $s^2 = \mathrm{Exp}(x)$ with x in S. Choose a C-basis for L for which x is diagonal. Then it is easily seen that if p is any polynomial function on E we may write $p(\mathrm{Exp}(rx)) = \sum_{i=1}^{q} c_i e^{rk_i}$, for all real numbers r, where the c_i's are real numbers independent of r and the k_i's are *distinct* real numbers independent of r. If p vanishes on H then $p(s^{2m}) = 0$, i.e., $\sum_i c_i(e^{2k_i})^m = 0$, for all integers m. Put $d_i = e^{2k_i}$. Then $d_1, \cdots, d_q$ are q distinct non-zero real numbers, so that the determinant with entries d_i^j ($j = 1, \cdots, q$) is different from 0. Hence the above relations imply that each $c_i = 0$, so that $p(\text{Exp}(rx)) = 0$ for every real number r. Hence, since H is a real algebraic subgroup of G, we have $\text{Exp}(rx) \in H \cap \Sigma$ for every real number r. Note that this proof has shown, generally, that if $\text{Exp}(x) \in H \cap \Sigma$, where $x \in S$, then $\text{Exp}(rx) \in H \cap \Sigma$ for every real number r. Hence

$$H \cap \Sigma = (H \cap \Sigma)_1 \subset H_1 \cap \Sigma = T_1 \cap \Sigma \subset T \cap \Sigma \subset H \cap \Sigma,$$

so that $H \cap \Sigma = T \cap \Sigma = (T \cap \Sigma)_1 = \text{Exp}(S_H)$, where S_H is a connected subset of S that is stable under the scalar multiplications with real numbers. If x is the above element of S such that $\text{Exp}(x) = s^2$ then $\frac{1}{2}x \in S_H$, $s = \text{Exp}(\frac{1}{2}x) \in \text{Exp}(S_H) = T \cap \Sigma$ and $t = su$, where $u = s^{-1}t \in T \cap U$. Thus we have $T = (T \cap \Sigma)(T \cap U)$.

In particular, this applies to the case where $H = A$. We have already seen that $(A \cap U)_1$ is the analytic subgroup of A whose Lie algebra consists of the derivations D_x with x in $L_\sigma \cap L_\tau$. On the other hand, $A \cap \Sigma = \text{Exp}(S_A)$ and, since S_A is stable under the scalar multiplications with real numbers, it follows that $S_A \subset \mathscr{L}(A) = D_{L_\sigma}$. Thus $S_A = S \cap D_{L_\sigma}$, so that $A \cap \Sigma$ consists of the elements $\text{Exp}(D_x)$, where $x \in L_\sigma$ and D_x is Hermitian, i.e., such that $F(D_x(y), z) = F(y, D_x(z))$ for all elements y and z of L. This last condition means that $B([x, y], \tau(z)) = B(y, [\tau(x), \tau(z)])$, which, in turn, is equivalent to $[x, y] = -[\tau(x), y]$ for all elements y of L, or to the condition $x = -\tau(x)$, i.e., to $x \in iL_\tau$. Thus we have $S_A = D_{L_\sigma \cap (iL_\tau)}$ and $T \cap \Sigma = \text{Exp}(D_{L_\sigma \cap (iL_\tau)})$. Now we see at once from this and the above result for G that the multiplication map $(T \cap \Sigma) \times (T \cap U) \to T$ is an isomorphism of disjoint unions of analytic manifolds (the factor $T \cap U$ need not be connected, but since it is a compact Lie group it has only a finite number of connected components). Hence $T \cap \Sigma$ is an exponential manifold factor of T_1 and, as a disjoint union of analytic manifolds, T is the Cartesian product of $T \cap \Sigma$ and the compact subgroup $T \cap U$. Furthermore, we know that $T \cap \Sigma$ is stable under the conjugations with the elements of $T \cap U$.

The case we are really interested in is the following. Suppose that L_σ is the Lie algebra of a Lie group X. The adjoint representation of X on L_σ extends by C-linearity to a representation of X by Lie algebra automorphisms of the complex Lie algebra $L = L_\sigma \otimes C$. Clearly, the image of X under its adjoint representation may be identified with the corresponding subgroup, T say, of G. Evidently, $T \subset A$ and T contains the image of X_1, which is the analytic subgroup of G that corresponds to the

Lie subalgebra D_{L_σ} of $\mathscr{L}(G)$. Since $D_{L_\sigma} = \mathscr{L}(A)$, it follows that $T_1 = A_1$. Hence our above results on the structure of T apply here to the adjoint image of X.

Finally, we shall use Theorem 1.2 in order to show that the above compact subgroup $T \cap U$ of the adjoint image T of X contains a conjugate of every compact subgroup of T. In order to do this, we show first that $T \cap \Sigma$ is a totally geodesic subset of Σ. Let h_0 and h_1 be points of $T \cap \Sigma$. Then the geodesic arc from h_0 to h_1 is given by

$$\eta(r) = h_0^{1/2} \cdot \mathrm{Exp}(r \, \mathrm{Log}(h_0^{-1/2} h_1 h_0^{-1/2})).$$

We know that $h_0^{1/2}$ and $h_0^{-1/2}$ still belong to $T \cap \Sigma$. Since h_1 belongs to Σ, so does $h_0^{-1/2} h_1 h_0^{-1/2}$. Hence $h_0^{-1/2} h_1 h_0^{-1/2} \in T \cap \Sigma$. We know from the above that this implies that $\mathrm{Exp}(r \, \mathrm{Log}(h_0^{-1/2} h_1 h_0^{-1/2})) \in T \cap \Sigma$ for all real numbers r, and since $h_0^{1/2} \in T$ it follows that $\eta(r) \in T \cap \Sigma$ for all real numbers r. Thus $T \cap \Sigma$ is indeed totally geodesic.

Now let K be any compact subgroup of T. If h is an element of $T \cap \Sigma$ and k is an element of K then khk^* evidently belongs to $A \cap \Sigma$. Since $A \cap \Sigma = T \cap \Sigma$, this means that $T \cap \Sigma$ is stable under the action of K that is involved in Theorem 1.2. Hence we conclude from Theorem 1.2 that there is an element h in $T \cap \Sigma$ such that $khk^* = h$ for every element k of K. Now $h^{1/2} \in T \cap \Sigma$, and

$$(h^{-1/2} k h^{1/2})^* = h^{1/2} k^* h^{-1/2} = h^{1/2}(h^{-1}k^{-1}h)h^{-1/2} = (h^{-1/2} k h^{1/2})^{-1},$$

so that $h^{-1/2} k h^{1/2} \in T \cap U$. Thus $h^{-1/2} K h^{1/2} \subset T \cap U$, which is what was to be proved.

3

In order to state the main result of this chapter, we must introduce a slightly generalized notion of *exponential manifold factor*. Let G be an analytic group, and suppose that, as an analytic manifold, G is a Cartesian product $E \times F$ and that there are vector subspaces $S_1, \cdots, S_k$ of $\mathscr{L}(G)$ whose sum in $\mathscr{L}(G)$ is direct such that the map $x_1 + \cdots + x_k \to \exp_G(x_1) \cdots \exp_G(x_k)$ is an analytic manifold isomorphism of $S_1 + \cdots + S_k$ onto E. Then we say that E is an *exponential manifold factor* of G. Note that then $E = E_1 \times \cdots \times E_k$, where $E_i = \exp_G(S_i)$ and is an exponential manifold factor of G in the sense of Section 2. We shall prove the following general structure theorem.

THEOREM 3.1. *Let G be a Lie group such that G/G_1 is finite. Then G has a compact subgroup K and there is an exponential manifold factor $E = E_1 \times \cdots \times E_k$*

of G_1, where $E_i = \exp_G(S_i)$, as above, such that the following conditions are satisfied:

(i) $xE_ix^{-1} = E_i$ *for each i and every element x of K;*

(ii) *the multiplication $E \times K \to G$ is an isomorphism of disjoint unions of analytic manifolds;*

(iii) *for every compact subgroup L of G, there is an element e in E such that $eLe^{-1} \subset K$.*

Note that the final result of Section 2 is the case of Theorem 3.1 where G is the image of a semisimple Lie group under the adjoint representation. In that case, we had $k = 1$. We shall prove Theorem 3.1 by a reduction to this special case. This reduction will be accomplished in a series of lemmas.

LEMMA 3.2. *Let A be a compact subgroup of a semidirect product $V \times_f T$, where V is a vector group and T a compact group. Then there is an element v in V such that $vAv^{-1} \subset T$.*

Proof. Write the elements a of A in the form $a = \sigma(a)\tau(a)$, where $\sigma(A) \in V$ and $\tau(a) \in T$. Writing V additively, we have then $\sigma(a_1 a_2) = \sigma(a_1) + f(\tau(a_1))(\sigma(a_2))$. Hence the translate $\sigma \cdot a$ of the V-valued function σ on A is equal to $\sigma(a) + f(\tau(a)) \circ \sigma$. If I_A denotes the normalized Haar integral for V-valued functions on A we have therefore

$$I_A(\sigma) = I_A(\sigma \cdot a) = \sigma(a) + f(\tau(a))(I_A(\sigma)).$$

In the multiplicative notation, this yields $\sigma(a) = v^{-1} f(\tau(a))(v)$, where $v = I_A(\sigma)^{-1}$. Now

$$a = \sigma(a)\tau(a) = v^{-1}f(\tau(a))(v)\tau(a) = v^{-1}\tau(a)v,$$

because $f(\tau(a))(v) = \tau(a)v\tau(a)^{-1}$. Thus $vav^{-1} = \tau(a) \in T$, so that Lemma 3.2 is proved.

LEMMA 3.3. *Let G be a Lie group such that G/G_1 is finite. Suppose that there is a discrete central subgroup D of G such that Theorem 3.1 holds for G/D. Then Theorem 3.1 holds for G.*

Proof. Let π be the canonical homomorphism of G onto G/D, and let E, E_i, S_i, K be the objects of Theorem 3.1 for G/D. Put $H = \pi^{-1}(E)_1$. By Lemma 1.2 of Chapter IV, $\pi_H \colon H \to E$ is a space covering. Since E is simply connected, π_H is therefore a homeomorphism. Hence we may endow H with the structure of an analytic manifold such that π_H is an analytic manifold isomorphism of H onto E and the manifold topology of H coincides with its topology as a subspace of G. The differential π° of π is an isomorphism of $\mathscr{L}(G)$ onto $\mathscr{L}(G/D)$ by means of which we shall identify these two Lie algebras. Then we have evidently $\exp_G(S_1)\cdots\exp_G(S_k) = H$. Let $\log_E$ denote the inverse of the analytic manifold isomorphism

$$x_1 + \cdots + x_k \rightarrow \exp_{G/D}(x_1)\cdots\exp_{G/D}(x_k)$$

of $S_1 + \cdots + S_k$ onto E. The injection map $H \rightarrow G_1$ is the composite of $\log_E \circ \pi_H$ with the map $x_1 + \cdots + x_k \rightarrow \exp_G(x_1)\cdots\exp_G(x_k)$ and is therefore analytic. Also, it is clear from the definition of the analytic manifold structure of H that the map $x_1 + \cdots + x_k \rightarrow \exp_G(x_1)\cdots\exp_G(x_k)$ is an analytic manifold isomorphism of $S_1 + \cdots + S_k$ onto H.

Now put $M = \pi^{-1}(K)$. Then M is a closed subgroup of G, and thus a Lie group. Since $D \subset M$ and $EK = G/D$, it is clear that $HM = G$. Moreover, if h_1 and h_2 are in H and m_1 and m_2 are in M and $h_1 m_1 = h_2 m_2$ then we find, on applying π and using that the multiplication $E \times K \rightarrow G/D$ is injective, that $\pi(h_1) = \pi(h_2)$, whence $h_1 = h_2$ and $m_1 = m_2$. Thus the multiplication map $H \times M \rightarrow G$ is bijective. Clearly, it maps each connected component of $H \times M$ analytically into a connected component of G. Since this map is bijective, there are maps $\eta: G \rightarrow H$ and $\mu: G \rightarrow M$ such that its inverse is given by $g \rightarrow (\eta(g), \mu(g))$.

Given an element g of G, we can evidently choose a connected neighborhood V of $\pi(\eta(g))$ in E and a connected neighborhood W of $\pi(\mu(g))$ in K such that the neighborhood VW of $\pi(g)$ in G/D is evenly covered by π. Let W^* be the connected component of $\mu(g)$ in $\pi^{-1}(W)$ and let $\tau: W \rightarrow W^*$ be the inverse of π_{W^*}. Let ε and γ denote the projections of G/D onto E and K, respectively. If $(VW)^*$ denotes the connected component of g in $\pi^{-1}(VW)$ then $(VW)^*$ is a neighborhood of g in G and, in fact, $(VW)^* = \pi_H^{-1}(V)W^*$. Hence if x is an element of $(VW)^*$ we have $\eta(x) = (\pi_H^{-1} \circ \varepsilon \circ \pi)(x)$ and $\mu(x) = (\tau \circ \gamma \circ \pi)(x)$. This shows that the map $x \rightarrow (\eta(x), \mu(x))$ maps each connected component of G analytically into a connected component of $H \times M$. Hence the multiplication $H \times M \rightarrow G$ is an isomorphism of disjoint unions of analytic manifolds. Moreover, it is clear from the construction that each factor $\exp_G(S_i)$ of H is stable under the conjugations with the elements of M.

Now observe that π° sends $\mathscr{L}(M)$ isomorphically onto $\mathscr{L}(K)$; in accordance with the identification we have already made, we identify $\mathscr{L}(M)$ with $\mathscr{L}(K)$. By Theorem 1.3 of Chapter XIII, $\mathscr{L}(K)$ is the direct sum of its center, Z say, and the semisimple ideal $([\mathscr{L}(K), \mathscr{L}(K)])$. Let P denote the analytic subgroup of M_1 whose Lie algebra is Z. Then P is evidently the connected component of 1 in the center of M_1. Hence it is a closed normal subgroup of M. Let Q denote the maximum compact subgroup of the abelian analytic group P. We know that Q is connected (actually, a toroid), and evidently Q is stable under the conjugations with the elements of M. Hence $\mathscr{L}(Q)$ is stable under the adjoint representation of M. Since M/M_1 is isomorphic with G/G_1, it is finite. Also, M_1 lies in the kernel of the adjoint representation of M on $\mathscr{L}(P)$. Hence $\mathscr{L}(P)$ is semisimple as an M-module with respect to the adjoint representation, so that there is an M-submodule S of $\mathscr{L}(P)$ such that $\mathscr{L}(P)$ is the direct sum of $\mathscr{L}(Q)$ and S. Let V denote the analytic subgroup of P whose Lie algebra is S. Clearly, $P = VQ$ and $V \cap Q$ is discrete. Since P/Q is a vector group (because Q is the maximum compact subgroup of P), we see by considering the canonical homomorphism $V \to P/Q$ that $V \cap Q = (1)$ and hence that the multiplication map $V \times Q \to P$ is an isomorphism of analytic groups. Hence P is the direct product $V \times Q$, and V is a closed normal subgroup of M (because V is closed in P and P is closed in M). The Lie algebra of M_1/P is isomorphic with $([\mathscr{L}(K), \mathscr{L}(K)])$, which is isomorphic with the Lie algebra of the compact semisimple group $K_1/Z(K_1)$, where $Z(K_1)$ is the center of K_1. Hence we know from Theorem 1.3 of Chapter XIII that M_1/P is compact. Now $(M_1/V)/(P/V)$ is isomorphic with M_1/P, and P/V is compact. Hence M_1/V is compact. Since M/M_1 is finite, this implies that M/V is compact. Now it follows from Theorem 2.3 of Chapter III that M is a semidirect product $V \times_f T$, where T is a compact group.

Now put $F = HV$. Then the multiplication $F \times T \to G$ is evidently an isomorphism of disjoint unions of analytic manifolds, and F is an exponential manifold factor of G_1; $F = \exp_G(S_1) \times \cdots \times \exp_G(S_k) \times \exp_G(S)$. Let t be any element of T. By the construction of V, we have $tVt^{-1} = V$. Thus each factor of F as written above is stable under the conjugations with the elements of T.

It remains only to show that condition (iii) of Theorem 3.1 is satisfied. Let L be any compact subgroup of G. Then $\pi(L)$ is a compact subgroup of G/D, so that there is an element e in E such that $e\pi(L)e^{-1} \subset K$. Choose an element h in H such that $\pi(h) = e$. Then $hLh^{-1} \subset M = V \times_f T$. By Lemma 3.2, there is an element v in V such that $vhLh^{-1}v^{-1} \subset T$. We know that $v \exp_G(S_i)v^{-1} = \exp_G(S_i)$, so that $vhv^{-1} \in H$. Thus $vh = (vhv^{-1})v \in HV$. This completes the proof of Lemma 3.3.

Note that Lemma 3.3, when combined with the result of Section 2, establishes Theorem 3.1 in the case where $\mathscr{L}(G)$ is semisimple; take D to be the kernel of the adjoint representation of G on $\mathscr{L}(G)$.

LEMMA 3.4.   *The conclusion of Lemma 3.3 holds also if D is a compact normal subgroup of G.*

Proof.   As before, let $M = \pi^{-1}(K)$. Then M is a compact subgroup of G. Hence $\mathscr{L}(G)$ is semisimple as an M-module under the adjoint representation. Since each S_i is K-stable under the adjoint representation of G/D, it is clear that each $(\pi^\circ)^{-1}(S_i)$ is an M-submodule of $\mathscr{L}(G)$. It contains $\mathscr{L}(D)$ as an M-submodule and hence is a direct sum $\mathscr{L}(D) + T_i$, where T_i is an M-submodule that is mapped isomorphically onto S_i by π°. Let ρ_i denote the isomorphism of S_i onto T_i that inverts the restriction of π° to T_i. Put $F_i = \exp_G(T_i)$. One sees immediately that $F_1 \cdots F_k M = G$. If $f_1, \cdots, f_k$ and $f_1', \cdots, f_k'$ are elements of $F_1, \cdots, F_k$ and m, m' are elements of M such that $f_1 \cdots f_k m = f_1' \cdots f_k' m'$ then $\pi(f_i) = \pi(f_i')$ for each i. Now $f_i = \exp_G(\rho_i(s_i))$ and $f_i' = \exp_G(\rho_i(s_i'))$, where s_i and s_i' belong to S_i. Hence $\exp_{G/D}(s_i) = \pi(f_i) = \pi(f_i') = \exp_{G/D}(s_i')$, which gives $s_i = s_i'$ and so $f_i = f_i'$. Thus the multiplication map $F_1 \times \cdots \times F_k \times M \to G$ is bijective, so that there are maps $\eta_i: G \to F_i$ and $\mu: G \to M$ such that, for every element g of G, we have $g = \eta_1(g) \cdots \eta_k(g)\mu(g)$.

In fact, we see from the definitions that $\eta_i = \exp_G \circ \rho_i \circ \log_{E_i} \circ \varepsilon_i \circ \pi$, where ε_i is the projection $G/D \to E_i$. Thus each η_i, and therefore also μ, is a continuous map, so that the multiplication $F_1 \times \cdots \times F_k \times M \to G$ is a homeomorphism. Following this up with $\varepsilon_i \circ \pi$, we obtain an open continuous map $F_1 \times \cdots \times F_k \times M \to E_i$ whose restriction to F_i is a homeomorphism of F_i onto E_i. We use this homeomorphism in order to transport the analytic manifold structure on E_i into an analytic manifold structure on F_i. Then the injection $F_i \to G_1$ is composed of the analytic manifold isomorphism $F_i \to E_i$ and the analytic map $\exp_G \circ \rho_i \circ \log_{E_i}$ of E_i into G_1, so that it is analytic. Its composite with η_i is the identity map on F_i. Since the composite of η_i with the analytic manifold isomorphism $F_i \to E_i$ is the analytic map $\varepsilon_i \circ \pi$, we conclude that $\eta_i: G \to F_i$ is analytic (on each connected component of G). Hence it is clear that the multiplication $F_1 \times \cdots \times F_k \times M \to G$ is an isomorphism of disjoint unions of analytic manifolds. Finally, it is clear from the definition of the analytic manifold structure on F_i that $\exp_G: T_i \to F_i$ is an analytic manifold isomorphism. Thus $F_1 \times \cdots \times F_k$ is an exponential manifold factor of G_1. Since T_i is M-stable under the adjoint representation, F_i is stable under the conjugations with the elements of M.

Finally, if L is any compact subgroup of G then there is an element e in E such that $e\pi(L)e^{-1} \subset K$. Choose an element f in $F_1\cdots F_k$ such that $\pi(f) = e$. Then $fLf^{-1} \subset M$. This completes the proof of Lemma 3.4.

LEMMA 3.5. *The conclusion of Lemma 3.3 holds also if D is a normal closed vector subgroup of G.*

Proof. Let $M = \pi^{-1}(K)$. Then $D \subset M$ and M/D is compact. By Theorem 2.3 of Chapter III, M is therefore a semidirect product $D \times_f T$ where T is a compact subgroup of G. As before, choose T-stable subspaces T_i of $\mathscr{L}(G)$ such that π° maps T_i isomorphically onto S_i. Put $F_i = \exp_G(T_i)$. The proof of Lemma 3.4 applies also here to show that $F_1\cdots F_k$ is an exponential manifold factor of G_1, that the multiplication $F_1 \times \cdots \times F_k \times M \to G$ is an isomorphism of disjoint unions of analytic manifolds, and that $tF_it^{-1} = F_i$ for every element t of T. Evidently, if $H = F_1\cdots F_k D$ then H is therefore still an exponential manifold factor of G_1 and the multiplication $H \times T \to G$ is an isomorphism of disjoint unions of analytic manifolds. Moreover, since D is normal in G, we have $tDt^{-1} = D$ for every element t of T.

Finally, let L be any compact subgroup of G. As before, we see that there is an element f in $F_1\cdots F_k$ such that $fLf^{-1} \subset M$. Now $M = D \times_f T$, and Lemma 3.2 shows that there is an element d in D such that $dfLf^{-1}d^{-1} \subset T$. Since $df = f(f^{-1}df) \in H$, this completes the proof of Lemma 3.5.

LEMMA 3.6. *Let G be a Lie group, and suppose that $\mathscr{L}(G)$ is not semisimple. Then G has a non-trivial closed normal subgroup that is either a vector group or a toroid.*

Proof. By assumption, the radical S of $\mathscr{L}(G)$ is not (0). Put $S_0 = S$, $S_{i+1} = ([S_i, S_i])$, and let S_p denote the last non-zero member of this sequence of ideals of $\mathscr{L}(G)$. Then S_p is evidently stable under every Lie algebra automorphism of $\mathscr{L}(G)$. Let A be the closure in G of the analytic subgroup of G_1 whose Lie algebra is S_p. Then A is clearly an abelian closed connected normal subgroup of G. Let B denote the maximum compact subgroup of A. Then A is a direct product $V \times B$, where V is a vector group. Moreover, B is normal in G. If B is non-trivial we have the desired result. If $B = (1)$ then $A = V$, a vector group, and the alternative conclusion of Lemma 3.6 is reached.

Now Theorem 3.1 is easily proved by induction on the dimension of G_1.

If this dimension is 0 then G is a finite group, and there is nothing to prove. Now suppose that the dimension of G_1 is not zero and that Theorem 3.1 has been established in the lower dimensional cases. If $\mathscr{L}(G)$ is semisimple, Theorem 3.1 holds, as we have already shown. If $\mathscr{L}(G)$ is not semisimple we know from Lemma 3.6 that there is a non-trivial closed normal subgroup D in G such that D is either a vector group or a toroid. By our inductive hypothesis, Theorem 3.1 holds for G/D. By Lemma 3.5, or by Lemma 3.4, it follows that Theorem 3.1 holds for G.

Observe that *the compact group K that figures in Theorem 3.1 is necessarily a maximal compact subgroup of G.* Indeed, if M is a compact subgroup of G containing K there is an element x in G such that $xMx^{-1} \subset K$. Thus we have $xKx^{-1} \subset xMx^{-1} \subset K$, whence it is easily seen (by comparing dimensions and numbers of components) that these inclusions are actually equalities, so that $M = K$.

THEOREM 3.7. *Let G be a Lie group such that G/G_1 is finite, and suppose that G has a closed connected normal subgroup N such that G/N is compact. Let L be any maximal compact subgroup of G. Then $G = LN$.*

Proof. We show first that we assume G to be connected. Note that $L \cap G_1$ is a maximal compact subgroup of G_1; for if M is a compact subgroup of G_1 containing $L \cap G_1$ there is, by Theorem 3.1, an element x in G such that $xMx^{-1} \subset L$. Hence $x(L \cap G_1)x^{-1} \subset xMx^{-1} \subset L \cap G_1$, which implies that $L \cap G_1 = M$. If Theorem 3.7 is established in the connected case we have therefore $(L \cap G_1)N = G_1$. On the other hand, it is clear from Theorem 3.1 that L meets each connected component of G. Hence $LG_1 = G$, and so $LN = G$.

Now assume that G is connected. Let P be the subgroup of G that contains N and is such that P/N is the center of G/N. Then G/P is isomorphic with the factor group of the compact group G/N mod. its center and is therefore compact and semisimple. The Lie algebra of G/P is isomorphic with $\mathscr{L}(G)/\mathscr{L}(P)$. Since it is semisimple, it follows from Theorem 3.1 of Chapter XI that there is a subalgebra S of $\mathscr{L}(G)$ such that $\mathscr{L}(G) = \mathscr{L}(P) + S$ and $S \cap \mathscr{L}(P) = (0)$. Now S is isomorphic with the Lie algebra of a compact semisimple analytic group, so that it follows from Theorem 1.3 of Chapter XIII that the analytic subgroup, H say, of G that corresponds to S is compact. Hence HN is a closed connected subgroup of G. From $\mathscr{L}(G) = \mathscr{L}(P) + S$, we have $G = HP$. Moreover, since P/N is the center of G/N, one sees easily that the commutator subgroup of HP, i.e., of G, lies in HN. Thus HN is normal in G and $G/(HN)$ is abelian. Since it is compact and connected, it is therefore a toroid.

By Theorem 3.1 and the remark following its proof, H is contained in a maximal compact subgroup K of G, and the coset space G/K is simply connected. Now consider the canonical map $\eta: G/K \to G/(KN)$. Clearly, η is continuous open and surjective. The group KN is closed in G, because K is compact. Since KN contains HN, it is normal in G and $G/(KN)$ is a homomorphic image of the toroid $G/(HN)$ and hence is also a toroid. On the other hand, if xKN is any point of $G/(KN)$ then $\eta^{-1}(xKN)$ is the canonical image in G/K of the connected subset xKN of G and is therefore connected. Hence we can apply the result of Exercise 1 of Chapter IV to conclude that $G/(KN)$ is simply connected. Since it is a toroid, it must therefore be trivial, i.e., $KN = G$. By Theorem 3.1, if L is any maximal compact subgroup of G there is an element g in G such that $gLg^{-1} = K$, whence also $LN = G$, so that Theorem 3.7 is proved.

EXERCISES

1. Let G be an analytic group, and let T and T' be maximal toroids in G. Show that there is an element x in G such that $xTx^{-1} = T'$. Also show that G/T is simply connected. [Use Theorem 3.1, Corollary 4.2, of Chapter XIII and Theorem 4.3 of Chapter XIII.]

2. Show that the adjoint image of a non-trivial semisimple analytic group has a non-trivial connected compact subgroup. [Consider the proof of the relevant case of Theorem 3.1, as given in Section 2.]

3. Let G be the group of all linear automorphisms of determinant 1 of a two-dimensional real vector space. Show that a maximal compact subgroup of G is a one-dimensional toroid. Let $\pi: H \to G$ be a group covering, with H simply connected. Show that the manifold of H is R^3, and that H has no non-trivial compact subgroup. [Examine this situation in the light of the proof of Lemma 3.3.]

XVI. CENTERS OF ANALYTIC GROUPS AND CLOSURES OF ANALYTIC SUBGROUPS

1

We begin with an elementary result.

THEOREM 1.1. *The center of a nilpotent analytic group is connected.*

Proof. Let G be a nilpotent analytic group, Z its center, Z_1 the connected component of 1 in Z. We assume that $G \neq (1)$, and that Theorem 1.1 has been established for groups of smaller dimension than that of G. Since G is nilpotent, Z_1 is non-trivial, and the center of G/Z_1 is connected, by our inductive hypothesis. Write the center of G/Z_1 in the form T/Z_1. Then T is a closed analytic subgroup of G containing Z. The factor group T/Z is an abelian analytic group and thus is the direct product of a toroid and a vector group. The adjoint representation of G induces an injective representation ρ of T/Z on $\mathscr{L}(G)$, and the differential of ρ is a nilpotent injective representation of $\mathscr{L}(T/Z)$. Since the restriction of ρ to a toroid in T/Z is a semisimple representation, it follows that T/Z contains no non-trivial toroid. Hence T/Z is a vector group. The kernel of the canonical homomorphism $T/Z_1 \to T/Z$ is the discrete subgroup Z/Z_1 of T/Z_1. Since T/Z is a vector group and T/Z_1 is the direct product of a toroid and a vector group, this evidently implies that $Z/Z_1 = (1)$, i.e., that $Z = Z_1$. This completes the proof of Theorem 1.1.

In the general case, the following result serves as a substitute for Theorem 1.1.

THEOREM 1.2. *The center of an analytic group G is contained in an abelian analytic subgroup of G.*

Proof. Let Z denote the center of G, and let Z_1 be the connected component of 1 in Z. Let π denote the canonical homomorphism $G/Z_1 \to G/Z$, with the discrete kernel Z/Z_1. Let K be a maximal compact subgroup of G/Z, and put $M = \pi^{-1}(K)$. We know from the proof of Lemma 3.3 of Chapter XV that the analytic manifold G/Z_1 is a Cartesian product $H \times M$ (where H is an exponential manifold factor of G/Z_1). In particular, M is therefore connected.

Now let us first consider the case where G is solvable. In this case, K must evidently be abelian. Since the kernel of π is discrete, this implies that M is abelian. Write M in the form L/Z_1. Then L is a closed analytic subgroup of G and contains Z. Since M is abelian, the commutator subgroup of L lies in Z_1, whence L is nilpotent. By Theorem 1.1, the center of L is therefore connected. Since it contains Z, this proves Theorem 1.2 in the solvable case.

Now suppose that G is semisimple. Then $Z_1 = (1)$, so that $M \subset G$. Since M is a covering group of the compact analytic group K, we know that M is a direct product $P \times V$, where P is a compact analytic group and V is a vector group. Now Z is contained in the center of M, which is $T \times V$, where T is the center of P. By Corollary 4.2 of Chapter XIII, T is contained in a maximal toroid U of P. Hence Z is contained in the abelian analytic subgroup $U \times V$ of G, which proves Theorem 1.2 in the semisimple case.

Next, let us suppose that G is a semidirect product $S \cdot R$, where S is a semisimple analytic group and R is the maximum normal solvable analytic subgroup of G. (We write $S \cdot R$ for $S \,_\sigma\times\, R$ if the homomorphism σ of S into the automorphism group of R need not be exhibited.) Clearly, the center $Z(G)$ of G is then contained in $Z(S) \cdot R$, where $Z(S)$ is the center of S. We know already that $Z(S)$ is contained in an abelian analytic subgroup A of S. Hence $Z(G)$ is contained in the solvable analytic subgroup $A \cdot R$ of G. By the solvable case of Theorem 1.2, $Z(G)$ is therefore contained in an abelian analytic subgroup of $A \cdot R$.

In the general case, since $\mathscr{L}(G)$ is a semidirect sum of its radical and a semisimple subalgebra, G is of the form $(S \cdot R)/D$, where S and R are as above and D is a discrete central subgroup of $S \cdot R$. Hence the center of G is the canonical image of the center of $S \cdot R$, so that our result for $S \cdot R$ yields Theorem 1.2 in the general case.

2

We shall prove some results which describe the relation between an analytic subgroup and its closure.

THEOREM 2.1. *Let H be a dense analytic subgroup of an analytic group G. Then every normal analytic subgroup of H is normal also in G, the commutator subgroup of H coincides with the commutator subgroup of G, and there is an abelian analytic subgroup A of G such that G = HA.*

Proof. An analytic subgroup of H is normal in G if and only if its Lie algebra is stable under the adjoint representation of G. If it is normal in H then its Lie algebra is H-stable with respect to the adjoint representation. Since H is dense in G, this implies that the Lie algebra of the analytic subgroup is G-stable. This proves the first statement of Theorem 2.1.

Let $\pi: G^* \to G$ be a group covering, with G^* simply connected, and identify $\mathscr{L}(G^*)$ with $\mathscr{L}(G)$ by means of π°. Let H^* denote the analytic subgroup of G^* whose Lie algebra is $\mathscr{L}(H)$. Let F denote the kernel of π. Since π is an open map and H is dense in G, it is clear that H^*F is dense in G^*. Since H^* is normal in G^*, so is its commutator subgroup $(H^*)'$. Since G^* is simply connected, $(H^*)'$ is therefore closed in G^*, by Theorem 1.2 of Chapter XII. Now $(G^*)'$ is the commutator subgroup of the closure of H^*F and hence is contained in the closure of the commutator subgroup of H^*F, i.e., in the closure of $(H^*)'$, i.e., in $(H^*)'$. Hence $(G^*)' = (H^*)'$, whence also $G' = H'$.

By Theorem 1.2, F is contained in an abelian analytic subgroup B of G^*. Consider the analytic subgroup H^*B of G^*. Since this contains H^*F, it is dense in G^*. On the other hand, $(G^*)' \subset H^*$, so that H^*B is normal in G^*. By Theorem 1.2 of Chapter XII, H^*B is therefore closed in G^* and hence coincides with G^*. Hence $G = HA$, where A is the abelian analytic subgroup $\pi(B)$ of G. This completes the proof of Theorem 2.1.

We retain the above notation while we single out a few more facts concerning the situation of Theorem 2.1. Let R denote the maximum normal solvable analytic subgroup of H or, as we shall say from now on, the *radical* of H. Let S be a maximal semisimple analytic subgroup of H. It is clear from Theorem 2.1 that $\mathscr{L}(G)/\mathscr{L}(H)$ is abelian. Hence $\mathscr{L}(S)$ is a maximal semisimple subalgebra of $\mathscr{L}(G)$ as well as of $\mathscr{L}(H)$, so that, by Theorem 3.3 of Chapter XI, $\mathscr{L}(G)$ is the semidirect sum of its radical and

$\mathcal{L}(S)$. Hence G^* is the semidirect product $S^* \cdot T^*$, where S^* is the analytic subgroup whose Lie algebra is $\mathcal{L}(S)$ and T^* denotes the radical of G^*. The image T of T^* in G is the radical of G, $R \subset T$ and $G = ST$. If R^* is the analytic subgroup of G^* whose Lie algebra is $\mathcal{L}(R)$ then $R^* \subset T^*$ and $H^* = S^* \cdot R^*$.

LEMMA 2.2. *Let U be a closed analytic subgroup of S^* containing the center of S^*. Then $G = [\pi(U)R]H$, where $[\pi(U)R]$ denotes the closure of $\pi(U)R$ in G. Moreover, $[\pi(U)R] \cap H = \pi(U)R$.*

Proof. Let F denote the kernel of the covering $\pi\colon G^* \to G$, and let σ and τ denote the projections of F into S^* and T^*, respectively, corresponding to the decomposition $G^* = S^* \cdot T^*$. For any subset X of G^*, let $[X]$ denote the closure of X in G^*. We have $G^* = [FH^*] = [S^*\tau(F)R^*] = S^*[\tau(F)R^*]$, whence $T^* = [\tau(F)R^*]$. Clearly, $\sigma(F)$ lies in the center of S^* and so in U. Hence the last result gives $T^* \subset [FUR^*]$, whence $T \subset [\pi(U)R]$. Since $G = TS$, this gives $[\pi(U)R]H = G$.

Now $U \cdot T^*$ is closed in G^* and contains F. Hence its image $\pi(U)T$ in G is closed in G, whence $[\pi(U)R] \subset \pi(U)T$. Hence it suffices to show that $(\pi(U)T) \cap H \subset \pi(U)R$. Let x be an element of $(\pi(U)T) \cap H$. Then $x = \pi(u)t$ with u in U and t in T, and also $x = sr$ with s in S and r in R. Hence $s^{-1}\pi(u) = rt^{-1} \in S \cap T$. But $S \cap T$ is contained in the center of S and hence in $\pi(U)$, because the center of S is the canonical image of the center of S^*. Hence we find that $s \in \pi(U)$, so that $x \in \pi(U)R$. This completes the proof of Lemma 2.2.

We shall require the following elementary result concerning continuous homomorphisms of the additive group R of the real numbers into a locally compact group G.

PROPOSITION 2.3. *Let γ be a continuous homomorphism of the one-dimensional vector group R into a locally compact group G. Then either γ maps R homeomorphically onto $\gamma(R)$ or the closure of $\gamma(R)$ in G is compact.*

Proof. Suppose first that there is a positive real number M and a neighborhood V of 1 in G such that $\gamma(r) \in V$ implies that $|r| \leq M$. Then the kernel of γ is bounded, hence compact, hence (0). Furthermore, if I is the interval in R defined by $|r| \leq M$ then I is compact, so that γ maps I homeomorphically onto $\gamma(I)$. Hence γ^{-1} is continuous on the neighborhood $V \cap \gamma(R)$ of 1 in $\gamma(R)$, whence γ^{-1} is continuous on $\gamma(R)$, so that γ is a homeomorphism of R onto $\gamma(R)$.

Hence, if γ does not map R homeomorphically onto $\gamma(R)$, then, for every neighborhood V of 1 in G and every positive real number M, there is a point r in R such that $|r| > M$ and $\gamma(r) \in V$. Replacing G with the closure of $\gamma(R)$ in G, we may assume without loss of generality that $\gamma(R)$ is dense in G, and we must now show that G is compact. Let W be an open neighborhood of 1 in G such that $W = W^{-1}$ and the closure $[W]$ of W is compact. Given x in G, there is an r in R such that $\gamma(r) \in xW$. Choose a neighborhood V of 1 in G such that $V = V^{-1}$ and $\gamma(r)V \subset xW$. Now there is an s in R such that $|s| > |r|$ and $\gamma(s) \in V$. Put $t = r + |s|$. Then we have $t \geq 0$ and $\gamma(t) \in xW$, so that $x \in \gamma(t)W$. In particular, letting x range over $[W]$ and using the compactness of $[W]$, we find that there are positive real numbers $t_1, \cdots, t_n$ such that $[W] \subset \bigcup_{i=1}^{n} \gamma(t_i)W$. Let u be the largest one among these t_i's. Let x be an arbitrary element of G, and let v be the smallest non-negative real number such that $\gamma(v) \in x[W]$. Then $x^{-1}\gamma(v) \in \gamma(t_i)W$ for some i, whence (using that G is commutative) $\gamma(v - t_i) \in xW$. By the definition of v, this implies that $v - t_i \leq 0$, so that $0 \leq v \leq u$. Since $x \in \gamma(v)[W]$, this shows that $G = \gamma(J)[W]$, where J is the interval defined by $0 \leq r \leq u$. Since $\gamma(J)$ and $[W]$ are compact, so is therefore G, and Proposition 2.3 is proved.

Now we are in a position to prove the following closure criterion for analytic subgroups.

THEOREM 2.4. *Let H be an analytic subgroup of an analytic group G. Suppose that the closure in G of every one-dimensional analytic subgroup of H lies in H. Then H is closed in G.*

Proof. We shall assume, without loss of generality, that H is dense in G. By Theorem 1.2, we may choose the group U of Lemma 2.2 to be abelian. Then $\pi(U)R$ is a solvable analytic subgroup of G and, by the first part of Lemma 2.2, it suffices to show that $\pi(U)R$ is closed in G. Moreover, it is clear from the second part of Lemma 2.2 that the assumed property of H entails the same property for $\pi(U)R$. Hence it suffices to prove Theorem 2.4 in the case where H (and hence also G) is solvable.

In that case, assuming that $H \neq (1)$, H has a non-trivial normal abelian analytic subgroup A. Let $[A]$ denote the closure of A in G, and let A° denote the connected component of 1 in $[A] \cap H$, with respect to the analytic group topology of H. Then A° is clearly a non-trivial normal abelian analytic subgroup of H. Let h be a one-dimensional analytic subgroup of A°, and let $[h]$ denote the closure of h in G. By the assumption of the theorem, we have $[h] \subset H$, so that $[h] \subset [A] \cap H$. Since $[h]$ is an analytic subgroup of G and lies in H, it is clear from Theorem 4.1 of Chapter X that $[h]$ is an analytic subgroup of H, whence $[h] \subset A°$.

Now we make the inductive hypothesis that Theorem 2.4 has been proved for analytic subgroups of lower dimension than that of H. Thus if $A° \neq H$ it follows from the inductive hypothesis that $A°$ is closed in G. On the other hand, if $A° = H$ then the above $[h]$ is a normal analytic subgroup of H that is closed in G. Hence, in any case, H contains a non-trivial normal abelian analytic subgroup N that is closed in G. Since H is dense in G, it is clear that N is normal also in G.

Evidently, it suffices to show that H/N is closed in G/N. Using our inductive hypothesis, we see therefore that it is sufficient to show that the closure in G/N of every one-dimensional analytic subgroup of H/N lies in H/N. Now N is a direct product of a toroid and a vector group. If the toroid is non-trivial, we may evidently replace N with this toroid. Otherwise N is a vector group. Thus it suffices to dispose of the cases where N is a toroid or a vector group.

Suppose first that N is a toroid, and let k be a one-dimensional analytic subgroup of H/N. Evidently, there is a one-dimensional analytic subgroup h of H such that the canonical image of h in G/N is k. Since N is compact, the image of $[h]$ in G/N is the closure $[k]$ of k in G/N. Since $[h] \subset H$, we have therefore $[k] \subset H/N$.

Now suppose that N is a vector group, and let k again be a one-dimensional analytic subgroup of H/N. If $[k] = k$ there is nothing to prove. If $[k] \neq k$ then, with the topology induced from that of G/N, k cannot be homeo-morphic with the real line, since this would make k locally compact and hence closed in G/N. Hence we know from Proposition 2.3 that $[k]$ is compact. Now write $[k]$ in the form C/N. Since C/N is compact and N is a vector group, we know from Theorem 2.3 of Chapter III that C is a semidirect product $B \cdot N$, where B is compact. Now let h be a one-dimensional analytic subgroup of H whose canonical image in G/N is k. We must evidently have $[h] \subset C$. Let β be the projection of C onto B that corresponds to the decomposition $C = B \cdot N$. Then $\beta(h) \subset hN \subset H$, and $\beta(h)$ is a one-dimensional analytic subgroup of H whose image in G/N is still k. Thus we may take $h \subset B$. But then $[h]$ is compact, so that its image in G/N is closed and therefore coincides with $[k]$. Since $[h] \subset H$, we have again $[k] \subset H/N$. The proof of Theorem 2.4 is now complete.

1. Construct a simply connected solvable analytic group whose center is a discrete infinite cyclic group as a suitable semidirect product of a two-dimensional normal vector subgroup and a one-dimensional vector group.

2. Let H be an analytic subgroup of an analytic group G, and suppose that, for every compact subgroup K of G, $H \cap K$ is closed in K. Show that H is closed in G. [Use Theorem 2.4 and Proposition 2.3.]

3. Let G be an arbitrary analytic group. Prove that $\mathscr{L}(G)$ has a basis $(x_1, \cdots, x_n)$ such that, for each i, the one-dimensional analytic subgroup $\exp_G(Rx_i)$ is closed in G. [Use Proposition 2.3.]

XVII. COMPLEX ANALYTIC GROUPS [9]

1

The definition and the elementary theory of complex analytic manifolds are obtained simply by copying Chapter VI, using the field C of the complex numbers in the place of the field R of the real numbers throughout. If M is an m-dimensional complex analytic manifold then M carries also the structure $\mathscr{F}$ of a $2m$-dimensional real analytic manifold, which is completely determined by the condition that, for every open subset V of M, the complex analytic functions on V are *complexified real analytic functions* on V, i.e., are elements of $\mathscr{F}(V) \otimes_R C$ (but not every element of $\mathscr{F}(V) \otimes_R C$ is a complex analytic function, of course). The existence of this real analytic manifold structure $\mathscr{F}$ on M is easily established from the following. Let p be a point of M, and let U be a coordinate neighborhood of p belonging to a chart of the complex analytic manifold M at p. Let $(z_1, \cdots, z_m)$ be the system of coordinate functions on U corresponding to this chart. Write each of the complex-valued functions z_k in the form $x_k + iy_k$, where x_k and y_k are real-valued functions on U. Then the set $(x_1, \cdots, x_m, y_1, \cdots, y_m)$, restricted to a suitable subset of U, is a complete system of coordinate functions for a chart of the real analytic manifold M at p.

Let $\mathscr{F}(p)$ denote the R-algebra of the germs of real analytic functions at p, and let $\mathscr{F}^C(p)$ denote the C-algebra of the germs of complex analytic functions at p. Then $\mathscr{F}^C(p)$ is a subalgebra of the algebra $\mathscr{F}(p) \otimes_R C$ of the germs of complexified real analytic functions at p. Now let τ be any complex tangent vector to M at p. By definition, τ is a differentiation of the C-algebra $\mathscr{F}^C(p)$ into C. It is easy to see that there is a differentiation τ° of the C-algebra $\mathscr{F}(p) \otimes_R C$ into C such that, writing x_k, y_k, z_k also to denote the germs determined by the above coordinate functions,

$$\tau^\circ(x_k) = \tfrac{1}{2}(\tau(z_k) + \tau(z_k)^*) \quad \text{and} \quad \tau^\circ(y_k) = \tfrac{1}{2}i(\tau(z_k)^* - \tau(z_k)),$$

where the superscript * indicates the complex conjugate. Moreover, τ° is invariantly characterized as the unique extension of τ to a differentiation of $\mathscr{F}(p) \otimes_R C$ into C such that $\tau^\circ(f^*) = \tau^\circ(f)^*$ for every element f of $\mathscr{F}(p) \otimes_R C$, where f^* denotes the complex conjugate of f. Finally, one shows easily that the map sending each τ onto the restriction of τ° to $\mathscr{F}(p)$ is a real linear isomorphism of the complex tangent space to M at p onto the real tangent space to M at p.

The definition of a complex analytic group results from that of a real analytic group simply by replacing the real analytic manifold with a complex analytic manifold. The theory of real analytic groups, up to and including Chapter XII, carries over almost entirely to complex analytic groups, with exactly analogous proofs. An important exception is that a continuous homomorphism of one complex analytic group into another is not necessarily complex analytic, although it is real analytic. Similarly, a closed connected subgroup of a complex analytic group is not necessarily a complex analytic group, although it is a real analytic group. These differences between the real theory and the complex theory will cause no difficulty if one views complex analytic groups as real analytic groups with an additional structural element that is very easy to handle. This point of view is as follows.

Let G be a complex analytic group, let $\mathscr{L}^c(G)$ denote its complex Lie algebra, and let $\mathscr{L}(G)$ denote its real Lie algebra. The above tangent space isomorphisms at the various points of G are evidently compatible with the group translations on G and hence define an isomorphism of $\mathscr{L}^c(G)$, regarded as a real Lie algebra, onto $\mathscr{L}(G)$. We use this isomorphism in order to identify $\mathscr{L}^c(G)$, regarded as a real Lie algebra, with $\mathscr{L}(G)$. The structure of $\mathscr{L}^c(G)$ as a complex Lie algebra consists of its structure as a real Lie algebra together with a real linear automorphism γ, the multiplication by i, such that γ^2 is the negative of the identity map on $\mathscr{L}^c(G)$ and $[\gamma(u), v] = \gamma([u, v])$ for all elements u and v of $\mathscr{L}^c(G)$. Thus we view $\mathscr{L}^c(G)$ as the real Lie algebra $\mathscr{L}(G)$, equipped with a map γ satisfying the above conditions. Conversely, if L is any real Lie algebra equipped with a γ as above then L has one and only one structure of a complex Lie algebra that is compatible with its structure as a real Lie algebra and is such that γ is the multiplication by i.

Since the exponential map is a complex analytic manifold isomorphism of a neighborhood of 0 in $\mathscr{L}^c(G)$ onto a neighborhood of 1 in G, it is clear that the complex analytic manifold structure of G is already determined by the complex Lie algebra structure of $\mathscr{L}(G)$. Moreover, if G is a real analytic group such that $\mathscr{L}(G)$ can be equipped with a compatible structure of a complex Lie algebra, i.e., with a γ as above, then one can evidently equip G with the structure of a complex analytic group by means of the exponential map, such that $(\mathscr{L}(G), \gamma)$ is the complex Lie algebra of G.

A power series P in the variables $x_1, \cdots, x_m, y_1, \cdots, y_m$ can be written as a power series in $z_1, \cdots, z_m$ if and only if, for each k, the partial derivative of P with respect to y_k is the scalar multiple by i of the partial derivative of P with respect to x_k. If U is an open subset of G and λ is an element of $\mathscr{L}(G)$ then λ defines a derivation λ_U of $\mathscr{F}(U) \otimes_R C$ such that, for every point p of U and every element f of $\mathscr{F}(U) \otimes_R C$, $\lambda_U(f)(p) = \lambda_p{}^\circ(f_p)$. The restriction of λ_U to the subalgebra $\mathscr{F}^c(U)$ of the complex analytic functions on U is the usual derivation λ_U that corresponds to the element λ of the complex Lie algebra $\mathscr{L}^c(G)$ of the complex analytic group G. The restriction of λ_U to $\mathscr{F}(U)$ is the derivation corresponding to λ as an element of the real Lie algebra $\mathscr{L}(G)$ of the real analytic group G. By localizing and then using the above remark about power series, one sees that an element f of $\mathscr{F}(U) \otimes_R C$ belongs to $\mathscr{F}^c(U)$ if and only if $\gamma(\lambda)_U(f) = i\lambda_U(f)$ for every element λ of $\mathscr{L}(G)$.

Now let G and H be complex analytic groups, and let η be a continuous homomorphism of G into H. We know that η is a real analytic homomorphism of the real analytic group G into the real analytic group H. If η is complex analytic then its differential is complex linear. Conversely, if η° is complex linear it follows from the above characterization of the complex analytic functions among the complexified real analytic functions that η is complex analytic. If γ_G and γ_H denote the multiplications by i on $\mathscr{L}(G)$ and $\mathscr{L}(H)$, respectively, we may express this result by saying that η is complex analytic if and only if $\eta^\circ \circ \gamma_G = \gamma_H \circ \eta^\circ$. In this way the complex analytic homomorphisms are characterized in terms of the real analytic structures and the γ's alone.

2

We shall now prove a few basic results concerning semisimple complex analytic groups.

THEOREM 2.1.　*The center of a semisimple complex analytic group is finite.*

Proof.　Let Z be the center of the semisimple complex analytic group G. Then Z is discrete, and we shall identify $\mathscr{L}(G)$ with $\mathscr{L}(G/Z)$ by means of the differential of the canonical homomorphism $G \to G/Z$.　By Theorem 4.3 of Chapter XIV, $\mathscr{L}(G)$ has a real form of compact type.　Let K be a real analytic subgroup of G/Z such that $\mathscr{L}(K)$ is such a real form of $\mathscr{L}(G)$. Then K is a compact semisimple real analytic group.　We know that K is therefore contained in a maximal compact subgroup M of G/Z.

Let x be an element of the center of M.　Then the image of x under the adjoint representation of G leaves the elements of $\mathscr{L}(K)$ fixed.　Since it is a complex linear automorphism of $\mathscr{L}(G)$, it therefore must be the identity map on $\mathscr{L}(G)$, because $C\mathscr{L}(K) = \mathscr{L}(G)$.　Hence x lies in the center of G/Z, which is trivial.　Thus M is a compact analytic group with trivial center and, in particular, is therefore semisimple.

We know from Theorem 3.1 of Chapter XV that there is an exponential manifold factor E of G/Z (regarded as a real analytic manifold) such that $G/Z = E \times M$, as a real analytic manifold.　Now let $\mu \colon M^* \to M$ be a group covering with M^* simply connected.　By Theorem 1.3 of Chapter XIII, M^* is compact, so that the kernel of μ is finite.　Define a map $\mu^+ \colon E \times M^* \to G/Z$ by $\mu^+(e, m) = e\mu(m)$.　Then μ^+ is evidently a space covering.　In the language of Exercise 2 of Chapter IV, the mobility group of the covering μ^+ is isomorphic with the mobility group of the covering μ. By Exercise 3 of Chapter IV, the mobility group of the covering μ is isomorphic with the kernel of μ, and thus is finite.　Hence the mobility group of the covering μ^+ is finite.　On the other hand, if $\gamma \colon G^* \to G$ is a group covering with G^* simply connected, and if π is the canonical map $G \to G/Z$, then $\pi \circ \gamma$ is evidently a group covering of G/Z.　The mobility group of this covering is isomorphic with the mobility group of the covering μ^+, because both G^* and $E \times M^*$ are simply connected.　Thus the mobility group of the covering $\pi \circ \gamma$ is finite, whence the isomorphic kernel of $\pi \circ \gamma$ is finite. This evidently implies that Z is finite, so that Theorem 2.1 is proved.

THEOREM 2.2.　*Let G be a semisimple complex analytic group, and let K be a real analytic subgroup of G such that $\mathscr{L}(K)$ is a real form of compact type of $\mathscr{L}(G)$. Then K is a maximal compact subgroup of G.*

Proof.　Let M be a maximal compact subgroup of G containing K. Exactly as in the proof of Theorem 2.1, we see that the center of M is contained in the center of G and hence is discrete.　Hence M is a semisimple real analytic group. Since $\mathscr{L}(G) = \mathscr{L}(K) + i\mathscr{L}(K)$, we have $\mathscr{L}(M) = \mathscr{L}(K) + iS$, where S is a real vector subspace of $\mathscr{L}(K)$. Now

$$i[S, \mathscr{L}(K)] = [iS, \mathscr{L}(K)] \subset \mathscr{L}(M) \cap (i\mathscr{L}(K)) = iS,$$

so that $[S, \mathscr{L}(K)] \subset S$. Thus S is an ideal of $\mathscr{L}(K)$, whence $S + iS$ is an ideal of the complex Lie algebra $\mathscr{L}(G)$. Let P denote the corresponding complex analytic subgroup of G. Since $S + iS$ is an ideal of the semisimple Lie algebra $\mathscr{L}(G)$, it is semisimple. Furthermore, $S + iS$ is a real Lie subalgebra of $\mathscr{L}(M)$. Since M is compact, it follows from Corollary 1.2 and Theorem 1.3 of Chapter XIII that P is compact.

Now let f be any complex analytic function on P. Since P is compact, $|f|$ takes its maximum at some point p of P. If we use a chart of P at p and consider the function on an open neighborhood of 0 in C^m that corresponds to f we see from Exercise 1 of Chapter V that f must be constant on a neighborhood of p. Using this, one sees immediately that the set of points of P where f takes this value is both open and closed in P, and thus coincides with P. Hence we conclude that every complex analytic function on P (or on any compact complex analytic manifold) is constant. Since the adjoint representation of P on $\mathscr{L}(G)$ is complex analytic, it must therefore be trivial. Hence P is contained in the center of G. Since the center of G is discrete, it follows that $P = (1)$, so that $S = (0)$ and $M = K$. This completes the proof of Theorem 2.2.

3

It is a remarkable fact that a semisimple complex analytic group has a faithful finite-dimensional complex analytic representation. In order to prove this, we require the following elementary result on groups of linear automorphisms.

LEMMA 3.1. *Let G be a group of linear automorphisms of a finite-dimensional vector space V over an algebraically closed field F. Let Q be a finite central subgroup of G such that the characteristic of F does not divide the order of Q. Then there exists a finite-dimensional G-stable subspace W of the tensor space $T(V)$ such that the representation of G on W has Q for its kernel.*

Proof. Note first that the assumptions on Q imply that V is semisimple as a Q-module. Making an induction on the order of Q, we reduce the lemma to the case where Q has prime order q. Then, since F is algebraically closed, it follows from Schur's Lemma that V is the direct sum of subspaces

$V_1, \cdots, V_h$ such that a given generator x of Q acts as a scalar multiplication on each V_i, and more precisely as the multiplication by ε^{e_i}, where ε is a primitive q-th root of 1 in F and the e_i's are distinct elements of $Z/(qZ)$, Z being the additive group of the integers. Since x lies in the center of G, each V_i is G-stable. Since x is not the identity automorphism of V, $(e_1, \cdots, e_h)$ is a non-zero vector in the h-dimensional vector space $(Z/(qZ))^h$ over the field $Z/(qZ)$. The line spanned by this vector is the intersection of $h - 1$ hyperplanes in $(Z/(qZ))^h$, which means that there exist non-negative integers a_{rs} $(r = 1, \cdots, h - 1; s = 1, \cdots, h)$ such that a vector $(u_1, \cdots, u_n)$ is an integral multiple of $(e_1, \cdots, e_s)$ if and only if $\sum_{s=1}^{h} a_{rs} u_s = 0$ for all $r = 1, \cdots, h - 1$.

Let $T^r(V_i)$ denote the homogeneous component of degree r of $T(V_i) \subseteq T(V)$. Put

$$W = \sum_{i=1}^{h} T^q(V_i) + \sum_{r=1}^{h-1} T^{a_{r1}}(V_1) \otimes \cdots \otimes T^{a_{rh}}(V_h).$$

Clearly, W is G-stable. Moreover, by the definition of the integers a_{rs}, Q belongs to the kernel of the representation of G on W.

Conversely, suppose that z is an element of this kernel. Since F is algebraically closed, V_i contains a non-zero element v_i such that $z(v_i) = \sigma v_i$, with some element σ of F. Since z leaves the element $v_i \otimes \cdots \otimes v_i$ of $T^q(V_i)$ fixed, we have $\sigma^q = 1$, so that $\sigma = \varepsilon^{u_i}$, with some u_i in $Z/(qZ)$. We wish to show that z acts as the scalar multiplication by ε^{u_i} on V_i. This means showing that if w_i is an element of V_i such that v_i and w_i are linearly independent then $z(w_i) = \sigma w_i$. Applying z to the element $w_i \otimes v_i \otimes \cdots \otimes v_i$ of $T^q(V_i)$, we obtain the relation

$$w_i \otimes v_i \otimes \cdots \otimes v_i = (\sigma^{q-1}) z(w_i) \otimes v_i \otimes \cdots \otimes v_i.$$

If we write $z(w_i)$ in terms of a basis containing v_i and w_i we see from this that we must indeed have $z(w_i) = \sigma w_i$. Now it is clear that the action of z on $T^{a_{r1}}(V_1) \otimes \cdots \otimes T^{a_{rh}}(V_h)$ is the scalar multiplication by ε^{v_r}, where $v_r = \sum_{s=1}^{h} a_{rs} u_s$. Since z leaves the elements of W fixed, we must therefore have $v_r = 0$ for each r. By the definition of the a_{rs}'s, this implies that there is an integer m such that $u_s = m e_s$ for each s. But this implies that $z = x^m \in Q$, so that Lemma 3.1 is proved.

THEOREM 3.2. *Every semisimple complex analytic group has a faithful finite-dimensional complex analytic representation.*

Proof. Let G be a semisimple complex analytic group, and let $\pi: G^* \to G$ be a group covering, with G^* simply connected. Let K be a maximal compact subgroup of G^*. We know from Theorem 2.2 and the conjugacy of the maximal compact subgroups that $\mathscr{L}(K)$ is a real form of $\mathscr{L}(G^*)$. Since K is a compact Lie group, it has a faithful finite-dimensional real analytic representation, as follows almost immediately from the Peter-Weyl Theorem. Let ρ be such a representation, and let V be its representation space. The representation ρ° of $\mathscr{L}(K)$ on V extends canonically to a complex representation of $\mathscr{L}(G^*) = \mathscr{L}(K) \otimes_R C$ on $V \otimes_R C$. Since G^* is simply connected, this representation of $\mathscr{L}(G^*)$ is the differential of a real analytic representation σ of G^*. Since our representation of $\mathscr{L}(G^*)$ is complex linear, we know from Section 1 that σ is actually a complex analytic representation. Furthermore, it is clear from the construction of σ that the restriction of σ to K is the canonical complexification of the representation ρ on the real vector space V to the representation $\rho \otimes C$ of K by complex linear automorphisms of $V \otimes C$. In particular, the restriction of σ to K is therefore faithful.

Now let α be the adjoint representation of G^* on $\mathscr{L}(G^*)$, and consider the direct sum of the representations σ and α, which is the representation on the direct sum of $V \otimes C$ and $\mathscr{L}(G^*)$ obtained in the evident fashion from σ and α. The kernel of α is the center of G^*, which we know to be finite from Theorem 2.1, and which must therefore be contained in K. Since the intersection with K of the kernel of σ is (1), it follows that the direct sum of σ and α is a faithful representation of G^*. Evidently, it is a complex analytic representation. Now we may identify G with G^*/D, where D is the kernel of π. Since D lies in the center of G^*, it is finite. Hence we may apply Lemma 3.1 to our faithful representation of G^*. Clearly, the representation of G thus obtained is still complex analytic, so that Theorem 3.2 is proved.

The analogue of Theorem 3.2 for real analytic groups is false. However, Theorem 3.2 yields a useful criterion for the representability of a semisimple real analytic group. In order to state this, we introduce the following notation. If L is a real or complex Lie algebra we denote by $S(L)$ a simply connected real or complex, respectively, analytic group whose Lie algebra is isomorphic with L (and will be identified with L).

THEOREM 3.3. *Let G be a semisimple real analytic group, and let σ denote the real analytic homomorphism of $S(\mathscr{L}(G))$ into $S(\mathscr{L}(G) \otimes_R C)$ whose differential is the canonical injection $\mathscr{L}(G) \to \mathscr{L}(G) \otimes_R C$. Let Q denote the kernel of σ, and let π denote the group covering $S(\mathscr{L}(G)) \to G$ whose differential is the identification of the Lie algebra of $S(\mathscr{L}(G))$ with $\mathscr{L}(G)$. Then every finite-dimensional* *continuous representation of G is trivial on $\pi(Q)$, and there exists a finite-dimensional continuous representation of G whose kernel is precisely $\pi(Q)$.*

Proof. Let ρ be a finite-dimensional continuous representation of G. In proving that $\pi(Q)$ lies in the kernel of ρ, we may evidently assume that ρ is a representation of G by complex linear automorphisms of a complex vector space (such as would be obtained by complexifying ρ in the canonical fashion). Then $\rho°$ extends by C-linearity to a representation of the complex Lie algebra $\mathscr{L}(G) \otimes_R C$. Since $S(\mathscr{L}(G) \otimes_R C)$ is simply connected, this is the differential $\tau°$ of a complex analytic representation τ of $S(\mathscr{L}(G) \otimes_R C)$. Clearly, $(\tau \circ \sigma)° = \rho° = (\rho \circ \pi)°$, whence $\tau \circ \sigma = \rho \circ \pi$, so that $\pi(Q)$ lies indeed in the kernel of ρ.

Now let F denote the kernel of π. Then F lies in the center of $S(\mathscr{L}(G))$. Evidently, this implies that $\sigma(F)$ lies in the kernel of the adjoint representation of $S(\mathscr{L}(G) \otimes_R C)$, i.e., in the center of $S(\mathscr{L}(G) \otimes_R C)$. The factor group $S(\mathscr{L}(G) \otimes_R C)/\sigma(F)$ is evidently a semisimple complex analytic group, because $\sigma(F)$ is a discrete (even a finite) central subgroup. By Theorem 3.2, $S(\mathscr{L}(G) \otimes_R C)/\sigma(F)$ has therefore a faithful finite-dimensional complex analytic representation, which may be regarded as a complex analytic representation η of $S(\mathscr{L}(G) \otimes_R C)$ with kernel $\sigma(F)$. Now the representation $\eta \circ \sigma$ of $S(\mathscr{L}(G))$ has kernel precisely FQ and hence induces a representation of G whose kernel is precisely $\pi(Q)$. This completes the proof of Theorem 3.3.

4

Having discussed the main features of semisimple complex analytic groups, we shall now go to the opposite extreme and consider the abelian complex analytic groups. The following is a preliminary structure theorem which isolates the difficulties involved.

THEOREM 4.1. *Let A be an abelian complex analytic group, and let T (a toroid) be the maximum compact subgroup of A. Let T^* denote the smallest complex analytic subgroup of A that contains T. Then A is a direct product $T^* \times U$, where U is a complex vector group.*

Proof. Regard A as a real analytic group, and consider the real analytic factor group A/T. Since T is the maximum compact subgroup of A, the group A/T is a real vector group. We may regard T^*/T as a real analytic subgroup of A/T, whence it is clear, since A/T is a vector group, that T^*/T is closed in A/T. Hence T^* is closed in A.

Let U be a complex analytic subgroup of A whose Lie algebra is a linear complement in $\mathscr{L}(A)$ of $\mathscr{L}(T^*)$. Then it is clear that $A = T^*U$ and that the canonical map $A \to A/T^*$ induces a surjective complex analytic homomorphism of U onto A/T^*. The kernel of this homomorphism is $T^* \cap U$, which is a discrete subgroup of the complex analytic group U. On the other hand, it is clear that, as a real analytic group, A/T^* is a vector group, and thus simply connected. Hence the kernel $T^* \cap U$ of the group covering $U \to A/T^*$ must be trivial. Hence the multiplication map $T^* \times U \to A$ is a real analytic isomorphism. Since its differential is complex linear, so is the differential of its inverse. Hence the multiplication $T^* \times U \to A$ is an isomorphism of complex analytic groups, which completes the proof of Theorem 4.1.

THEOREM 4.2. *Let T be a toroid contained in a complex analytic group T^* such that $\mathscr{L}(T)$ spans $\mathscr{L}(T^*)$ over C, and suppose that ρ is a complex analytic finite-dimensional representation of T^* whose restriction to T is faithful. Then ρ is faithful, and T^* is complex analytically isomorphic with the direct product of d copies of the multiplicative group C^* of the non-zero complex numbers, where d is the real dimension of T.*

Proof. Let V be the representation space of ρ. We can evidently decompose V into a direct sum of one-dimensional T-stable C-subspaces $V_1, \cdots, V_n$. The differential ρ° of ρ gives us real linear functions f_k from $\mathscr{L}(T)$ to R such that, for every element x of $\mathscr{L}(T)$, $\rho^\circ(x)$ acts as the multiplication by $if_k(x)$ on V_k. Let g_k denote the canonical extension of f_k to a complex linear map of $\mathscr{L}(T) \otimes_R C$ into C.

Now let D denote the direct product of d copies of C^*, and identify T with the subgroup of D consisting of all d-tuples of complex numbers of absolute value 1. This identifies $\mathscr{L}(T)$ with a real Lie subalgebra of $\mathscr{L}(D)$, and $\mathscr{L}(D)$ may compatibly be identified with $\mathscr{L}(T) \otimes_R C$. Then it is clear that the kernel of $\exp_D$ coincides with the kernel of $\exp_T$. For every element y of $\mathscr{L}(T) \otimes_R C$, let $\sigma(y)$ be the C-linear automorphism of V that coincides with the multiplication by $\exp(ig_k(y))$ on V_k, for each k. Evidently, σ is a complex analytic representation of the complex vector group $\mathscr{L}(T) \otimes_R C$ on V, and the restriction of σ to $\mathscr{L}(T)$ coincides with $\rho \circ \exp_T$. Hence the kernel of σ contains the kernel of $\exp_T$, i.e., the kernel of $\exp_D$. It follows that σ induces a complex analytic representation τ of D on V such that $\tau \circ \exp_D = \sigma$. Evidently, the restriction of τ to T coincides with the restriction of ρ to T.

Let u be an element of the kernel of τ. We have $u = \exp_D(y)$ with y in $\mathscr{L}(T) \otimes_R C$. Write $y = p + q \otimes i$, with p and q in $\mathscr{L}(T)$. Then $\tau(u)$ coincides with the multiplication by $\exp(if_k(p) - f_k(q))$ on each V_k, so that $\exp(if_k(p) - f_k(q)) = 1$, which implies that $f_k(q) = 0$. Since the restriction of ρ° to $\mathscr{L}(T)$ is faithful, the intersection of the kernels of the f_k's is (0). Thus we obtain $q = 0$, so that $y \in \mathscr{L}(T)$ and $u \in T$. Thus the kernel of τ lies in T and is therefore trivial.

Clearly,

$$\rho^\circ(\mathscr{L}(T^*)) = \rho^\circ(\mathscr{L}(T) + i\mathscr{L}(T)) = \rho^\circ(\mathscr{L}(T)) + i\rho^\circ(\mathscr{L}(T))$$
$$= \tau^\circ(\mathscr{L}(T)) + i\tau^\circ(\mathscr{L}(T)) = \tau^\circ(\mathscr{L}(D)).$$

Hence $\rho(T^*) = \tau(D)$. Hence we have a surjective complex analytic homomorphism $\tau^{-1} \circ \rho$ of T^* onto D. Evidently, this induces a real analytic surjective homomorphism of T^*/T onto D/T. Since $\mathscr{L}(T^*)$ is spanned over C by $\mathscr{L}(T)$, the dimension of T^*/T cannot exceed the dimension of D/T, so that the kernel of the homomorphism $T^*/T \twoheadrightarrow D/T$ must be discrete. But D/T is a vector group, and therefore simply connected. Hence the covering $T^*/T \to D/T$ must be an isomorphism. This implies that the kernel of $\tau^{-1} \circ \rho$ is contained in T, and therefore trivial. Thus $\tau^{-1} \circ \rho$ is a complex analytic isomorphism of T^* onto D and ρ is faithful. This completes the proof of Theorem 4.2.

5

Let G be a real analytic group. A *universal complexification* of G is a continuous homomorphism γ of G into a complex analytic group G^+ having the following property. For every continuous homomorphism η of G into a complex analytic group H, there is one and only one complex analytic homomorphism η^+ of G^+ into H such that $\eta^+ \circ \gamma = \eta$. It is clear from this definition that any two universal complexifications of G are equivalent in the evident appropriate sense. The existence of a universal complexification is easily established by means of the construction of the proof of Theorem 3.3. Let $\sigma \colon S(\mathscr{L}(G)) \to S(\mathscr{L}(G) \otimes_R C)$ be the homomorphism used there, and let F denote the kernel of the group covering $\pi \colon S(\mathscr{L}(G)) \to G$. Let η be a continuous homomorphism of G into a complex analytic group H. The differential η° of η extends canonically to a homomorphism of $\mathscr{L}(G) \otimes_R C$ into $\mathscr{L}(H)$, which is the differential of a complex analytic homomorphism η^* of $S(\mathscr{L}(G) \otimes_R C)$ into H. Clearly, $\eta^* \circ \sigma = \eta \circ \pi$. Let P denote the intersection of all kernels of homomorphisms like η^*

(with varying H's). Since the Lie algebra of the connected component of the identity in P is an ideal of the complex Lie algebra $\mathscr{L}(G) \otimes_R C$, it is clear that $S(\mathscr{L}(G) \otimes_R C)/P$ is a complex analytic group. Now η^* induces a complex analytic homomorphism η^+ of this factor group, which we shall now denote by G^+, into H. Since P contains $\sigma(F)$, the composite of σ with the canonical map δ of $S(\mathscr{L}(G) \otimes_R C)$ into G^+ determines a continuous homomorphism $\gamma \colon G \to G^+$ such that $\gamma \circ \pi = \delta \circ \sigma$. One sees readily that this homomorphism γ is a universal complexification of G.

In general, it is difficult to determine the universal complexification with precision. However, if G has a faithful continuous finite-dimensional representation, i.e., if there is an injective continuous homomorphism of G into the group L of automorphisms of a finite-dimensional real vector space V, then we may regard L as a subgroup of the complex analytic group of all C-linear automorphisms of $V \otimes_R C$, so that the given representation of G appears as a continuous homomorphism of G into a complex analytic group. Clearly, this implies that $\gamma \colon G \to G^+$ is injective. The complex conjugation of $\mathscr{L}(G) \otimes_R C$ is the differential of a real analytic automorphism α of $S(\mathscr{L}(G) \otimes_R C)$, and $\sigma(S(\mathscr{L}(G)))$ is evidently the connected component of 1 in the α-fixed subgroup. Hence $\sigma(S(\mathscr{L}(G)))$ is closed in $S(\mathscr{L}(G) \otimes_R C)$. Now it is clear that σ is a topological group isomorphism of $S(\mathscr{L}(G))$ onto the subgroup $\sigma(S(\mathscr{L}(G)))$ of $S(\mathscr{L}(G) \otimes_R C)$, whence $\sigma(F)$ is actually discrete, and $P = \sigma(F)$. In particular, this applies to the case where G is compact, which is the case we are interested in.

We shall say that a complex analytic group H is *reductive* if H has a faithful finite-dimensional complex analytic representation and every finite-dimensional complex analytic representation of H is semisimple. We shall prove that the reductive complex analytic groups are precisely the groups obtained from the universal complexifications of the compact real analytic groups.

THEOREM 5.1. *Let $\gamma \colon G \to G^+$ be a universal complexification of a compact real analytic group G. Then γ is injective, $\gamma(G)$ is a maximal compact subgroup of G^+, and $\mathscr{L}(\gamma(G))$ is a real form of $\mathscr{L}(G^+)$.*

Proof. We have already seen, even under the more general circumstances where G has a faithful representation, that γ is injective and that $\mathscr{L}(\gamma(G))$ is a real form of $\mathscr{L}(G^+)$.

We may take γ to be the homomorphism constructed above. Since G is compact, we have $S(\mathscr{L}(G)) = V \times K$, where V is a real vector group and K

is a simply connected compact semisimple real analytic group. It follows that $S(\mathscr{L}(G) \otimes_R C) = W \times L$, where W is a complex vector group and L is a simply connected semisimple complex analytic group containing $\gamma(K)$. Moreover, W may be identified with $V \otimes_R C$ in such a way that the restriction of σ to V becomes the canonical injection of V into $V \otimes_R C$. Now we may factor the group covering π according to the scheme

$$V \times K \to \pi(V) \times K \to \pi(V)\pi(K) = G.$$

The kernel of the first of these homomorphisms is $F \cap V$, which is the discrete subgroup of V generated by an R-basis of V. Since $\pi(V) \times K$ is compact, the kernel of the second homomorphism is finite. Thus $F/(F \cap V)$ is finite.

Let $Z(G)$ and $Z(G^+)$ denote the connected components of 1 in the centers of G and G^+, respectively. Clearly, $Z(G^+)$ is the smallest complex analytic subgroup of G^+ containing $\gamma(Z(G))$, and is also the canonical image of W in G^+, which is isomorphic with $W/(\sigma(F) \cap W)$. This last group is the factor group of $W/\sigma(F \cap V)$ mod. the finite group $(\sigma(F) \cap W)/\sigma(F \cap V)$. Since $\sigma(F \cap V)$ is the discrete subgroup of W generated by a C-basis of W, it is clear that $W/\sigma(F \cap V)$ is the direct product of d copies of C^*, where d is the complex dimension of W, which is equal to the real dimension of V and thus to the real dimension of $Z(G)$. In particular, $W/\sigma(F \cap V)$ has therefore a faithful finite-dimensional complex analytic representation. By Lemma 3.1, the same is therefore true for $W/(\sigma(F) \cap W)$ and so for $Z(G^+)$. Hence we conclude from Theorem 4.2 (with $\gamma(Z(G))$ taking the place of what was denoted T there) that $Z(G^+)$ is the direct product of d copies of C^*. Hence the maximum compact subgroup of $Z(G^+)$ is of real dimension d. Since γ is injective, the compact real analytic subgroup $\gamma(Z(G))$ of $Z(G^+)$ is of real dimension d. Hence it must coincide with the maximum compact subgroup of $Z(G^+)$.

Now let M be a compact subgroup of G^+ containing $\gamma(G)$. Then the canonical image of M in $G^+/Z(G^+)$ is a compact subgroup containing the canonical image of $\gamma(G)$. One sees immediately from the construction of γ given above that the real dimension of the canonical image of $\gamma(G)$ in $G^+/Z(G^+)$ is equal to the complex dimension of $G^+/Z(G^+)$. Now $G^+/Z(G^+)$ is a semisimple complex analytic group. Hence it is clear from Theorem 2.2 (with the canonical image of $\gamma(G)$ taking the place of what was denoted K there) that the canonical image of $\gamma(G)$ is a maximal compact subgroup of $G^+/Z(G^+)$. Hence we must have $M \subset \gamma(G)Z(G^+)$, so that

$M = \gamma(G)(M \cap Z(G^+))$. Since $\gamma(Z(G))$ is the maximum compact subgroup of $Z(G^+)$, this gives $M = \gamma(G)$, so that Theorem 5.1 is proved.

Next we shall prove a generalization of Theorem 4.2. Let us say that a compact subgroup Q of a complex analytic group G is *full* in G if $\mathscr{L}(Q)$ spans $\mathscr{L}(G)$ over C.

THEOREM 5.2. *Let G be a complex analytic group having a full compact subgroup Q. Suppose that ρ is a finite-dimensional complex analytic representation of G that is faithful on Q. Then ρ is a faithful representation of G.*

Proof. Let σ denote the restriction of ρ to Q, regarded as a representation by real-linear automorphisms of a real vector space. Since σ is faithful, it is clear from Exercise 5 of Chapter II (an application of the Stone-Weierstrass Theorem) that the space $S(\sigma)$ of the real-valued representative functions associated with σ generates the algebra of all real-valued representative functions on Q. Let $S(\rho)$ denote the space of the complex-valued representative functions on G associated with ρ, and let $S(\rho)_Q$ denote the restriction image of $S(\rho)$ in the space of the complex-valued representative functions on Q. Then $S(\sigma)$ is contained in the C-space spanned by the elements of $S(\rho)_Q$ and their complex conjugates. We know from a discussion following the proof of Theorem 2.5 in Chapter II that the complex conjugates of the elements of $S(\rho)_Q$ are the elements of $S(\rho^*)_Q$, where ρ^* is the dual of ρ. Hence $S(\rho)_Q$ and $S(\rho^*)_Q$ generate the algebra of all complex-valued representative functions on Q.

Now observe that if f is any complex analytic function on G whose restriction to Q is 0 then $f = 0$. Indeed, the assumption implies that if $\eta_1, \cdots, \eta_k$ are elements of $\mathscr{L}(Q)$ then $\eta_1 \cdots \eta_k(f)$ also vanishes on Q. Since $\mathscr{L}(Q)$ spans $\mathscr{L}(G)$ over C, the same holds therefore if the η_i's are arbitrary elements of $\mathscr{L}(G)$. By choosing a chart of G at 1, for instance, we see that this implies that f vanishes on some neighborhood of 1 in G. Since f is complex analytic, this implies that $f = 0$ (the set of points where f and all its derivatives vanish is both open and closed in G, and thus must coincide with G).

In particular, it follows that the restriction map of the algebra of all complex analytic representative functions on G to the algebra of the complex-valued representative functions on Q is injective. Since the restrictions to Q of the elements of $S(\rho)$ and $S(\rho^*)$ generate the algebra of all complex-valued representative functions on Q, we conclude that $S(\rho)$ and $S(\rho^*)$ generate the algebra of all complex analytic representative functions on G.

This evidently implies that the kernel of ρ is contained in the kernel of every finite-dimensional complex analytic representation of G.

Hence Theorem 5.2 will be established as soon as we have shown that G has a faithful finite-dimensional complex analytic representation. Since G has a full compact subgroup, it is clear (noting that the Q-stable C-subspaces of a complex analytic representation space for G are also G-stable) that every complex analytic representation of G is semisimple. If we apply this to the adjoint representation of G, we conclude that $([\mathscr{L}(G), \mathscr{L}(G)])$ is semisimple and that $\mathscr{L}(G)$ is the direct sum of its center and $([\mathscr{L}(G), \mathscr{L}(G)])$. The same is true for $\mathscr{L}(Q)$. Hence it is clear that the center of $\mathscr{L}(Q)$ spans the center of $\mathscr{L}(G)$ over C. Let $Z(G)$ denote the connected component of 1 in the center of G. Then the Lie algebra of $Q \cap Z(G)$ is evidently the center of $\mathscr{L}(Q)$, so that $Q \cap Z(G)$ is a full compact subgroup of $Z(G)$. Since ρ is faithful on Q, it follows therefore from Theorem 4.2 that ρ is faithful on $Z(G)$.

On the other hand, since $G/Z(G)$ is a semisimple complex analytic group, we know from Theorem 3.2 that it has a faithful finite-dimensional complex analytic representation, i.e., that there is a finite-dimensional complex analytic representation τ of G whose kernel is precisely $Z(G)$. Now the direct sum of ρ and τ is evidently a faithful finite-dimensional complex analytic representation of G, so that the proof of Theorem 5.2 is complete.

THEOREM 5.3. *Let $\gamma: G \to G^+$ be a universal complexification of a compact analytic group G. Then G^+ is a reductive complex analytic group. Conversely, if H is a reductive complex analytic group and G is a maximal compact subgroup of H then the injection $G \to H$ is a universal complexification of G.*

Proof. The first part follows immediately from Theorems 5.1 and 5.2. In order to prove the second part, we show first that G is full in H. Since H is reductive, it follows from the same Lie algebra argument that we made in the proof of Theorem 5.2 that $H = Z(H)H'$, where $Z(H)$ is the connected component of 1 in the center of H and where H' is the commutator subgroup of H. Moreover, H' is a semisimple complex analytic subgroup of H. Let T denote the maximum compact subgroup of $Z(H)$, and let T^* be the smallest complex analytic subgroup of $Z(H)$ containing T. By Theorem 4.1, $Z(H)$ is a direct product $T^* \times U$, where U is a complex vector group. Since H' is a semisimple complex analytic group, its center is finite, whence $Z(H) \cap H'$ is finite and therefore contained in T. Hence $U \cap (T^*H') \subset U \cap T^* = (1)$. Now T^*H' is evidently a complex analytic subgroup of H, and by the last result the multiplication map $U \times (T^*H') \to H$ is injective. Since it is a complex analytic homomorphism, it is therefore an isomorphism of complex analytic groups. Hence every complex analytic representation of U may be regarded as a complex analytic representation of H that is trivial on T^*H'. Since H is reductive, this implies that every complex analytic representation of U is semisimple. Since U is a complex vector group, it follows that U must be trivial, so that T is a full compact subgroup of $Z(H)$. On the other hand, we know that the semisimple complex analytic group H' has a full compact subgroup, Q say. Clearly, TQ is a full compact subgroup of H. Since G is maximal compact in H, it contains a conjugate of TQ, so that G is full in H.

Since, by assumption, H has a faithful finite-dimensional complex analytic representation, we may identify it with a complex analytic subgroup of a full complex linear group, L say. Now let $\gamma: G \to G^+$ be a universal complexification of G. Then the injection $G \to H$ determines a complex analytic homomorphism $\rho: G^+ \to H$. We may regard ρ as a complex analytic representation of G^+. Since ρ is faithful on $\gamma(G)$, it follows from Theorem 5.2 that ρ is faithful. Moreover, since G is full in H, it is clear that $\rho(G^+) = H$. Thus ρ is a complex analytic isomorphism of G^+ onto H, which evidently gives an equivalence of the injection $G \to H$ with the universal complexification $\gamma: G \to G^+$, so that Theorem 5.3 is proved.

In this chapter, we have confined ourselves to connected groups in order to eliminate some awkward but comparatively superficial details. By a complex Lie group, one means a Lie group G together with the structure of a complex analytic group on the connected component G_1 of 1 in G such that the conjugations effected by the elements of G on G_1 are complex analytic automorphisms of G_1 (which is true, a priori, only for the elements of G_1). A reductive complex Lie group is a complex Lie group G such that G_1 is a reductive complex analytic group and G/G_1 is finite. Universal complexifications exist as complex Lie groups also for non-connected real Lie groups, the requisite construction being somewhat more complicated than that for real analytic groups. A full compact subgroup of a complex Lie group G is a compact subgroup Q such that Q_1 is full in G_1 and $QG_1 = G$. The results for reductive complex Lie groups are the evident modifications of the results for reductive complex analytic groups. In particular, these groups are the universal complexifications of compact Lie groups.

1. Let G be the semisimple real analytic group of all linear automorphisms of determinant 1 of a two-dimensional R-space, and let H be the semi-simple complex analytic group of all linear automorphisms of deter-minant 1 of a two-dimensional C-space. Note that G may be identified with a real analytic subgroup of H, and that $\mathscr{L}(G)$ thus becomes a real form of $\mathscr{L}(H)$. Show that the subgroup of H consisting of the auto-morphisms that are unitary with respect to some positive definite Hermitian form is a maximal compact subgroup of H, and hence that H is simply connected. Now use Theorem 3.3 to show that if $\pi\colon K \to G$ is any group covering of G then every continuous finite-dimensional representation of K is trivial on the kernel of π (by Exercise 3 of Chapter XV, non-trivial π's exist).

2. Let G be a complex analytic group, and suppose that G has a faithful finite-dimensional complex analytic representation. Show that then the real dimension of any connected compact subgroup of G does not exceed the complex dimension of G. [Show first that one may assume G to be reductive, and then use Theorems 5.3 and 5.1.]

3. Let G be a complex analytic group, and suppose that G has a closed normal complex analytic subgroup S such that S is solvable and simply connected and G/S is reductive. Prove that, as a complex analytic group, G is a semidirect product of S and a complementary complex analytic subgroup. [Use Theorem 3.2 of Chapter XII and some of the results of Section 5.]

4. Let Z denote the additive group of the integers, and let G denote the complex analytic group $(C/Z) \times (C/Z)$. Let S be the closed complex analytic subgroup of G consisting of the elements of the form $(c + Z, ic + Z)$. Show that S is not a semidirect factor of G in the complex analytic sense, although G/S is compact.

5. In the notation of the beginning of Section 5, show that if G is solvable then $\sigma(F)$ is discrete in $S(\mathscr{L}(G) \otimes_R C)$, $G^+ = S(\mathscr{L}(G) \otimes_R C)/\sigma(F)$, and $\gamma\colon G \to G^+$ is injective. [Use Theorem 2.2 of Chapter XII.]

XVIII. FAITHFUL REPRESENTATIONS

1

We shall require a few simple notions and facts concerning general representation theory. Let G be a topological group, and let V be a finite-dimensional continuous G-module over the field F, where F is either the field R of the real numbers or the field C of the complex numbers. Let $S(V)$ denote the F-space of the representative functions associated with V; we recall from Chapter II that the elements of $S(V)$ are the composites of the representation of G on V with the linear functionals on the space $E(V)$ of all linear endomorphisms of V. We make the tensor product space $S(V) \otimes_F V$ into a representation space for G such that, for f in $S(V)$, v in V, and x in G, we have $x \cdot (f \otimes v) = (x \cdot f) \otimes v$. This representation space for G is evidently G-isomorphic with the direct sum of n copies of $S(V)$, where n is the dimension of V. If x is an element of G, let $\delta(x)$ be the linear endomorphism of $S(V) \otimes_F V$ that is characterized by the property that $\delta(x)(f \otimes v) = (f \cdot x) \otimes v - f \otimes (x \cdot v)$ for all elements f of $S(V)$ and all elements v of V. Let V^* denote the intersection of the kernels of these endomorphisms $\delta(x)$, as x ranges over G. Evidently, V^* is G-stable.

Let ε be the linear map of $S(V) \otimes_F V$ onto V such that $\varepsilon(f \otimes v) = f(1)v$ for every f in $S(V)$ and every v in V. We claim that *the restriction σ of ε to V^* is a G-module isomorphism of V^* onto V.* Noting that $(x \cdot f)(1) = f(x) = (f \cdot x)(1)$, we see immediately from the definition of V^* that σ is a G-module homomorphism. Let $(v_1, \cdots, v_n)$ be a basis of V and let $(\mu_1, \cdots, \mu_n)$ be the dual basis of the space V° of the linear functions on V. If v is an element of V then each function μ_i/v on G, defined by $(\mu_i/v)(x) = \mu_i(x \cdot v)$, is an element of $S(V)$. Define the linear map τ on V by $\tau(v) = \sum_{i=1}^{n}(\mu_i/v) \otimes v_i$. It is easy to verify that $\tau(V) \subset V^*$, that $\sigma \circ \tau$ is the identity map on V, and that $\tau \circ \sigma$ is the identity map on V^*. Thus σ is indeed a G-module isomorphism of V^* onto V, its inverse being τ. We shall need only the crude form of this conclusion, saying that *every finite-dimensional continuous G-module V is isomorphic with a G-submodule of the direct sum of a finite number of copies of $S(V)$*.

With G and V as above, let $(0) = V_q \subset \cdots \subset V_0 = V$ be a composition series for the G-module V. The direct sum of the factor modules V_i/V_{i+1} is evidently a semisimple continuous G-module. By the Jordan-Hoelder Theorem for groups with operators, this semisimple G-module is determined uniquely to within G-module isomorphisms by V. Taking the point of view that a choice of a composition series for each V is made in advance, we shall call the direct sum of the factor modules V_i/V_{i+1} *the semisimple G-module associated with V*, and we shall denote it by V'. If ρ denotes the representation of G on V then the representation of G on V' is denoted ρ' and is called *the semisimple representation associated with ρ*. If ρ' is trivial then we shall say that ρ is a *unipotent* representation of G. The representation ρ is unipotent if and only if the set of endomorphisms $\rho(x) - I$, where I denotes the identity map on V and x ranges over G, is nilpotent on V.

A final general remark is the following. *Let K be a normal subgroup of G, and let V be a finite-dimensional semisimple G-module. Then V is semisimple also as a K-module.* The proof is as follows. Since V is a sum of simple G-submodules, it suffices to prove the result in the case where V is a simple G-module. Let W be a minimal non-zero K-submodule of V. Then W is evidently a simple K-module. The sum of the transforms $x \cdot W$, with x ranging over G, is a G-stable subspace of V, and thus coincides with V. Since K is normal in G, each $x \cdot W$ is a K-submodule of V, and it is evidently still a simple K-module. Thus V is the sum of simple K-submodules, which means that it is semisimple as a K-module.

2

Let G be an analytic group, and let P be the radical of G. Recall that the radical of G is the unique maximum normal solvable analytic subgroup of G. It is easy to see that the closure in G of a normal solvable analytic subgroup is still a normal solvable analytic subgroup of G. Hence P is closed in G.

The following lemma is basic for the development of a criterion for the extendibility of a representation of a normal subgroup to a representation of the whole group.

LEMMA 2.1.   *Let G be an analytic group, and let P be the radical of G.   Let S be a maximal semisimple analytic subgroup of G.   Let ρ be a finite-dimensional continuous representation of G, and let ρ' be the semisimple representation associated with ρ.   Let A be a set of topological group automorphisms of G satisfying the conditions*
(i) $\rho'(\alpha(x)x^{-1}) = 1$ *for all α in A and all x in P;*
(ii) $\rho(\alpha(x)x^{-1}) = 1$ *for all α in A and all x in S.*
Then if f is any representative function associated with ρ the space spanned by the functions $f \circ \alpha$, with α in A, is finite-dimensional.

Proof.   We show first that it suffices to prove the lemma in the case where G is simply connected.   Let $\pi: G^* \to G$ be a group covering with G^* simply connected.   Then $f \circ \pi$ is a representative function on G^* that is associated with the representation $\rho \circ \pi$ of G^*.   The map $h \to h \circ \pi$ of the space of continuous functions on G into the space of the continuous functions on G^* is evidently injective.   Hence it suffices to show that the space spanned by the functions $f \circ \alpha \circ \pi$, where α ranges over A, is finite-dimensional.   We know from Chapter XII that, for each α in A, there is one and only one topological group automorphism α^* of G^* such that $\pi \circ \alpha^* = \alpha \circ \pi$.   Let A^* denote the image of A under the map $\alpha \to \alpha^*$.   We show that conditions (i) and (ii) of Lemma 2.1 extend to $(G^*, A^*, \rho \circ \pi)$.

Clearly, $\rho' \circ \pi$ is the semisimple representation associated with $\rho \circ \pi$. If P^* is the radical of G^* then we have evidently $\pi(P^*) = P$.   Hence if α is an element of A and x^* is an element of P^* we have

$$(\rho' \circ \pi)(\alpha^*(x^*)(x^*)^{-1}) = \rho'(\alpha(\pi(x^*))\pi(x^*)^{-1}) = 1.$$

Similarly, if S^* is the maximal semisimple analytic subgroup of G^* such that $\pi(S^*) = S$ and if x^* is an element of S^* we have

$$(\rho \circ \pi)(\alpha^*(x^*)(x^*)^{-1}) = \rho(\alpha(\pi(x^*))\pi(x^*)^{-1}) = 1.$$

Thus conditions (i) and (ii) of Lemma 2.1 hold for $(G^*, A^*, \rho \circ \pi)$.   Therefore, if the lemma holds for simply connected groups we conclude that the space spanned by the functions $f \circ \pi \circ \alpha^* = f \circ \alpha \circ \pi$ is finite-dimensional. The reduction to the simply connected case is therefore complete.

Now we assume that G is simply connected.   Since $\mathscr{L}(S)$ is a maximal semisimple subalgebra of $\mathscr{L}(G)$, we know from Theorem 3.3 of Chapter XI that $\mathscr{L}(G)$ is the semidirect sum $\mathscr{L}(S) + \mathscr{L}(P)$.   Since G is simply connected, this implies that G is the semidirect product of P and S.

Let T denote the kernel of the restriction ρ'_P of ρ' to P.   Since P is normal in G, we know from the end of Section 1 that ρ'_P is a semisimple representation of P. Hence it is clear from Theorem 1.3 of Chapter XI that $[\mathscr{L}(P), \mathscr{L}(P)] \subset \mathscr{L}(T)$. It follows that if $x_1, \cdots, x_p$ are representatives in $\mathscr{L}(P)$ for the elements of a basis of $\mathscr{L}(P)/\mathscr{L}(T)$ then

$$\mathscr{L}(T) \subset \mathscr{L}(T) + Rx_1 \subset \cdots \subset \mathscr{L}(T) + Rx_1 + \cdots + Rx_p = \mathscr{L}(P)$$

is a series of ideals of $\mathscr{L}(P)$. Let T_1 denote the connected component of 1 in T. By Theorem 1.2 of Chapter XII, P and T_1 are simply connected, and closed in G. Hence P can be reached from T_1 by successively constructing semidirect products in accordance with the above series of ideals, as in the proof of Theorem 1.1 of Chapter XII. Moreover, since T_1 is simply connected and solvable, there is a composition series $Ry_1 \subset \cdots \subset Ry_1 + \cdots + Ry_q = \mathscr{L}(T)$ and T_1 is reached by successively constructing semidirect products in accordance with this series.

This shows that there is an analytic manifold isomorphism $\mu: \mathscr{L}(P) \to P$, given by

$$\mu(t_1y_1 + \cdots + t_qy_q + s_1x_1 + \cdots + s_px_p)$$
$$= \exp(t_1y_1) \cdots \exp(t_qy_q)\exp(s_1x_1) \cdots \exp(s_px_p),$$

where the t_j's and the s_i's are arbitrary real numbers.

Every element α of A induces a Lie algebra automorphism α° of $\mathscr{L}(G)$ under which $\mathscr{L}(P)$ is stable. Condition (i) of our lemma evidently implies that $\mathscr{L}(T)$ is also stable under α° and that, for each i, we have $\alpha^\circ(x_i) = u_i + x_i$, with u_i in $\mathscr{L}(T)$. Write z for $t_1y_1 + \cdots + t_qy_q + s_1x_1 + \cdots + s_px_p$. Then we have

$$\alpha(\mu(z)) = \exp(t_1\alpha^\circ(y_1)) \cdots \exp(t_q\alpha^\circ(y_q))\exp(s_1(u_1 + x_1)) \cdots \exp(s_p(u_p + x_p)).$$

If ρ° denotes the differential of ρ this gives

$$\rho(\alpha(\mu(z))) = \mathrm{Exp}(t_1\rho^\circ(\alpha^\circ(y_1))) \cdots \mathrm{Exp}(t_q\rho^\circ(\alpha^\circ(y_q)))$$
$$\times \mathrm{Exp}(s_1(\rho^\circ(u_1) + v_1)) \cdots \mathrm{Exp}(s_p(\rho^\circ(u_p) + v_p)),$$

where $v_i = \rho^\circ(x_i)$.

Now let $(0) = V_{d+1} \subset \cdots \subset V_1 = V$ be a composition series for the representation space V of ρ. Then it is clear from the definition of ρ' and T that $\rho^\circ(\mathscr{L}(T))(V_i) \subset V_{i+1}$ for $i = 1, \cdots, d$. Hence every monomial in elements of $\rho^\circ(\mathscr{L}(P))$ having more than $d - 1$ factors in $\rho^\circ(\mathscr{L}(T))$ is equal to 0. Clearly, the elements $\rho^\circ(\alpha^\circ(y_j))$ and $\rho^\circ(u_i)$ are linear combinations with coefficients $c_k(\alpha)$ and $d_k(\alpha)$ depending only on α of the elements $\rho^\circ(y_k)$. Hence if $p_1, \cdots, p_s$ are all the polynomials of total degree less than

d in $2q$ commuting variables we have from the above, on writing out the exponential series and collecting terms appropriately, that

$$\rho(\alpha(\mu(z))) = \textstyle\sum_{r=1}^{s} p_r(c_1(\alpha), \cdots, c_q(\alpha), d_1(\alpha), \cdots, d_q(\alpha)) f_r(z),$$

where the f_r's are (analytic) maps of $\mathscr{L}(P)$ into the endomorphism algebra of V that do not depend on α.

Now let π be the projection of G onto P corresponding to the semidirect product decomposition $G = P \times_\eta S$, and put $g_r = f_r \circ \mu^{-1} \circ \pi$. Then the last result gives, for every x in G,

$$\rho(\alpha(\pi(x))) = \textstyle\sum_{r=1}^{s} p_r(c_1(\alpha), \cdots, c_q(\alpha), d_1(\alpha), \cdots, d_q(\alpha)) g_r(x).$$

Noting that $x\pi(x)^{-1}$ lies in S and using condition (ii) of our lemma, we obtain, from the last result,

$$\begin{aligned}
\rho(\alpha(x)) &= \rho(\alpha(x\pi(x)^{-1}))\rho(\alpha(\pi(x))) = \rho(x\pi(x)^{-1})\rho(\alpha(\pi(x))) \\
&= \textstyle\sum_{r=1}^{s} p_r(c_1(\alpha), \cdots, c_q(\alpha), d_1(\alpha), \cdots, d_q(\alpha)) h_r(x),
\end{aligned}$$

where $h_r(x) = \rho(x\pi(x)^{-1})g_r(x)$. Now if f is a representative function associated with ρ then $f = \gamma \circ \rho$, where γ is a linear functional on the endomorphism algebra of V. Hence the last result shows that $f \circ \alpha$ lies in the space spanned by the functions $\gamma \circ h_1, \cdots, \gamma \circ h_r$, so that Lemma 2.1 is proved.

THEOREM 2.2. *Let K be an analytic group, and suppose that K is a semidirect product $H \times_\eta G$, with G normal in K. Let P be the radical of G, and let ρ be a finite-dimensional continuous representation of G such that $\rho'(yxy^{-1}x^{-1}) = 1$ for all y in K and all x in P. Then the representation space V of ρ is contained as a G-stable subspace in a finite-dimensional representation space W of a continuous representation σ of K, and the kernel of σ' contains the kernel of ρ'.*

Proof. Let S be a maximal semisimple analytic subgroup of G, and let $Z(S)$ denote the centralizer of S in K. We wish to show first that $K = Z(S)G$. For y in K, consider the automorphism of G/P that is induced by the conjugation $x \to y^{-1}xy$ on G. This automorphism evidently belongs to the connected component of the identity in the group of all topological group automorphisms of G/P, whose Lie algebra consists of derivations of $\mathscr{L}(G/P)$. Since G/P is semisimple, we know (see Exercise 5 of Chapter XI) that every derivation of $\mathscr{L}(G/P)$ is of the form D_x with some x in $\mathscr{L}(G/P)$, i.e., belongs to the Lie algebra of the image of G/P under its adjoint representation. Hence the connected component of the identity in the group of all topological group automorphisms of G/P consists of the conjugations effected by the elements of G/P. It follows that there is an element u in G such that the conjugation $x \to (yu)^{-1}x(yu)$ induces the identity automorphism on G/P. In particular, for every element s of S, we have $(yu)^{-1}s(yu)s^{-1} \in P$.

Now S and $(yu)^{-1}S(yu)$ are two maximal semisimple analytic subgroups of G. It follows therefore from Theorem 3.3 of Chapter XI that there is an element p in P such that $(yu)^{-1}S(yu) = pSp^{-1}$, whence $(yup)^{-1}s(yup)s^{-1} \in S$ for every element s of S. On the other hand, this element may be written $p^{-1}((yu)^{-1}s(yu)s^{-1})(sps^{-1})$, showing that it also belongs to P. The analytic map $s \to (yup)^{-1}s(yup)s^{-1}$ from S to S therefore sends S into the discrete subset $S \cap P$ of S, so that it must be trivial. Thus $yup \in Z(S)$, so that $y \in Z(S)G$. We have shown, therefore, that $K = Z(S)G$.

Now let $\mathscr{F}(G)$ denote the space of all continuous real-valued functions on G. Regard this as a G-module, with G acting from the left by $f \to x \cdot f$. We extend this G-module structure on $\mathscr{F}(G)$ to a K-module structure as follows. Let f be in $\mathscr{F}(G)$, h in H, x and y in G. Then we define the element $(hx) \cdot f$ of $\mathscr{F}(G)$ by $((hx) \cdot f)(y) = f(h^{-1}yhx)$. One verifies directly that $(h_1x_1) \cdot ((h_2x_2) \cdot f) = (h_1x_1h_2x_2) \cdot f$, so that we have indeed defined a K-module structure on $\mathscr{F}(G)$. Now suppose that f is a representative function on G, so that the transforms $x \cdot f$ with x in G lie in a finite-dimensional subspace $(G \cdot f)$ of $\mathscr{F}(G)$. Then we have, for all x_1 in G,

$$x_1 \cdot ((hx) \cdot f) = (x_1hx) \cdot f = (h(h^{-1}x_1hx)) \cdot f = h \cdot ((h^{-1}x_1hx) \cdot f) \in h \cdot (G \cdot f),$$

whence it is clear that $(hx) \cdot f$ is still a representative function. Thus the space $\mathscr{R}(G)$ of the representative functions on G is a K-submodule of $\mathscr{F}(G)$.

Since $K = Z(S)G$, given h in H, we can find an element z in G such that hz commutes with every element of S. Let α be the automorphism $x \to (hz)^{-1}x(hz)$ of G. Then one sees directly that $h \cdot f = (z^{-1} \cdot f \cdot z) \circ \alpha$ for every f in $\mathscr{F}(G)$. Let A be the set of all these automorphisms α. The assumption of Theorem 2.2 evidently implies that condition (i) of Lemma 2.1 is satisfied by (A, ρ), while condition (ii) is trivially satisfied because the elements of A leave the elements of S fixed. Now let f be a representative function associated with ρ. Then each $z^{-1} \cdot f \cdot z$ lies in the finite-dimensional space $S(V)$ of the representative functions associated with ρ, so that we conclude from Lemma 2.1 that the space spanned by the functions $h \cdot f = (z^{-1} \cdot f \cdot z) \circ \alpha$, as h ranges over H, is finite-dimensional. It follows that the K-transforms of the elements of $S(V)$ span a finite-dimensional subspace U

of $\mathscr{R}(G)$. Evidently, U is the representation space for a continuous representation of K and contains $S(V)$ as a G-stable subspace.

Now we know from Section 1 that V may be identified with a G-stable subspace of the direct sum of a finite number of copies of $S(V)$. This, in turn, is a G-stable subspace of the direct sum W of the same number of copies of U, so that the first part of Theorem 2.2 is proved.

It remains to show that if σ is the representation of K on W then the kernel of σ' contains the kernel of ρ'. Note first that the conditions of Theorem 2.2 imply that the kernel of ρ' is normal in K, not only in G. In fact, let z be an element of this kernel, and let y be an element of K. Write $z = sp$, with s in S and p in P (note that $G = SP$, because S is a maximal semisimple analytic subgroup of G). We have shown above that there is an element u in G such that uy commutes with every element of S. Hence we have

$$yzy^{-1} = (ysy^{-1})(ypy^{-1}) = (u^{-1}su)(ypy^{-1}) = (u^{-1}zu)(u^{-1}pu)^{-1}(ypy^{-1}).$$

Since the kernel of ρ' is normal in G, we have $\rho'(u^{-1}zu) = 1$, so that the above and the assumption of our theorem give

$$\rho'(yzy^{-1}) = \rho'(u^{-1}p^{-1}u)\rho'(ypy^{-1}) = \rho'(p^{-1})\rho'(p) = 1.$$

Thus the kernel of ρ' is normal in K. Hence we can apply the last remark of Section 1 to conclude that the restriction of σ' to the kernel of ρ' is semisimple. In order to conclude that it is trivial, it suffices therefore to show that the original representation of the kernel of ρ' on U is unipotent.

The elements of U are linear combinations of functions $y \cdot f$, with y in K and f in $S(V)$. By the definition of ρ', the representation of its kernel on V is unipotent. This is easily seen to imply that the representation of the kernel of ρ' on $S(V)$ is also unipotent. Now if z is in the kernel of ρ' then so is $y^{-1}zy$ for every y in K, and $z \cdot (y \cdot f) = y \cdot (y^{-1}zy \cdot f)$. It is clear from this that the representation of the kernel of ρ' on U is indeed unipotent, so that Theorem 2.2 is proved.

We observe that *the condition* $\rho'(yxy^{-1}x^{-1}) = 1$ *for all y in K and all x in P is necessary*. In fact, the group generated by these elements is the analytic subgroup of K whose Lie algebra is $([\mathscr{L}(K), \mathscr{L}(P)])$. Since $\mathscr{L}(P)$ is contained in the radical of $\mathscr{L}(K)$, it follows from Theorem 3.2 of Chapter XI that the differential of σ' is trivial on $([\mathscr{L}(K), \mathscr{L}(P)])$, so that σ' is trivial on $[K, P]$, the group generated by the above commutators. Hence if σ extends ρ in the sense of Theorem 2.2 then these commutators must lie in the kernel of ρ'.

THEOREM 2.3.   *In the situation of Theorem 2.2, suppose that ρ is a unipotent representation of G and that the restriction to H of the adjoint representation of K on $\mathscr{L}(G)$ is unipotent.   Then the representation σ of K obtained in the proof of Theorem 2.2 is unipotent.*

Proof.   In this case, ρ' is trivial, so that we know from the proof of Theorem 2.2 that the representation of G on U is unipotent.   Let us denote this representation by μ.   Let f be an element of U, and let $f*$ denote the linear function on the space $E(U)$ of all linear endomorphisms of U that is given by $f*(e) = e(f)(1)$ for every e in $E(U)$.   Then, as a function on G, f coincides with $f* \circ \mu$.   Now we have $f \circ \exp_G = (f* \circ \mu) \circ \exp_G = f* \circ \operatorname{Exp} \circ \mu^\circ$.   Since μ is unipotent, μ° is a nilpotent representation of $\mathscr{L}(G)$, so that $\operatorname{Exp} \circ \mu^\circ$ is a polynomial map of $\mathscr{L}(G)$ into $E(U)$.   Hence the above shows that $f \circ \exp_G$ is a polynomial function on $\mathscr{L}(G)$.   Moreover, it is clearly a polynomial function of degree $< d$, where d is the dimension of U, because every product of d elements of $\mu^\circ(\mathscr{L}(G))$ is 0.   Since μ is unipotent, the map $\operatorname{Exp}: \mu^\circ(\mathscr{L}(G)) \to \mu(G)$ is surjective (the logarithm is defined on $\mu(G)$).   Hence the above shows that the map $f \to f \circ \exp_G$ is injective on U.

If h is any element of H we have $(h \cdot f) \circ \exp_G = f \circ \exp_G \circ (h^{-1})*$, where $(h^{-1})*$ denotes the image of h^{-1} under the adjoint representation of K on $\mathscr{L}(G)$.   By assumption, the restriction of this representation to H is unipotent, and so is therefore its dual.   This is easily seen to imply that the canonical extension of this last representation to a representation of H on the space of all polynomial functions on $\mathscr{L}(G)$ of degree $< d$ is also unipotent.   The above shows that the map $f \to f \circ \exp_G$ is an injective H-module homomorphism of U into this space of polynomial functions.   Hence we conclude that the representation of H on U is unipotent.   Clearly, this implies that the restriction to H of the representation σ constructed in the proof of Theorem 2.2 is unipotent.   On the other hand, since ρ' is trivial and since the kernel of σ' contains the kernel of ρ', it is clear that the restriction of σ to G is also unipotent.

It remains to show that the unipotency of σ on H and on G implies that σ is unipotent on $H_n \times G = K$.   Let h be an element of H, let g be an element of G, and let I stand for the identity map on the representation space W of σ.   Then we have

$$I - \sigma(hg) = \sigma(h)(I - \sigma(g)) + (I - \sigma(h)).$$

Hence a product of q endomorphisms of the form $I - \sigma(hg)$ can be written as a sum of products of the form $\sigma(h)u$, where h is in H and u is a product whose factors are either of the form $I - \sigma(g)$ with g in G or of the form $I - \sigma(h)$ with h in H, the total number of factors being q.   Now

$$(I - \sigma(g))(I - \sigma(h)) = (I - \sigma(g)) - \sigma(h)(I - \sigma(h^{-1}gh)).$$

Hence each u can be written as an integral linear combination of products

$$\sigma(h)(I - \sigma(h_1)) \cdots (I - \sigma(h_s))(I - \sigma(g_1)) \cdots (I - \sigma(g_t)),$$

where h and the h_i's are in H, the g_j's are in G, and t is the number of factors of the form $I - \sigma(g)$ with g in G that occurred in the original form of u. Hence we have $u = 0$ whenever $t > D - 1$, where D is the dimension of W. On the other hand, if $t < D$ and if we choose $q \geq D^2$ then we see from the above that u must contain at least D successive factors $I - \sigma(h)$ and hence must again be 0.   Thus, if $q \geq D^2$ then every product of q endomorphisms of the form $I - \sigma(hg)$ is 0, so that σ is indeed unipotent.   This completes the proof of Theorem 2.3.

3

Now we are in a position to prove the basic results on the existence of faithful representations.   From now on, we shall permit ourselves to write "representation" for "finite-dimensional continuous representation."

THEOREM 3.1.   *Let G be a simply connected solvable analytic group, and let N denote the maximum nilpotent normal analytic subgroup of G.   There exists a faithful continuous finite-dimensional representation of G that is unipotent on N.*

Proof.   We make an induction on the dimension of G.   Thus we suppose that G is non-trivial, and that Theorem 3.1 has been established in the lower dimensional cases.   Let Z be the connected component of 1 in the center of N.   We claim that Z is non-trivial.   This is clear if G is abelian, for then $Z = G$.   Otherwise $([\mathscr{L}(G), \mathscr{L}(G)])$ is a non-zero nilpotent ideal of $\mathscr{L}(G)$, which is therefore contained in $\mathscr{L}(N)$, so that N is non-trivial. Since a non-trivial nilpotent Lie algebra has a non-trivial center, it follows that Z is non-trivial.   By Theorem 1.2 of Chapter XII, G/Z is simply connected.   Hence we may apply our inductive hypothesis to conclude that there is a faithful representation of G/Z that is unipotent on N/Z.   We may regard this as a representation of G whose kernel is Z and whose restriction to N is unipotent.

Since N is simply connected and solvable, we can reach N from Z by making a series of semidirect product constructions, and it is clear that the unipotency condition of Theorem 2.3 is satisfied by each semidirect product obtained in this process. Since Z is a vector group, it has a faithful unipotent representation. By Theorem 2.3, this can be extended, in the sense of Theorem 2.2, to a unipotent representation of N. Now we can reach G from N by a series of semidirect product constructions. Since the commutator subgroup of G is contained in N, Theorem 2.2 is applicable at each stage to yield a representation of G that is unipotent on N and faithful on Z. The direct sum of this representation and the representation obtained from the inductive hypothesis evidently satisfies the requirements of Theorem 3.1.

THEOREM 3.2. *Let G be a solvable analytic group, G' the commutator subgroup of G. Then G has a faithful finite-dimensional continuous representation if and only if G' is closed in G and has no non-trivial compact subgroup.*

Proof. Suppose that ρ is a faithful representation of G. By Theorem 1.3 of Chapter XI, ρ° is nilpotent on $([\mathscr{L}(G), \mathscr{L}(G)])$, whence the restriction of ρ to G' is unipotent. Hence Exp is a homeomorphism of $\mathscr{L}(\rho(G'))$ onto $\rho(G')$, topologized by the topology induced from that of the full linear group on the representation space of ρ. Hence $\rho(G')$ is a closed simply connected analytic subgroup of $\rho(G)$. Since ρ is faithful, it follows that G' is closed in G and simply connected. As a simply connected solvable analytic group, G' has no non-trivial compact subgroup.

Now suppose that G' is closed in G and has no non-trivial compact subgroup. As an abelian analytic group, G/G' has the form $T \times V$, where T is a toroid and V is a vector group. Let M be the full inverse image of V in G under the canonical map $G \to G/G'$. Then $G' \subset M$ and $V = M/G'$. Since the vector group V has no non-trivial compact subgroup, every compact subgroup of M must lie in G' and hence must be trivial. Evidently M is connected. Hence M is a solvable simply connected analytic group. By Theorem 3.1, M has therefore a faithful representation μ that is unipotent on G'. Now G/M is isomorphic with T and hence compact. By Theorem 3.2 of Chapter XII, G is therefore a semidirect product $H_n \times M$. Hence we may apply Theorem 2.2 to extend μ to a representation σ of G. On the other hand, since G/M is compact, there is evidently a representation τ of G whose kernel is precisely M. The direct sum of σ and τ is a faithful representation of G, so that Theorem 3.2 is proved.

4

Now we shall deal with the existence of faithful representations for not necessarily solvable analytic groups. The following elementary fact will be used later on.

PROPOSITION 4.1.   *If a semisimple analytic group has a faithful finite-dimensional continuous representation then its center is finite.*

Proof. Let G be a semisimple analytic group, and let ρ be a faithful representation of G with representation space V. Replacing V with $V \otimes_R C$, we may suppose that V is a complex vector space and that $\rho(G)$ consists of complex linear automorphisms of V. Since G is semisimple, V is the direct sum of simple G-submodules $V_1, \cdots, V_k$. Let Z denote the center of G. By Schur's Lemma, Z acts by scalar multiplications on each V_i. Thus there are functions $f_i \colon Z \to C^*$ such that the restriction of $\rho(x)$ to V_i is the scalar multiplication by $f_i(x)$ for every i and every element x of Z. Hence the determinant of the restriction of $\rho(x)$ to V_i is equal to $f_i(x)^{n_i}$, where n_i is the dimension of V_i. Since $G = G'$, these determinants are all equal to 1, i.e., $f_i(x)^{n_i} = 1$ for every x in Z. Hence it is clear that $\rho(Z)$ is finite, whence Z is finite.

THEOREM 4.2.   *Let G be an analytic group, P its radical, S a maximal semisimple analytic subgroup of G. Suppose that both S and P have faithful continuous finite-dimensional representations. Then the same is true for G.*

Proof. We know from the proof of Theorem 3.2 that P is a semidirect product $A_{\alpha} \times M$, where M is a simply connected solvable normal analytic subgroup of P and A is a toroid. Now $\mathscr{L}(G)$ is a semisimple A-module with respect to the adjoint representation. It follows easily from this that $\mathscr{L}(G)$ is the direct sum of $([\mathscr{L}(A), \mathscr{L}(G)])$ and the centralizer, U say, of $\mathscr{L}(A)$ in $\mathscr{L}(G)$.

Let U_r denote the radical of U, and let U_s be a maximal semisimple subalgebra of U, so that U is the semidirect sum $U_s + U_r$. We claim that $\mathscr{L}(P) + U_r$ is a solvable ideal of $\mathscr{L}(G)$. Indeed, we have

$$[\mathscr{L}(G), \mathscr{L}(P) + U_r] \subset [([\mathscr{L}(A), \mathscr{L}(G)]), \mathscr{L}(P) + U_r] + [U, \mathscr{L}(P) + U_r].$$

The first summand lies in $\mathscr{L}(P)$, because $\mathscr{L}(A) \subset \mathscr{L}(P)$. The second summand evidently lies in $\mathscr{L}(P) + U_r$. Thus $\mathscr{L}(P) + U_r$ is an ideal of $\mathscr{L}(G)$. For any Lie algebra L, let $L_0 = L$, $L_{i+1} = ([L_i, L_i])$. Then we have $(\mathscr{L}(P) + U_r)_i \subset \mathscr{L}(P) + (U_r)_i$, whence we see that $\mathscr{L}(P) + U_r$ is solvable. Since $\mathscr{L}(P)$ is the maximum solvable ideal of $\mathscr{L}(G)$, we must therefore have $U_r \subset \mathscr{L}(P)$. Hence $\mathscr{L}(G) = U_s + \mathscr{L}(P)$, so that U_s is a maximal semisimple subalgebra of $\mathscr{L}(G)$. Hence the analytic subgroup of G whose Lie algebra is U_s is a conjugate of the given maximal semisimple analytic subgroup S of G (we have given the argument for this in the proof of Theorem 2.2). Hence we may assume without loss of generality that $\mathscr{L}(S) = U_s$, so that $[\mathscr{L}(S), \mathscr{L}(A)] = (0)$.

Then $\mathscr{L}(A) + ([\mathscr{L}(P), \mathscr{L}(P)])$ is evidently an $\mathscr{L}(S)$-submodule of $\mathscr{L}(G)$. Moreover,

$$\mathscr{L}(A) \cap ([\mathscr{L}(P), \mathscr{L}(P)]) \subset \mathscr{L}(A) \cap \mathscr{L}(M) = (0).$$

Since $\mathscr{L}(S)$ is semisimple, $\mathscr{L}(P)$ is semisimple as an $\mathscr{L}(S)$-module. Since it contains $\mathscr{L}(A) + ([\mathscr{L}(P), \mathscr{L}(P)])$ as a submodule, it may therefore be written as a direct sum $\mathscr{L}(A) + W$, where W is an $\mathscr{L}(S)$-submodule of $\mathscr{L}(P)$ containing $([\mathscr{L}(P), \mathscr{L}(P)])$. Clearly, W is an ideal of $\mathscr{L}(G)$. The corresponding analytic subgroup, B say, of P is therefore normal in G, and we have $P = AB$.

Since P has a faithful representation, we know from Theorem 3.2 that P' is closed in P and has no non-trivial compact subgroup. In particular, P' is therefore closed in the analytic subgroup B of P. Since A is compact, it follows also that AP' is closed in P.

Now consider the canonical surjective homomorphism $B/P' \to P/(AP')$. Its kernel is $(B/P') \cap ((AP')/P')$, which is a discrete subgroup of the analytic group B/P', because $\mathscr{L}(B) \cap (\mathscr{L}(A) + \mathscr{L}(P')) = \mathscr{L}(P')$. On the other hand, $P/(AP')$ is isomorphic with M/P', which we know to be simply connected. Thus $P/(AP')$ is simply connected. Hence the discrete kernel of the canonical homomorphism $B/P' \to P/(AP')$ must be trivial, i.e., $(B/P') \cap ((AP')/P') = (1)$, and B/P' is simply connected. Hence every compact subgroup of B must lie in P', which has no non-trivial compact subgroup. Thus B has no non-trivial compact subgroup. Moreover, $(AP') \cap B \subset P'$, whence $A \cap B \subset A \cap P'$, which is a compact subgroup of P', and hence is trivial. Hence $A \cap B = (1)$, so that B is a semidirect factor in $P = AB$. In particular, B is therefore closed in P, and hence also in G.

Now let H be the analytic subgroup SA of G. Since S has a faithful representation, we know from Proposition 4.1 that its center $Z(S)$ is finite. The center of H is $Z(S)A$, and is therefore compact. Since $H \cap B$ is a discrete normal subgroup of H, it lies in the center of H, and is therefore finite. Since B has no non-trivial compact group, we have therefore

$H \cap B = (1)$, so that G is the semidirect product $H_{\,\eta} \times B$. Moreover, we know that B is simply connected (because it has no non-trivial compact subgroup) and solvable.

By Theorem 3.1, there is a faithful representation β of B that is unipotent on the maximum nilpotent normal analytic subgroup, N say, of B. Since $([\mathscr{L}(H), \mathscr{L}(B)]) \subset \mathscr{L}(N)$ (by Theorem 3.2 of Chapter XI), we may apply Theorem 2.2 to extend β to a representation γ of G. On the other hand, $S \times A$ has evidently a faithful representation. Since H is isomorphic with $(S \times A)/F$, where F is a finite central subgroup, it follows from Lemma 3.1 of Chapter XVII that H has a faithful representation. This may be regarded as a representation ρ of G with kernel B. Now the direct sum of γ and ρ is a faithful representation of G, so that Theorem 4.2 is proved.

We shall define a *reductive* real analytic group by exact analogy with the case of a complex analytic group: a real analytic group G is called reductive if it has a faithful finite-dimensional continuous representation and if every finite-dimensional continuous representation of G is semisimple. The proof of Theorem 4.2 almost contains the proof of the following result.

THEOREM 4.3. *Let G be an analytic group. Then G has a faithful finite-dimensional continuous representation if and only if G is a semidirect product $H_{\,\eta} \times B$, where H is a reductive analytic group and B is a simply connected solvable analytic group, normal in G.*

Proof. Suppose first that G has a faithful representation. Then the assumptions of Theorem 4.2 are evidently satisfied, and we let H and B be the groups obtained in the proof of Theorem 4.2. The necessity part of Theorem 4.3 will be established as soon as we have shown that H is reductive. Since H, as a subgroup of G, has a faithful representation, it suffices to show that every representation ρ of H is semisimple. We know that the center Z of H is compact and that H/Z is semisimple. In particular, the adjoint representation of $\mathscr{L}(H)$ is therefore semisimple, so that $([\mathscr{L}(H), \mathscr{L}(H)])$ is semisimple and $\mathscr{L}(H) = \mathscr{L}(Z) + ([\mathscr{L}(H), \mathscr{L}(H)])$. Hence H' is semisimple and $H = H'Z$. We may evidently take ρ to be a representation of H by complex linear automorphisms of a complex vector space V. Since Z is compact, V can be decomposed into the direct sum of subspaces $V_1, \cdots$, V_p to which there correspond maps $f_i: Z \to C^*$ such that, for every x in Z, the restriction of $\rho(x)$ to V_i is the scalar multiplication by $f_i(x)$. If these are chosen so that the f_i's are all distinct, it is clear that each V_i is H-stable. Moreover, the H'-submodules of V_i are also the H-submodules of V_i. Since H' is semisimple, each V_i is therefore a semisimple H-module. Hence ρ is indeed a semisimple representation of H.

Now suppose that G has a semidirect product decomposition as stated in Theorem 4.3. Then the last part of the proof of Theorem 4.2 shows that G has a faithful representation. This completes the proof of Theorem 4.3.

THEOREM 4.4. *Let G be an analytic group having a faithful finite-dimensional continuous representation. Then G is reductive if and only if the center Z of G is compact and G/Z is semisimple.*

Proof. In proving Theorem 4.3, we have already shown that if Z is compact and G/Z is semisimple then G is reductive. Now suppose that G is reductive. Then G is a semidirect product $H_n \times B$, as in the proof of Theorem 4.2, and it suffices to show that B must be trivial. Now if B is non-trivial then also the maximum nilpotent normal analytic subgroup N of B is non-trivial. The proof of Theorem 4.2 has shown that there is a faithful representation τ of G that is unipotent on N. Since G is reductive, τ is semisimple. As we have shown in Section 1, this implies that the restriction of τ to the normal subgroup N of G is also semisimple. Since τ is unipotent on N, it is therefore trivial on N. Since τ is faithful, this gives $N = (1)$, so that also $B = (1)$, which completes the proof of Theorem 4.4.

THEOREM 4.5. *Let G be an analytic group that has a faithful finite-dimensional continuous representation. Then G' is closed in G.*

Proof. Let P be the radical of G, and let S be a maximal semisimple analytic subgroup of G, so that $G = SP$. Since G has a faithful representation, so has S, so that the center of S is finite. Hence $S \cap P$ is finite, so that also the kernel of the multiplication map $S_\sigma \times P \to G$ is finite, where $S_\sigma \times P$ is the appropriately defined semidirect product. Now G' is the image of $(S_\sigma \times P)'$ which, as an analytic group, is the semidirect product $S_\sigma \times [G, P]$, where $[G, P]$ is the group generated by the commutators formed with the elements of G and P. Now if γ is the given faithful representation of G then γ is unipotent on $[G, P]$ (by an argument used before), whence $\gamma([G, P])$ is closed in the full linear group on the representation space of γ, and hence also is closed in the analytic group $\gamma(P)$. Since γ is faithful, it follows that $[G, P]$ is closed in P, whence it is clear that $(S_\sigma \times P)'$ is closed in $S_\sigma \times P$. The surjective homomorphism $S_\sigma \times P \to G$ is a closed map, because its kernel is finite. Hence we conclude that the image G' of $(S_\sigma \times P)'$ is closed in G, so that Theorem 4.5 is proved.

It is not difficult to see that the analogues of the results of this chapter for complex analytic representations of complex analytic groups hold also, and can be proved by essentially the same method, supplemented by some of the results of Chapter XVII. We shall not carry this out, but we prove one result whose real analogue is not true.

THEOREM 4.6. *Let G be a complex analytic group, and suppose that the radical of G is simply connected. Then G has a faithful finite-dimensional complex analytic representation.*

Proof. Exactly as in the real case, one shows that there is a faithful complex analytic representation π of the radical P of G that is unipotent on the maximum nilpotent normal complex analytic subgroup N of P. Let S be a maximal semisimple complex analytic subgroup of G. Exactly as in the real case, one sees (by the complex analogue of Theorem 2.2, whose proof is almost identical with the one given above) that π can be extended to a complex analytic representation μ of the (appropriately defined) semidirect product $S_\sigma \times P$. On the other hand, we know from Theorem 3.2 of Chapter XVII that S has a faithful complex analytic representation, which we regard as a representation ρ of $S_\sigma \times P$ with kernel P. Now the direct sum of μ and ρ is a faithful complex analytic representation of $S_\sigma \times P$. Since the center of S is finite, so is the kernel of the multiplication homomorphism $S_\sigma \times P \to SP = G$. Hence we can apply Lemma 3.1 of Chapter XVII to conclude that G has a faithful complex analytic representation. This completes the proof of Theorem 4.6.

EXERCISES

1. Let G be the group of matrices of the form $\begin{pmatrix} 1 & 0 & 0 \\ a & 1 & 0 \\ c & b & 1 \end{pmatrix}$ where a, b and c are arbitrary real numbers. Let D be the discrete central subgroup consisting of the matrices in which a and b are 0 and c is an integer. Show that G/D has no faithful finite-dimensional continuous representation. [Use Theorem 3.2.]

2. Let G be a reductive real analytic group, and let $\gamma: G \to G^+$ be a universal complexification of G. Show that G^+ is a reductive complex analytic group. [G is isomorphic with $(S \times T)/F$, where S is a semisimple analytic group, T is a toroid and F is a finite central subgroup.

Let $\sigma: S \to S^+$ and $\tau: T \to T^+$ be universal complexifications, and show that G^+ is isomorphic with $(S^+ \times T^+)/(\sigma \times \tau)(F)$.]

3. Let G be a real analytic group having a faithful finite-dimensional continuous representation, and let $\gamma: G \to G^+$ be a universal complexification of G. Show that G^+ has a faithful finite-dimensional complex analytic representation. [Write $G = H_{\eta} \times B$, as in Theorem 4.3. Show that B^+ is simply connected and solvable, and that G^+ is isomorphic with $H^+_{\eta^*} \times B^+$ (with a suitably defined η^*). Now use the complex analogues of Theorems 3.1 and 2.2.]

4. Let G be a complex analytic group, and suppose that G coincides with its commutator subgroup G'. Show that the radical P of G has a unique maximum compact subgroup Q. Let Q^* be the smallest complex analytic subgroup of G containing Q. Prove that every finite-dimensional complex analytic representation of G is trivial on Q^*, and that there is a finite-dimensional complex analytic representation of G whose kernel is exactly Q^*. [For the last part, show that P/Q^* is simply connected, and apply Theorem 4.6.]

SUPPLEMENTARY READING

1. Chevalley, C., *Theory of Lie Groups*, Princeton University Press, 1946
2. ———, *Théorie des Groupes de Lie*, II, Hermann & Cie, Paris, 1951
3. ———, *Théorie des Groupes de Lie*, III, Hermann & Cie, Paris, 1955
4. Helgason, S., *Differential Geometry and Symmetric Spaces*, Academic Press, New York, 1962
5. Jacobson, N., *Lie Algebras*, Interscience Publishers, New York, 1962
6. Loomis, L. H., *An Introduction to Abstract Harmonic Analysis*, Van Nostrand, New York, 1953
7. Montgomery, D., and L. Zippin, *Topological Transformation Groups*, Interscience Publishers, New York, 1955
8. Pontrjagin, L., *Topological Groups*, Princeton University Press, 1939
9. *Séminaire "Sophus Lie"* (mimeographed), Ecole Normale Supérieure, Paris, 1955
10. Weil, A., *L'intégration dans les groupes topologiques et ses applications*, Hermann & Cie, Paris, 1938

INDEX

229

Index